OUR GARDEN SOILS

By CHARLES E. KELLOGG

THE SOILS THAT SUPPORT US
OUR GARDEN SOILS

OUR
GARDEN
SOILS

by

CHARLES E. KELLOGG,

New York
THE MACMILLAN COMPANY
1952

PREFACE

So many good garden books are available that anyone writing another should have a special excuse. This book was prompted by experience and by many questions about garden soils. It is about garden soils, not gardening in general. It does not attempt to deal with matters that lie mainly in the field of horticulture, or landscape gardening, or insect and disease control, or engineering. Where it does pass slightly beyond the border into these fields, I ask the tolerance of readers who really know them.

"Garden" is used here in the broad sense of all the combinations of cared-for soils and plants about the home—the kitchen garden, the flower beds, the lawn, and the plantings of trees and shrubs.

I wish to help gardeners who must work with soils unsuited to their purpose, to help them choose plants that will grow well on such soils after proper treatment, and to help any who want a superior garden to have it.

Every soil is productive of some kinds of plants. In the wide range of garden plants, some can be found for almost any situation. Many plants grow well, or moderately well at least, in a great variety of soil conditions; others are particular. Some of the nice plants that are particular do well on soils poor for most vegetables and flowers.

By observing a few general principles, one can have a good garden on good soil. Under many individual plants, the books and catalogues recommend planting "in a rich loam soil." If the reader has that kind of soil, perhaps he needs only tools and seeds. But few do have it. This book is primarily for people who do not have it—who have soil that is too sandy, too wet, too sloping, too thin, too clayey, too dry, or too infertile for gardens. For success, they must choose their plants carefully, perhaps change the soil, and certainly give it special management.

Any gardener needs specific suggestions that fit his situation. Still one cannot deal with the thousands of kinds of soil and kinds of plants individually, and the almost infinite number of combinations. I have therefore given both principles and specific suggestions. Several of the tables and lists may be used together to find the recommendation for a specific soil-plant combination. Even with these tables and lists, some generalization has been necessary. Nor is every possible soil-plant combination provided for. Yet nearly all situations for the majority of gardeners in temperate regions can be worked out. Then too, many gardeners will find it possible to follow up and adjust the recommendations made with detailed advice based upon local research in their states or communities.

Because the several important aspects of soil productivity are closely interrelated, it is suggested that readers page rapidly through the whole book, including the tables, in advance of careful reading of individual sections.

CHARLES E. KELLOGG

Beltsville, Maryland,
January, 1952

CONTENTS

OUR GARDEN SOILS

1

NATURAL SOILS

It has been said that "Nature seldom gives us the very best; for that we must have recourse to art." So it is with our garden soil. Although a few natural soils are nearly perfect for gardens as they are, not many people have them in their own back yards. Even the lucky ones who do will need to give them some fixing to grow the finest plants, and indeed to grow some plants at all. If the soil is sweet enough for cabbages it will be too sweet for blueberries. The sandy acid soils that azaleas like best will hardly do for roses.

Well, of course, one can skip the roses and have azaleas, or leave out carrots if the soil is wrong. But even such selecting supposes that we know what plants our own particular soil will support and what it will refuse. Some gardeners mostly "leave out," others do a lot of "fixing" of their soil, and all do some of both.

A garden is a highly personal thing to many people—a part of home. They go a long way toward making soils right for this plant and that. Such doing offers a kind of mind-over-matter challenge, like the red apple at the very top of the tree to the boy on the ground.

Other people won't bother. Instead, they may try to knock a little white ball into a sunken cup, or click little black boxes at big mountain peaks and granite monuments. So what is practical for one gardener is impractical for another, because of differences in the value they put on their garden, in the fun of doing, and in the result.

Garden soil is made from the natural soil. Sometimes a lot of things have been done to the natural soil before the gardener gets hold of it,

1

especially by careless builders who leave their scrappings lying about, covered, perhaps, with a shallow "topsoil" of doubtful origin.

Natural soils vary from one another in over a thousand ways, indeed in more than ten thousand ways; for that many soil types exist in the United States alone. Each has a unique combination of characteristics like that of no other soil type. Some pairs are different in every way, while others are nearly alike as far as gardening is concerned. No more than he needs to know the details of botanical classification does the gardener need to learn all the intricacies of soil classification.[1] But those qualities of his own soil that influence its behavior should be learned. Some gardeners, especially those on a small city lot, have only one kind of soil; others have two or more. Some suburban gardeners and many on farms have a chance to select their garden sites from several kinds of soil, but city dwellers must use what they have. Even many country houses are located for reasons other than the quality of soil immediately around them.

(First of all, soil is much more than a mixture of sand and clay and organic matter; it is teeming with living matter and is continual host to thousands of chemical and biological reactions. Living forms rise from the soil and return to it. In this thin film beneath earth and sky are mingled the physical processes of earth and atmosphere and the living processes upon which all life depends.

The gardener (and the farmer and forester as well) must guard against two common fallacies in thinking about his soil and how to manage it that have persisted for many years: the first because it is so simple, and the second because it is so appealing to our love of mystery.

The fallacy of the storage bin is the more common of the two. It came from the writings of a popular German chemist of one hundred years ago—Baron Justus von Liebig—and his followers. According to this concept a soil is simply a reservoir for plant nutrients. (If one knows the analysis of the soil, the total plant nutrients in it, and the analysis of the plant, the nutrients taken up by the roots, then a simple balance sheet may be prepared as a guide to fertilization. This idea is not even approximately true. The amounts of available plant nutrients in soils and the amounts required by plants are both very important. But we need to know a great deal more. Many processes

---

[1] A little more is said in the Appendix dealing with soil maps; and books on the subject are listed among the references.

that go on in the soil diminish or increase the supply of nutrients besides their removal by plants or addition as fertilizers. Nor can we depend on manures and fertilizers alone to make the soil productive, important as they are. The structure of the soil and its water relations are as vital to productivity as nutrients. Of greatest importance are the reciprocal relationships between the soil characteristics and the behavior of growing plants and micro-organisms.)

A second fallacy is that *all* chemical fertilizers are bad in all situations, and that complete dependence should be placed upon manures, composts, and cover crops. This came about partly as an extreme reaction against the fallacy of the storage bin. Organic matter is very important to the gardener. On most soils (although not all) gardening with neither manures nor composts would be impracticable, if not impossible. But having said this much we need go no further. Organic matter has great value in maintaining soil structure, in furnishing a slow, continuous supply of the many plant nutrients, and as sources of food for micro-organisms. But it has no mysterious power that can be substituted for phosphorus, calcium, or potash where needed. A good commercial source of these nutrients is as good as a so-called "natural" source, and often better. Even chemical nitrogen has an important place in the gardener's kit if he doesn't use too much, and especially if he doesn't try to use it as a substitute for organic matter and cover crops where they are essential to maintain soil structure.

(Soils are so complex and differ so much from place to place that someone is usually advocating practices for all soils that were found to be good for certain ones. Thus some soils require deep spading or plowing while others should have only shallow surface tillage. Some are subject to erosion and others are not.[2])

Continually the gardener must be on his guard against recommendations that apply to a different type of soil than the one he has. Before he attempts to follow his successful neighbor's example, he should be sure that the soils are similar.

Before going into detail about ways to make a good garden soil from the natural soil or from one that has been mucked about, let us

[2] These and other doctrines are reviewed for the layman by the author in "Conflicting Doctrines About Soils," in the *Scientific Monthly*, June, 1948, vol. 66, pp. 475–87. It is also published as a bulletin of the Food and Agriculture Organization of the United Nations, 1201 Connecticut Avenue, N.W., Washington, D.C., and Viale delle Terme di Caracalla, Rome, Italy.

look at some of the important characteristics that cause us to use different methods.

GRAINS AND CLODS

Soils are made up of two sorts of particles, not counting water, soluble salts, and organic matter: the individual mineral grains and the clusters or aggregates of grains. Soil *texture* refers to the relative proportion of individual grains of various sizes. Sandy and clayey are adjectives denoting texture. Soil *structure* refers to the form of the groups of particles. Granular and blocky are adjectives indicating structure.

Most people have learned something about texture, and easily recognize sand or clay. But actually, structure is of more general importance—especially to the gardener.

Texture. The size of individual soil grains changes very slowly. Except as he may add sand or clay to the soil, texture must be accepted by the gardener.

Groups of particles, defined according to size, are called *separates* and are given names as follows:

Separate	*Diameter in millimeters*
Clay	below .002
Silt	.002 to .05
Very fine sand	.05 to .10
Fine sand	.10 to .25
Medium sand	.25 to .50
Coarse sand	.50 to 1.0
Very coarse sand	1.0 to 2.0
Pebbles and stones	above 2.0

Of these separates, clay is by far the most active. Individual kinds of clay are quite different, however, depending upon the sort of weathering that produced them. Thus clays formed in the tropics are not so sticky when wet and not so hard when dry as those found in semiarid grasslands, like central North Dakota; but the leached clays of the humid temperate regions, like New York and Pennsylvania, are still more sticky than those in North Dakota.

Very rare indeed is a soil composed entirely of one separate; rather a soil is a mixture of sand, silt, and clay. These various mixtures are given textural *class* names. The more important of these, in order of increasing content of clay, are: sand, loamy sand, sandy loam and fine sandy loam, loam, silt loam, clay loam, silty clay loam, silty clay, and clay.[3]

Only by analyses in the laboratory can the textural class of a soil be determined precisely. It can be recognized, however, with a little experience, by feeling the moist soil between the fingers. (See page 16.) The gardener should know the class for the various layers of his soil down to 3 or 4 feet. So many recommendations of soil management and descriptions of plant requirements are given, in part, in terms of soil texture that he needs to know the textural class of his own garden soils.

Not everyone can be counted on to use soil class terms correctly—unfortunately, not even all writers of garden books. None of these terms should refer to anything other than particle size; yet some people think of "loam" as necessarily mellow and rich in organic matter. But this is not always so: a loam soil may have any structure and may be nearly white. Then too, silt loams, clay loams, and clay are often lumped together as clay. Actually a silt loam is handled much more easily in the garden than a clay.

Generally speaking, the sandy soils hold the least water, are the most open to roots, and are the least sticky, while clay is at the other extreme. But several factors other than texture influence these things; chiefly structure, content of organic matter, and the arrangement of the layers in the soil profile.

Instead of sandy and clayey soils, people often speak of "light" and "heavy" soils. The terms refer to the "light" or "heavy" pull required to plow the soil, and the clayey soils, which require more power for plowing, are said to be heavy. (Actually a cubic foot of dry sand weighs more than a cubic foot of clay.)

Within one soil region, where the processes of soil formation dominated by climate and vegetation are similar, differences in texture and structure are quite closely related in natural soils. But comparing the texture of soils from different regions may not indicate much about structure; that is, loam soils in western Nebraska, in Costa Rica, and in Maryland have quite different structures.

It should be added that soils developed wholly or largely from peat

---

[3] It will be noted that "sand" and "clay" are each used as the name of a separate class and of a soil class. The sand class contains a small amount of clay and silt; soil of the clay class may have as little as 40 per cent of clay separate. See also page 180.

—accumulations of organic matter in wet places—are not given class names. If well decomposed, they are called muck, and not peat.

Structure. The maintenance of good structure is the greatest single problem for most gardeners—not more important than maintaining the proper balance of plant nutrients, but more difficult.

Some soils are structureless. At one extreme are the nearly pure sands with each grain by itself, or *single grain*. At the other extreme the grains are bound together in masses without definite form or regular breakage, as in hardpans or puddled clays. Such soils are said to be *massive*. Both these extremes must be avoided.

Natural soil aggregates have either irregular curved surfaces or plane surfaces. The first group is called *granular* or sometimes *crumb* structure. The second is called *blocky, prismatic*, or *platy*, according to whether the pieces have dimensions similar in each direction, greater vertically than horizontally, or greater horizontally than vertically. The structural pieces in different soils or in different layers of one soil vary greatly in size and consistence as well as in form. A granular structure can be developed easily from some types of blocky structure and only with great difficulty from others.

Although the soil scientist lays great emphasis upon fine distinctions in natural soil structure, because of what they tell him about the formative process going on, the gardener needs to concentrate on developing and maintaining a granular structure. A well developed blocky structure in the lower part of a clay soil indicates at least fair permeability to water, air, and roots, but a massive condition must be avoided or changed.

Fortunate indeed is the gardener whose soil is granular for a considerable depth to begin with. Soil developed under a good cover of grass has a granular structure naturally. The surface layers of many soils under forests have granular structure; but these layers may be quite thin, and, generally, this structure is easily destroyed by careless tillage. Many of the naturally forested soils have a granular structure in the surface soil, say to 6 or 12 inches, and a blocky structure beneath. Tree roots penetrate between the blocks and the soil is well drained so long as the blocky structure remains. Yet if the trees are removed and only shallow-rooted plants grown, the soil may "run together" into a massive condition if no provision is made to keep this lower soil supplied with organic matter. Then the soil becomes only slowly permeable to water: it is often too wet in spring and too dry in summer. If the soil is spaded and cultivated a great deal without the addition of organic matter, the surface soil may lose its granular structure and become massive too. When plowed or spaded, massive soil breaks into irregular clods (rather than aggregates) which run together into a mass when moistened.

In common terms, the structure of a tilled soil is called *tilth*. Soil in good tilth for gardening has a granular structure, and not one made by purely mechanical means alone. No matter how much one breaks up and pulverizes clods or masses of clayey soil, after a good soaking rain the individual pieces "run together" or puddle again into masses. A lot needs to be said later about how to develop and maintain good structure.

Consistence. Closely related to texture and structure, or tilth, is consistence. Soils that are plastic and sticky when wet are likely to be hard when dry. Such soils that may be spaded easily when moist nearly resemble concrete when dry—"freeze in August," as some say. Of course the higher the content of active clay, the more plastic the soil may become. But the chemical nature of the clay, and especially the amount and kind of organic matter, influence consistence very much.

Ideally, the soil is friable when dry or simply moist. That is, clods or structural pieces are easily crushed with the fingers. Depending upon their nature and previous treatment, loam soils with only 25 per cent clay, or even less, may be hard and cloddy, whereas heavy clays with over 60 per cent clay may be easily friable. Thus, even though the natural soil has a blocky structure, if the pieces are friable, good tilth can be developed.

NOTE THE COLOR SCHEME

Color is the most obvious characteristic of soil. Even though black soils may adsorb somewhat more heat than white ones, the direct effects of color are relatively insignificant. But soil color indicates a lot about other important characteristics. Yet it cannot be followed blindly.

Although we talk about red soils and black soils, and yellow ones and white ones, nearly all of them are really some shade of brown.

Generally, the black soils are rich in humus—the stable product of decomposed organic matter. The soils developed under luxuriant grass vegetation are black, or nearly so, like the famous black soils (Chernozem) of the Ukraine and the Prairie soils of Iowa. The normal well drained soils of eastern North Dakota, for example, have deep, black, highly productive surface layers. But in humid forested regions, like the eastern part of the United States, the very black soils are developed under poor drainage. Thus a black color there suggests such wetness that the soil needs artificial drainage for most vegetable crops and common flowers, although it would be suited to a good many flowering shrubs, trees, and other plants adapted to swampy conditions.

Occasionally, black soils may be too alkaline or too acid for ordinary garden plants, but on the whole they are the most productive of any on account of the supply of humus and good structure.

Deep brown soils are generally next in line. The best garden soils of humid temperate regions, as in New York and Maryland, have a rich brown color.

Red soils are usually good, if the red color is developed and not simply an inheritance from the underlying rock. A developed red color means that the soil has formed under good drainage. But a wet soggy soil from red shale may be red in color and not be well drained. In tropical regions red soils are generally much better than yellow or white ones, although they need much fertilizer and organic matter.

Yellow soils in temperate regions are often well drained and suitable for gardens if well fertilized and supplied with organic matter. In tropical regions the yellow color suggests restricted drainage, for a part of the time at least, and very low fertility.

White or light gray soils are almost universally low in fertility. If the lower layers are brown or red and have good structure, a productive garden soil can be made. Gray layers beneath the surface may indicate poor drainage in moist regions or accumulations of salt or lime in dry regions.

If the soil is mottled gray, brown, and yellow just beneath the surface, one may suspect poor drainage part of the time. In such soils the roots of plants may be killed during moist periods.

In regions where the soils are normally black, light colors in the surface suggest that the soil has been eroded and a raw subsoil exposed. Similarly, in most parts of the United States it is not usual for the surface soil to be red. Even though the subsoils of many of our soils in the South are red, the natural surface soil is yellowish-, grayish-, or reddish-brown. Red clay soil in the very surface, then, usually means that the original surface has been removed by running water, or in some other way, or that excavated subsoil has been dumped over the surface.

Many a city dweller has yellow, white, or red clay to deal with that was scraped out of the basement and spread over the surface of his lot instead of being carted away as it should have been.

BY THE PROFILE WE KNOW THEM

As we dig into a soil, we see that it is made up of a series of layers, called *horizons,* which are roughly parallel to the surface of the ground. They may appear to vary from one another simply in color, or in color, texture, and structure. Collectively, the horizons of a soil are called its *profile.* In soil classification soils are defined chiefy, although not entirely, by their profiles.

Each soil type has a characteristic profile, which has developed from a particular combination of climate, native vegetation, parent rock, slope, and time. Thus each soil type is a particular kind of natural landscape, identified by its profile, which reflects the whole history of its formation over the years.

The gardener will be well repaid to examine with some care the profile of each kind of soil he expects to use. Normally, soil profiles extend down some 20 to 60 inches. Beneath the soil is usually rotten rock or other loose material; although sometimes the whole soil is shallow over hard rock if the soil is young or on a rocky slope.

Such examinations help the gardener directly: he can see the evidences for good or poor drainage and any massive horizons that might interfere with roots. (*Many* people underestimate the depth of roots.) He can see whether he needs to double spade or dig deep holes or trenches in order to incorporate organic matter to develop a proper structure for certain plants.

Then to make the maximum use of the results of scientific research on soil management and soil-plant relationships, the gardener needs to know the name of his soil or be able to describe it in some detail so that he can discover which results apply to his soil, or so that others can help him do so. A large program of research significant to the gardener is going forward in most of the state agricultural experiment stations on the important soil types—or at least a part of them.

If the scientists conducting these researches know the soil type of an inquiring gardener, or can determine it from his description of the soil slope and the color, texture, structure, and thickness of the various horizons of the complete soil profile, they can usually give him specific information on how his soil responds to various treatments, based upon scientific experiments.[4]

Most natural soil profiles may be divided into three principal horizons, called A, B, and C, corresponding roughly to the common terms: surface soil,[5] subsoil, and substratum. Surface soil includes the upper part ordinarily moved in spading or plowing. But, of course, the lower layers are just as much a part of the soil as the surface layer. The substratum is the disintegrated but otherwise unchanged rock material beneath the true soil, or *solum*. The B horizon (or subsoil) is the lower part of the solum between the upper A horizon and the C horizon, or substratum. In humid regions the B horizon is often higher in clay content than either the surface soil or substratum. In extreme cases it is a very dense claypan or hardpan.

In the dark-colored soils of the grasslands the A horizon is normally very dark brown and granular; the B horizon is simply a transitional horizon to the loose material underneath the solum. In semiarid regions soils normally have a layer of concentrated lime carbonate just beneath the B horizon, often called the "lime zone." For most garden crops and trees it is *very* important that the solum be deep over this lime zone, certainly not shallower than 15 inches.

In humid forested regions, like the eastern part of the United States, the A horizon consists of important subdivisions. In the woods one finds a covering layer of loose leaves over a mat of partly decomposed organic matter called leaf mold. (This leaf mold is nearly ideal

---

[4] In making such inquiries it is helpful to give the exact location, especially where detailed soil maps are available. Many experiment stations are equipped to make tests on soil samples for residents of the state to help in determining needs for specific fertilizers or other amendments for particular plants or groups of plants.

[5] "Topsoil" is another common term, sometimes used as equivalent to surface soil, sometimes for A horizon, and sometimes only for the dark-colored surface part of the soil, which may be less than an inch or more than 2 feet in thickness, depending on the type of soil. Others mean by "topsoil" fertile soil material, rich in humus, used to cover other soil in making lawns and flower beds. The term is used in such different senses by various writers that its meaning is often obscure. This author uses it only in the sense of fertile soil material used to cover other soil.

mulch for shrubs and other plants where it can be gathered in some quantity.) Under the dense evergreen forests of New England this organic mat may be several inches thick while in the South it is not more than an inch or two. Severe burning of the woods destroys it.

The upper layer of dark-colored soil, containing a mixture of mineral soil grains and humus, is called the A_1 horizon. This black soil may be 1 to 2 feet deep in the subhumid grasslands, but is only 1 to 3 inches thick under the forest mat. As soon as the soil is cultivated, a shallow surface horizon is mixed with those beneath and loses its identity. Yet it is the most important horizon of the soil. In it, biological activity is at the maximum. The small animals and micro-organisms tear up and decompose the organic litter and release the minerals and nitrogen for other plants. Where this layer is reasonably thick, say 2 to 4 inches, and nearly black, granular, and neutral or slightly acid in reaction, one knows that the forest trees have been growing well—that they have found a good supply of mineral nutrients in the lower soil, have brought them up by their processes of growth, and have returned them to the surface soil as the leaves and twigs have died.

Just beneath the dark-colored A_1 horizon is the A_2 horizon, generally the most leached and lightest in color of any horizon in forested soils. It may be very thin or well over a foot in thickness. Normally after spading, a garden soil developed from a well drained, mature soil in the humid forested region has a surface soil of 6 to 8 inches that consists of a mixture of the natural A_1 and the upper part of the A_2. Underneath will be, perhaps, the lower part of the old A_2, a transitional horizon 2 to 6 inches thick between the A and B, and then the B horizon.

In addition to these normal soil horizons are others found in some soils, including hardpans, claypans, and salty layers. Deep hardpans and claypans may not do too much harm to common plants if good drainage can be developed. If they are near the surface, they will need to be removed, or else only shallow-rooted plants grown that can endure alternately wet and dry conditions. Such layers may cause considerable difficulty if the soil must be irrigated a great deal, as in desert regions. Hardpans impede drainage, and any salt in the lower layers gradually rises into the root zone with ascending capillary water that moves up when the surface begins to get dry.

In young soils one may find all sorts of layers of rock or sediments that have not yet been changed to soil. Whether or not good garden soil can be developed from fills and raw substrata depends upon their structure, or rather how much work will be necessary to give them a good structure. Almost any material can be used for at least some plants. Even in rocky ledges pockets of good soil can be developed with a little effort. In fact some plants grow best under such conditions.

EACH SOIL HAS ITS HOME PLACE

Each soil has its own profile, but that profile is the result of its environment. Thus, each kind of soil has also a characteristic climate, native vegetation, slope, and parent rock. Climate and vegetation are the active factors that determine the processes of weathering and soil formation, while the parent rock and slope are the passive factors that modify these processes locally.

If we compare the brownish-black, granular soils of central Nebraska with the light-colored soils of Maryland we shall see that the outstanding differences between them are due to the great difference in climate and vegetation. But within either region the local differences —differences between the natural soil in one garden and that in another—are directly related to differences in slope, parent material, or the length of time that soil processes have been going on.

Those who look carefully at soils in a local region, but never have the opportunity to compare them with soils in some other region, of course fail to see the characteristics that the local soils have in common. Since most of the local differences are directly related to slope and parent rock, people have wrongly assumed that the main soil characteristics were due to rock. One even hears such expressions as "limestone soils" or "granite soils." Actually, dozens of different soils may be developed from identical rocks, depending upon the other environmental factors. And also similar soils may arise from quite different rocks in the same region.

Thus the effects of climate and soil on plants are not easily separated. To be sure, climatic conditions obviously restrict the growth of many plants. But where the climates are different the soils are also unlike.

ALL SOILS ARE PRODUCTIVE

Only with some definite plant or group of plants in mind can it be said that some soils are productive and others not. Usually when one says that a soil is productive, he means that it will produce well (and without too much trouble or pains) the common grasses and crops of the locality. A productive soil in Iowa produces good corn; in southern Georgia, good watermelons; in southern Maryland, good tobacco; in New York, good grass. A productive soil for corn or beans can produce most of the vegetable crops well or fairly well. Yet there are exceptions. Strawberries and cabbage need different kinds of soil. On a productive soil for blueberries, most vegetable crops would do nothing.

The gardener grows, or can grow, an exceedingly wide range of vegetables, flowers, and shrubs. No matter how poor his soil may seem to be, it probably will produce a good many plants, at least with some help from the gardener. One of the main problems is to discover which plants. Attractive shrubs, for example, may be had for almost any kind of soil if one knows how to select the shrubs that fit the type of soil to be used.

Most soils are slow to change. After all, this may be a good thing. From time to time people have had such wrong notions of fertilizers and other treatments that if soils were easily ruined, many would have been. And, in making additions of fertilizer, lime, and other soil amendments, there is a fairly wide margin of safety.

This is especially true of soils fairly rich in clay—loams, silt loams, and clay loams—and more particularly those high in organic matter. But a very heavy clay soil, acid and low in organic matter, is a stubborn one to improve for ordinary cultivated plants; and even more so if it is either wet or steeply sloping. So too are soils shallow over rock or gravel.

Light sandy soils are more easily changed. Here the factor of safety with chemical treatments is narrow. Many a gardener with sandy soil has applied too much lime, for example, and injured his soil.

If the natural soil to be used is a normal sandy loam, loam, or silt loam for the region, nearly level, and without hard layers underneath —or the "rich loam" recommended by most garden manuals and on the backs of most seed packets—the necessary changes will not be difficult. With a great many plants fair results can be had with little modification of such a soil.

But a good garden can be had on the other soils. This book is chiefly concerned with these—with the majority that call for something special. When understood, there are really no *bad* soils. Some are stubborn, very stubborn, and others simply coy, but all will respond to the gardener's art.

2

WHAT PLACE?

The garden is part of the home and closely associated with the house. If one can choose a good soil when locating the house, fine; but ordinarily other factors dominate. Once the position of the house is fixed, lawns, trees, shrubs, and flower gardens need to be grown as best they can on whatever soil is there. And this is true too for the kitchen garden, although there may be a little more opportunity for choosing its location. Yet a distant tract should have much better soil, or some other compelling advantage, to take even the vegetables away from the house.

All plants, even trees and shrubs, need to be looked after. "The shadow of the master is the best fertilizer." If they can be seen every day, trouble may be sensed before it has become serious. A few minutes' work may stop insects or diseases at the start that would require hours some two or three days later, if indeed they may be stopped at all. Weeds are easily controlled when small. Then there is time to do the little things, if the garden is near at hand. Having it far away makes a job out of fun.

An ideal location is not necessary. Most garden books and bulletins calmly advise: "Select a smooth-lying, rich sandy loam or loam soil, where there is plenty of sunlight, no competition from trees. . . ." If taken literally, such advice would have eliminated a very large percentage of the city and suburban kitchen gardens so important to our food supply during war.

But it is important for the gardener to know the kind of soil he has.

15

He can prepare for the hazards and choose his plants and methods. Taking the soil he has, he can plan his lawns and gardens according to plant requirements and his own wishes. There is a great advantage in having a garden plan, not entirely fixed, of course, but as an orderly pattern of judgments based upon the best ideas he can form. Such a plan saves time and expense.

WHAT KIND OF SOIL?

In the previous chapter the nature of soils was outlined briefly and it was suggested that the gardener examine the profile of each kind of soil he has.[1] In unplanted ground it is best to make the holes with a spade, but in lawns and beds a soil auger is better. This is simply a large carpenter's auger, about 1½ inches in diameter, welded to a small steel rod or pipe and fitted with a cross bar about 14 inches long at the top, so that one may bore a hole about 40 inches deep into the soil. (This same tool is very useful in making holes around trees for adding phosphatic fertilizers.) The structure of the soil removed is nearly destroyed with the auger, but the other characteristics—color, texture, and consistence—may be observed on the soil taken out with it.

Texture. With a little trying it is not too difficult to estimate the textural class. Sands are very coarse and gritty, and any loose aggregates fall apart in the hands as separate grains. Clays, at the other extreme, when moist and forced between the fingers, make a smooth, thin, continuous smear. Dry soil must be moistened a little, else hard structural pieces may be taken for sand or pebbles. The silt loams make a fair smear, but they do not rub out thin like clay before becoming rough and broken. Clay loams are intermediate. Loams give only a rough smear and much sand is felt. Sandy loams hold together when moist, but scarcely make any smear. A loamy sand holds together a little when slightly moist. It takes some practice not to overestimate the amount of sand in gritty clays and clay loams, and the amount of clay in fine sandy loams.

[1] This may sound a bit academic at first; but many times the author has seen wastes of hundreds of dollars and much time, to say nothing of the disappointments, that could have been avoided by looking at the soil beneath. If the gardener has an old house or an old city lot, he may discover almost anything. More than once the author has seen people trying to grow grass on soil only a few inches thick over paving stones, concrete, and even old tar-bound roads!

Often the lower soil is entirely unlike the surface in texture, especially in humid regions where a loam or silt loam surface soil is commonly underlain by clay loam or clay. For plants normally having deep root systems, but accommodated only to pervious soils, massive clay needs to be removed, say to 2 or 3 feet, depending on the plants, and replaced with lighter soil. For some plants the soil may be made open enough by mixing organic matter into the clay subsoils.

If the texture of the soil a few inches beneath the surface is sand, loamy sand, or gravel, the chances are that many kinds of plants will suffer from drought during dry periods between rains. The gardener needs to water plants on such soils frequently or else grow plants that can endure such droughty conditions if given a good surface mulch of organic matter.

For most plants a sandy loam or loam surface soil with a slightly heavier soil beneath, say a loam or silt loam that holds water well but lets any excess drain through, is ideal. Yet radishes, carrots, azaleas, and many others really prefer a more sandy soil, while squash, beans, and roses do as well or better in more clayey soils.

Structure. The more nearly granular or crumblike the soil, the better. Loose, open sands need much well decomposed organic matter, and perhaps some clay, for the maintenance of a granular structure. In massive clay, coarse organic matter, like peat or leaf mold, is needed. Many thousands of dollars in plants and seeds come to nothing because of massive clay just beneath the surface that neither roots nor water can penetrate.

Roots of existing plants may give some leads as to how well others will grow. But caution is required. Some trees, like the oaks, for example, have strong roots that may penetrate coarsely blocky or nearly massive soils that the roots of tender plants cannot. In fact the structure in the heavy B horizons of forested soils often worsens after clearing. The swaying in the wind of deep-rooted trees moves the roots enough to help maintain a blocky structure through which air and water may pass. But shortly after clearing and cultivating, the old roots rot away; and if other deep-rooted plants are not grown, the soil in the B horizon gradually loses its blocky structure and "runs together" into massive soil. In such cases the drainage gradually gets poorer after clearing away the trees.

Color. The color profile helps to show the depth of surface soil. If no definite soil horizons or layers are to be seen, it can be assumed with fair certainty that the soil is either very young, as along a stream, or has been disturbed and moved about in the past. The general significance of soil color was explained in the first chapter. Note how deep the dark-colored surface soil is and watch for gray colors or mottled patterns that suggest imperfect drainage.

Depth. The term *depth* is applied to soil very differently by different people. Some use it for the dark-colored surface layers, either natural or cultivated; others refer to the depth of granular or friable blocky soil over some claypan or hardpan; still others refer to the total A and B horizons, or true soil, over the parent rock material; but most commonly the total depth of soil and loose material over hard rock is meant.

All these "depths" are important, which is simply saying one needs to see the whole soil profile in order to predict how roots may grow and how water will pass through the soil; or, perhaps, to see what changes must be made for particular plants.

Contamination. The soil near houses and in city lots is commonly contaminated with all sorts of materials. Often the earth excavated from basements is spread over the surrounding area. In humid regions this may be sticky clay very difficult to get into a granular condition. In dry regions such earth may be much too limy or salty for plants.

Special care must be taken to examine the soil immediately next to the house itself. Excavations for basements are frequently made a few feet wider than needed; and after the walls are built the trenches left outside are then filled with all sorts of building rubble—pieces of brick, wood, tile, conduit, tar paper, and what not—that must be removed and replaced with good soil. Where acid-loving plants, such as azaleas and rhododendrons, are to be grown, special precautions must be taken to remove any waste plaster, concrete, or ashes that may have been dropped into such places and only lightly covered.

Ashes often cause trouble. Wood ashes can be used to furnish some potash and lime to acid soils, either directly or through the compost, and sifted coal ashes are used to lighten heavy clay soils; but the gardener does not want too much of either. Some kinds of soft coal ashes, until leached, contain substances toxic to plants. *Ashes from lignite coal are especially bad.* They contain toxic caustic alkali compounds that injure plants directly, and make the soil too alkaline and cause it to puddle or "run together."

Old pavements and walks are sometimes lightly covered in grading. These must be removed for almost any sort of plants to grow well.

Although broken glass, wire, and sticks are a nuisance, they can be removed by working over the soil carefully when spading, or double-spading where necessary. For grass and ordinary garden plants this trash does not do much harm beyond the space it robs from roots and the hazards offered to the gardener's hands and knees.

Where beds or vegetable gardens must be made from old fills, it is far better to do a thorough job of soil preparation in a small area as time is available than to plant a large space without first cleaning out the rubbish.

Acidity. It is very important to know the reaction—the degree of acidity or alkalinity—of the soil throughout the zone occupied by roots, but more especially the surface soil. Soils vary widely in reaction and plants vary as widely in their tolerance of acidity. Some require acid soils; others require alkaline soils; while the majority grow best in slightly acid to neutral soils. Yet among this last group there are wide differences in their tolerance for reactions different from the ideal.

This subject is so important that a special chapter is devoted to it. The approximate reaction preferences of many garden plants are suggested in the lists of Appendix II. The gardener can use these lists in deciding what plants will grow on his soil as it is, as far as acidity is concerned, what plants may be grown together in the same bed or group, and what changes he must make in reaction for growing specific plants. Directions for determining acidity and for increasing and decreasing acidity in soils are given in Chapter 6.

For flowering plants especially, the gardener will do well to study his soil and site and the requirements of various plants before starting any operations. That is, one may have a beautiful flower garden on an area of forested, acid soil. Rather than cutting down the trees and adding lime in order to grow roses, for example, it may be much better to select acid-loving, shade-tolerant shrubs and flowers that may be naturalized in the area. Less work and expense are required in both establishment and maintenance, with as good or better effects.

Slope. Soil slope must be thought of in relation to the other soil characteristics and the plant cover. If the soil is relatively impermeable to water, the greater the slope the greater the difficulty of getting water to enter the soil and the greater the erosion hazard. Yet pervious sandy soils may be quite sloping without excessive runoff.

But before deciding that the soil is too open and porous to offer an erosion hazard, one must be certain that it is pervious throughout. If only the surface layers are porous and are underlain by impervious clay or hardpans, serious erosion may be expected with bare soil. As soon as the surface soil gets saturated with water, the whole mass becomes soft and yielding and flows as mud.

Then too, relatively pervious soils may erode very badly in winter and early spring if left bare. If the soil freezes to a depth of several inches, the surface may thaw and erode easily during heavy late-winter rains while the frozen soil beneath acts as an impermeable hardpan. But this problem of guarding against erosion is taken up in more detail later.

The length of slope is also important. That is, if the gardener is working near the lower part of a long gentle slope, he may have a great excess of surface water to deal with during heavy rains—water that has accumulated from the upper part of the slope. On such slopes diversion ditches or terraces become imperative, or the results of months of work may be washed out in one big storm.

Attention also needs to be given the direction of the slope. In the Northern Hemisphere soils with south or southwest-facing slopes, exposed to the most direct rays of the sun, become warmer and drier than level soils; while those with north-facing slopes are cooler and more moist. With plants easily hurt by heat and drought these differences in slope are often critical. Gardeners maintaining lawns on exposed south-facing slopes of heavy clay soils where hot dry periods are common can testify on this point. By careful planning of lawns and gardens such problems can often be avoided by the use of drought-resistant shrubs instead of grass or, at least, by providing for moving shade over the slopes to reduce the heat. In extreme cases a stone wall to eliminate the earth slope may be the only practical remedy.

Drainage. Soil drainage has two aspects: (1) the surface drainage, or runoff—the ease with which excess water flows off the soil; and (2) internal drainage—the ease with which excess water drains through the soil. If the watertable is deep, level soils underlain by porous sands and gravels are well drained, whereas level soils with impervious layers in them are wet much of the time.

In humid regions poorly drained soils are usually dark in color and have a mucky or peaty surface underlain by gray soil. The surface soils of imperfectly drained soils are often more grayish, less brown than those of the associated well drained soils, and they are mottled underneath. The presence of sedges and other plants common to wet places indicates poor drainage.

In semiarid or arid regions excess salts accumulate in poorly drained areas, making a white crust on the surface. Irrigation usually intensifies the difficulty with salts in such situations.

Although some plants are more particular than others, the majority of the ones that most people want to grow in their lawns and gardens require well drained soils. Yet there are many excellent flowering shrubs, trees, and other plants that thrive in wet soils, some in wet acid soils and some in wet neutral soils. Soils that are wet and soggy during autumn, winter, and spring but dry in summer are especially difficult to manage. But plants can be found even for such places. Or the soil may be drained, as explained later.

WHAT ABOUT AIR DRAINAGE AND FROST?

As the air just above the ground cools, the soil gives heat to it. How well the soil can supply heat to the surface depends upon the rate at which heat can be transferred from the warmer soil underneath. With muck or peat soils the transfer is very slow since heat can move only very slowly through the organic matter. Thus on cold nights— just cold enough to cause frost injury—plants on muck soils are killed while those on adjacent mineral soils, other things being equal, are not.

Of more importance, however, are differences in air drainage. As the air cools, it becomes heavier and slides down the slopes into the hollows. Thus fruits and flowers planted high on slopes are less subject to frost than those in the hollows where the cold air accumulates. It is not uncommon to have several days more between spring and autumn killing frosts on slopes than in hollows a few hundred feet away, because of local differences in air drainage. The climate becomes cooler and the growing season shorter with big increases in elevation, say on very high hills or mountains contrasted to valleys a thousand feet lower.

The gardener cannot do much about air drainage unless he is lucky enough to have a wide choice of locations so that he can place his fruit trees and tender plants on soils with good air drainage. But he can size up his own situation and, if the air drainage is poor, avoid plants that require a longer growing season than he can depend upon. That is, the growing season given by his local weather station may be shorter or longer than that at his own place, perhaps a mile or so away. Also, he should be on guard against trying tender plants, requiring a long season, in his garden simply because a neighbor grows them successfully. The neighbor may have much better air drainage than he has.

WATER SUPPLY

Even in humid regions some plants usually need extra water, at least once in a while, other than what may be counted on from rain. This is one of the important advantages of locating the kitchen garden near the house rather than on even better soil far away. Of course shrubs and trees may be selected that can withstand severe drought, but the majority of the better sorts do not.

Strangely, there are people who spend a great deal of time and money on vegetable and flower gardens, lawns, and shrubbery without adequate provisions for watering. This is a poor place to save. Much better results would be obtained with a given amount of money to provide water for a more modest planting. This does not mean that plants need to be kept supplied with ideal moisture conditions all of the time. But when they are young or first put out, and during periods of extremely dry weather, careful watering is important, in winter as well as summer.

For many it is easy to use the city water supply or a home pressure system. Elsewhere a reservoir filled by pumping from a well or one made by a small dam on a stream can often be provided in a location *above* the garden.

ARRANGE FOR LIGHTING

Each plant has its own needs of light and shade. Most vegetable crops need at least 4 to 6 hours of sun and either do best with full sun or at least endure full sun; although lettuce and the other salad crops do a little better with some shade, especially "moving shade," like that from a tall tree. Generalization on this point is difficult because of the great differences in normal sunshine from place to place. In places having nearly the maximum sunshine, along with high air temperatures, plants require more shade than in cool, cloudy areas.

Reference is made here to shade. Much of the damage laid to shade is really not due to shade at all, but to root competition. The roots of large trees often extend for long distances and rob other plants of water and nutrients.

Many plants require shade, especially in naturally sunny areas. Many of the azaleas and rhododendrons, for example, do only fairly well, or even poorly, in full sun, although they need to have a little sun—say 2 to 5 hours, preferably in morning or late afternoon—for good flowering. A few, like the Christmasrose (Hellebore), for example, need shade in summer and full sun in winter. Most ferns require full or partial shade.

Many plants have a rather wide range of adaptability. English ivy grows in either sun or shade. No good lawn grasses tolerate dense shade; yet few do best in full sun and strong heat. In northern areas, where summer temperatures do not become very high, lawns and vegetable gardens do well or best in full sun; but where temperatures are very high, light shade, especially moving shade, is better.

By careful plant selection beautiful flowers, flowering shrubs, and excellent ground covers can be had even with heavy shade. In fact the shade that some gardeners assume to be detrimental can often be turned to their distinct advantage with proper plant selection.

Much remains to be learned about the effect of light and shade on plants. Many of our present notions are in error because all or part of the effects thought to be due to shade are really due to root competition. Also the continuous shade of a building has a different effect on many plants from the uneven, moving shade of a tree, especially a fairly open tree like an oak.

PROTECTION

The garden plan needs to provide protection for many plants from strong winds, tree roots, and animals.

Wind. Some plants require protection from cold wintry winds, some from the hot, dry winds of summer, and many from both. Generally in the United States, protection is required from the north and west winds, although in Kansas and adjoining parts of the Great Plains more protection is needed in summer from the south than from the north.

Evergreen hedges or plantings of cedars or hemlocks furnish good protection for vegetable and flower gardens. For small gardens in humid regions these may be kept down to a height of 6 or 10 feet by pruning so that the garden may be planted within 8 or 10 feet of the trees. In the Great Plains and Southwest higher windbreaks of adapted trees, such as Russian olive, are useful. Such windbreaks protect both soil and plants from hot scorching winds in summer and hold the snow on the soil in winter. Often fruit-bearing trees and shrubs and flowering shrubs can be used in protective plantings and windbreaks.

Such trees and shrubs require water. In dry regions plants will need to be used that are hardy under such conditions with whatever water can be supplied through irrigation. Where tall trees are used, the kitchen garden should be 25 feet or more away to avoid competition with the roots.

If insufficient water is available for shelter belts, or for temporary protection, picket fences or snow fences may be used; but there effects are quite local, for scarcely more than a few feet. For narrow vegetable gardens, rows of thickly planted sunflowers and corn on the west side or south and west sides protect tender plants satisfactorily.

The need for windbreaks depends upon local relief, but all gardens should be planned so that tender plants are protected from strong winds. Although in cities buildings may give considerable protection, many exposed places are unsatisfactory for tender plants. Often the wind whips around a particular corner in such a way that tender azaleas or roses die in one place from winter injury and yet thrive only 10 feet away. These exposed places are easily seen as the bare spots after winter snowstorms. Tender plants should not be planted where the ground has been thus left bare of snow without having first established hardy evergreens to give the necessary protection.

The gardens, including all the lawn and yard space, of country houses should be protected from strong winds by trees wherever possible. These may be arranged in broad strips or in irregular clumps according to convenience and taste. During the past fifteen years a great deal has been learned about the planting and care of shelter belts or windbreaks for the Prairie and Great Plains states. Advice may be had locally from county agricultural agents or from state or federal foresters about the best adapted species to use and how nursery stock may be obtained conveniently.

Trees. Although trees are often necessary for shade and protection —indeed they are essential to a well planned garden—other plants may need to be protected from them. Many hardy shrubs and flowers may be naturalized with trees; but tree roots can seriously injure flower beds and borders and vegetable gardens. If such plantings must be placed near trees, their roots must be cut off occasionally or, better still, permanent protection given.

Some trees have more troublesome roots than others. Generally, trees like cottonwood and the poplars should be avoided since their long roots work into drains and cause other trouble as well. Bamboo should not be planted near vegetable gardens or flower beds because of its vigorous roots. Elm and maple trees offer much more competition than oaks to shrubs.

In the tropics where trees, shrubs, and some of the grasses grow with great vigor, open trenches are maintained around the garden to protect it from roots.

Since it is time-consuming to dig around the gardens and beds each year, some provide permanent concrete walls deep enough in the soil to prevent root spreading. Heavy asphalt-soaked roofing paper may be used instead. Such protective barriers must be deep enough to prevent roots coming across even at considerable depth, for, once across, they grow upward again and cause as much trouble as if there were no barrier.

With normally growing trees cutting the roots along one side, or even two sides if not too close to the trunk, does not injure them. Trees that are not entirely thrifty may be injured by cutting the roots; but such trees usually do little harm or else should be replaced.

Animals. Each locality has its own peculiar pests—mice, dogs, rabbits, birds, or even tigers. In considering the site these handicaps should be evaluated—although it is hard to predict when the neighbors may get a troublesome dog that is not kept at home. Near old barns, rats are likely to cause trouble. A vegetable garden near the woods offers a temptation that rabbits often cannot resist. But they can be trapped, and so can woodchucks. Tigers in the tropics are a special problem—probably unsolvable by the ordinary householder.

Scares for birds usually fail. Since most people who like gardens also like birds, it is best to plan on covers of netting for blueberries, strawberries, and the like.

GARDENS ARE TO BE LIVED IN

Above all, in sizing up the garden site and planning the changes, we must remember that a garden is for people. Tender plants should not be walked on, nor should wet soils that contain much clay, but what is the use of a garden that cannot be walked through? Grassy paths can be laid out for light traffic, and steppingstones where traffic is heavy.

One needs some wide vistas with grass in sun and shade, and some flower beds and clumps of shrubs. Such planning is largely a matter of design and taste, with which this book does not deal.

Each gardener needs plans—long-time plans and short-run seasonal plans. But these should not be too fixed or rigid. As the gardener's tastes change, so will his plants. Rarely is it wise to follow a set plan of someone else, out of a book. Rather use the principles as they relate to the individual site to be dealt with, fitting the plants to the soil as much as possible, using the banks for rock gardens, and naturalizing shade-tolerant shrubs and flowers under the trees.

One needs variety without confusion, among both flowers and vegetables, strength and daintiness, and a pleasant place to live; and a garden that is pleasant to work in as well as to enjoy with leisure.

3

THE GARDEN SOIL NEEDS
A GOOD SKELETON

The productivity of a soil for a particular plant or group of plants depends upon several factors in *combination*, including structure, nutrient supply, moisture, temperature, freedom from disease (sanitation), and exposure, each of which influences the others. But, of course, all cannot be discussed at once. So while thinking about the physical structure and tillage it must be recalled that the physical skeleton, organic matter, nutrient supply, water relations, and, above all, the living roots within the soil are closely interrelated.

First of all, plants have roots. Some are deep, others shallow. The reader probably thinks, "Of course, everyone knows that." Yet, it is amazing how many people know this without its being a part of their everyday thinking in the garden. If a plant does poorly, they may examine the stems, leaves, and flowers very carefully, without thinking whether the roots are cramped, too wet, too hot, or what not. On the whole the roots of most common plants go much more deeply into the soil, when growing normally, than is commonly realized. Even though the mass of feeding roots is in the very surface—1 inch to 8 inches—other roots may go to 2 or 3 feet. Some go even deeper; a few are shallower.

Roots must be able to extend themselves easily, and find nutrients, air, and water. Many require protection against extremes of cold or heat, of dryness or wetness, or of excesses or deficiencies of nutrient salts.

The gardener's ultimate success depends a great deal on how well he maintains or, more commonly, how well he creates and maintains a granular or crumblike structure in his soil. This cannot be done by tillage alone. In fact tillage—spading, plowing, cultivating, or hoeing —by itself generally injures the permanent structure, perhaps just a little or maybe a lot, depending upon conditions. The apparent granular structure of mellow soil developed by careful tillage should not fool us. If massive clay is simply broken up and made mellow by mechanical means alone, after a short time it will revert to its former state. But at least some tillage is necessary to prepare a proper seed bed, to incorporate organic material and nutrients into the soil, to make the soil most receptive of water, and to kill weeds.

Although a great deal is said about soil fertility, the maintenance of structure is just as important and indeed often more of a problem because of the greater difficulty of correction. It is comparatively easy to buy a few bags of chemical fertilizers and apply them. But these cannot substitute for good structure and organic matter. (These two usually go together.) In fact, excessive use of nitrogen fertilizer with poor soil structure is the perfect combination for great early promise and poor final results.

PLOWING AND SPADING

Usually careful plowing or spading is the first step in preparing the garden. Some advocate complete dependence upon an organic mulch with no plowing. Occasionally it may be possible to prepare a satisfactory seed bed in this way, but not often. In the subhumid and semiarid regions it is commonly better to use shallow, broad cultivator blades or sharp discs instead of complete turning with the ordinary plow or spade. Soils that are mellow and permeable to roots and water and that are well supplied with nutrients and organic matter in the lower part do not require deep spading or plowing; indeed they may be better off without it since plowing or spading does tend to shear the granules or crumbs. By leaving the surface "trashy," hazards of soil blowing and erosion are reduced.

But most garden soils need to be "turned" in order to incorporate organic matter into the lower soil where it is needed. Further, trash on the surface may present disease and insect hazards. Enthusiasts for surface tillage should not permit us to forget the need for organic matter, phosphates, and limestone in the *lower* soil, as well as in the surface, especially with soils of humid regions. For good garden soil there is no choice between organic matter within the lower soil, within the surface soil, or on the very surface; it must be abundant in all three places. Further, plenty of air is needed for plant roots, for the useful micro-organisms, and for the bio-chemical reactions that change mineral and organic compounds of plant nutrients into forms available to plants.

Time of tillage. First of all, the soils should not be handled when they are wet, except for very sandy soils or the deep red crumbly soils in the tropics. If a soil has any tendency to become hard and massive when dry, stirring it when wet greatly intensifies the trouble. The plowing or spading of silt loams and clay loams when very wet may nearly destroy their granular structure, especially if they are low in organic matter. Such soils should not be walked on when wet; indeed, one may nearly ruin their structure for a whole season. If plants must be weeded or otherwise tended when the soil is wet, the gardener should lay down wide boards to walk on.

Where the soil freezes in winter, it is often best to plow or spade the garden in late fall *without any other tillage.* The exposure of the clods to alternate freezing and thawing helps to promote natural granulation. Alternate wetting and drying helps some too. By leaving the surface rough and broken, water and air may enter freely. Many kinds of insects that live over in the soil are killed in this manner. And the spring work can be undertaken more promptly if this basic job is out of the way.

But fall plowing should not be done where there is much slope because of the hazard of erosion. If the plowing is done on the contour so that each furrow may act as a tiny terrace, gently sloping soil may be plowed in the fall.

There is no advantage in the fall plowing of well drained sandy soils, and it is better to carry these over the winter under a cover of rye, crimson clover, or other cover crops that protect the surface, take up nutrients that otherwise would be lost by leaching, and supply fresh succulent organic matter when turned under in the spring.

A good cover crop is an advantage on most soils and must be weighed against the advantage of fall plowing. Erosive soils should be carried over the winter under a cover crop seeded early enough to make a good growth before winter. (See page 57.)

Often one can make a good compromise by growing the cover crop and then spading in February or early March when the weather and moisture content of the soil become favorable.

At the proper moisture content for spading or plowing, the soil should just crumble in the hand after squeezing into a ball. Soil that works into a sticky ball is too wet for handling. The impatient gardener who works his soil too wet will be sorry. It is much better to have a good late garden than a poor early one.

Plowing or spading during the summer for late crops should be done when the soil is neither wet nor extremely dry. Hard dry clods are difficult to work down into a good seed bed except by strong-arm mechanical crushing, which injures the natural granular structure.

In simple plowing or spading the soil should not be turned completely upside down, but at an angle, wide enough to cover surface sod or organic matter. If sod is turned completely over, a continuous layer of spongy organic matter is formed that is too loose and dry for good root growth during summer. By turning at an angle a good seed bed can be had, firmly connected to the underlying soil, and the organic matter is mixed throughout the surface soil.

Depth. Plowing or surface spading in the northern part of the country, east of the Mississippi, normally should turn over about 6 to 8 inches of soil. Usually, plowing is a little shallower in the South and West. In the Great Plains, 4 to 5 inches is deep enough. If the darker-colored surface soil is thin, not more than an inch or so of light-colored soil from beneath should be stirred into the surface at any one time.

In double spading and in making holes or trenches, care should be taken to avoid mixing soil from the lower layers into the surface soil.

Subsurface tillage and double spading. Some plows or other implements are fitted with a deep knife that breaks up the lower soil. Such a tool has little use in any but farm gardens. Double spading is often very helpful, especially with soils having heavy subsoils or B horizons. In this process the surface soil of the first slice at the edge of the garden, say 6 to 8 inches deep and 8 to 12 inches wide, is laid aside. Then the subsoil within the trench is spaded. After that is done, this spaded subsoil is covered with surface soil from an adjoining strip. The process is repeated across the garden, mixing organic matter and fertilizer into both layers as needed. Finally, the soil from the first trench is carried across to fill the last one. In extreme cases of massive subsoil it may be advisable to "triple" spade; that is, lay aside the surface soil for a trench about 24 inches wide, then the subsoil for a trench about 12 inches wide and 8 or 10 inches deep within the first trench, and finally spade to about a total depth of 24 to 30 inches. Materials are added, as needed, to each of the three layers.

Such double or triple spading gives the gardener the opportunity to incorporate organic matter deeply in the soil, and also ground lime-stone, where needed, and fertilizer—especially phosphorus. The organic matter has a direct mechanical effect in maintaining pore spaces for water, air, and roots. The basic aim should be to develop conditions of fertility, organic matter, and structure favorable for the growth of both roots and micro-organisms in the lower layers and thus promote natural granulation of the soil.

Leaving ridges or spading into raised beds has no general advantage on all soils, yet may be necessary to prevent erosion, improve drainage, or insure proper irrigation. Such special practices are explained in the section on control of water.

Covering materials. Sometimes the surface soil is inadequate for plants to be grown, and other soil—locally called topsoil—must be used as a surface covering. This is often the case if lawns are to be established at once around buildings or along roadways where the natural surface soil has been destroyed.

If the present soil is not too raw, one can often use a surface mulch of peat worked into the surface. But ordinarily this is very expensive. After seeding grass, 50 to 100 pounds per 1000 square feet of hay or straw may be applied, or enough to make a light covering through which one may still see the soil beneath. If too much is used, especially of leafy hays, a dense mat may form that prevents growth.

To avoid blowing by the wind, the straw may be worked into the very surface soil with a disc or spade, not by turning the soil but by pressing the cutting edge down into it enough to fasten the straw. The straw does not want to be worked into the surface too deeply else it makes the soil dry out too easily. One may also fasten the straw down by strings held by small stakes. Some dealers supply an erosion netting that may be staked over the soil to hold it from blowing or washing while the grass is getting established. This is better than chicken wire, since it gradually rots away and does not need to be removed. Such nets are very useful when establishing grass on banks. Coarsely woven burlap can be used also.

If the natural surface soil is all destroyed and the existing surface consists largely of raw soil material low in organic matter, it is necessary to bring in surface soil or to grow some locally adapted field crop and work it into the soil until a suitable surface soil has been developed. Wheat, rye, ryegrass, and similar crops can be grown, but the deep-rooted legumes like alfalfa and sweet clover are much better.

Of course, if one has just built a home, he usually doesn't want to wait two or three years until he can have a lawn. The depth of covering necessary depends somewhat on the existing soil. Usually it should be at least 2 to 5 inches thick; and 8 inches may be better. The source of topsoil bought should always be investigated. The surface from a field that has been producing good alfalfa or market-garden crops for several years and that has a dark-brown color should be suitable. Dark-colored soil from swampy places may be fairly good, but good field soil is preferable. It should be mellow and have a natural granular structure. One should be certain that the field is reasonably free of weed seeds, especially of the kinds most troublesome in lawns, like crabgrass, plantain, dandelions, chickweed, and dock.

After the area has been smoothed and made ready for the surface covering of new soil, a good dressing of phosphatic fertilizer, and perhaps other fertilizers, should be added before the new soil is added. The amounts to use are discussed in Chapter 7.

YOU CAN MAKE IT OVER

Holes or trenches often need to be prepared for trees, flower borders, and clumps of shrubs in about the same way as described under triple spading, except that the soil is all excavated and the different layers are kept in separate piles. It is preferable to prepare the soil some time in advance of setting out the plants, especially where chemicals are used to increase soil acidity, as for blueberries, azaleas, or other acid-loving shrubs, in order to give the made soil some chance to settle and "cure" in advance.

While the holes or trenches are open, one may easily test the drainage by filling them with water and noting how rapidly it soaks away. Most plants require good drainage. Holes dug into heavy clay soils, without underdrainage, may become, in effect, cisterns. During moist periods the water accumulates enough to kill plant roots and to prevent the normal micro-organisms from growing. If proper under-drainage cannot be obtained by digging down a reasonable depth in the hole or trench, tile needs to be laid to take care of it. In such cases the bottom of the hole or trench (say at about 30 inches, where the tile leads out) should be covered with a layer of coarse gravel, crushed rock, or other porous material about 4 to 6 inches thick in which the water can collect and flow into the tile. The good soil above needs to be at least 20 to 30 inches thick, if possible, to insure a proper rooting zone; although ivy, cacti, and many other orna-mental plants can be grown satisfactorily even on rocky ledges with only shallow pockets of good soil.

If the lower layers of soil consist of extremely heavy clay, hardpan material, or loose rock, these should be removed entirely and replaced with good soil such as is used as the surface for lawns, or with a few inches of surface soil from a natural woods. The latter is preferred for acid-loving plants. Where acid soils are unavailable, the garden soil can be made more acid, as explained in Chapter 6. If the soil is very heavy clay, a part may be discarded, and organic matter, like compost or manure, and sand or sandy soil [1] mixed with that to be used. For acid-loving plants leaf mold or weathered sawdust is better than manure or compost to which any limestone has been added. Of course, brick, plaster, or other rubbish needs to be removed.

If such holes or beds are made on a slope, the rim on the down side needs to be built up with stones so that neither the soil nor the surface mulch can wash out and, more especially, so that water will soak in around the roots. Rock slabs, flagstone, or slate shingles set edgewise in the soil are fine for this purpose. A well made rock garden is simply a compound series of such holes and rocky rims.

In preparing all such places so that the soil may have a suitable physical condition, the gardener needs to have in mind the nutrient requirements of the plants to be grown and choose or modify the soil used accordingly. In practically all instances he shall need to mix in organic matter and phosphorus generously. But with the same kind

---

[1] Many gardeners mix sifted coal ashes or cinders with clay soil to make it more mellow. They are also recommended to be used as the 4 to 6-inch-deep layer under specimen plants and beds for drainage. Despite this common recommendation and use, the author cannot recommend them because of the danger of sulphides and other toxic substances in some coal ashes. Probably it is a good practice in most instances.

of soil he shall need to add limestone to make the soil less acid for
some plants, and sulphur to make it more acid for other plants. Some
prefer a sandy soil, others a clayey one.

Seed beds. The soil may be allowed to settle for a while after plowing or spading, but it should not be permitted to become dry. The
loose soil needs to be packed with a roller or cultipacker to develop
a firm seed bed. In the small garden, where all the work is done by
hand, the soil usually gets sufficient packing, indeed usually too much,
while the smoothing and leveling is being done.

In large gardens the soil may be smoothed and made fine with a
harrow or cultivator. In small gardens the hoe and garden rake are
used. Lumps of soil need to be shattered and the surface made uniformly smooth and granular, but not powdery. Like plowing or spading this must *not* be done when the soil is wet, unless it is very sandy.
It is usually more convenient to sow seeds if the stones and coarse
organic matter are raked out of the immediate surface. Such obstruc-
tions within the normal depth of rooting cause deformed roots that
decrease the value of root crops. Ideally, the surface few inches should
be uniformly firm with a surface inch of fairly loose granular soil.
Unless the seed bed is uniform, the seeds do not come up evenly.

Cultivation. For over a century most farmers and gardeners have
cultivated the soil not simply more than necessary but actually too
much. About the turn of the century a "dust mulch" theory was
developed, according to which one should always keep the surface
finely pulverized to prevent the soil water underneath from rising to
the surface by capillary action (as in a lamp wick) and being lost.
This theory is no longer widely believed.

Excessive hoeing and cultivating should be avoided because they
are certain to harm the natural granular structure. When the soil is
wet, a great deal of harm is done. If the soil bakes hard to a considerable depth, a fundamental improvement of the granular structure
must be undertaken by mixing in organic matter, growing cover crops,
plowing in the fall, and so on, because continual deep cultivation and
hoeing hurt the surface roots. Rarely should the hoeing be deeper
than one-half to one inch. Soils rich in clay may develop a hard
surface crust upon drying after a beating rain. This crust should be

broken up just after it begins to form—while the soil is neither wet nor dry—so that water from the next rain can enter. If a shower comes when there is such a crust on the soil, a lot of water may run off before the soil gets soaked up enough for the rain water to enter.[2]

And, of course, weeds must be killed. This is the main reason for cultivation. It is easy to destroy tiny weeds with shallow surface cultivating or hoeing. If allowed to grow large, the weeds must be pulled out by hand or by deep hoeing. Either method injures the roots of other plants. Also by the time the weeds have reached this stage, they have already robbed the other plants of a good deal of water and nutrients. Above all, weeds should never be allowed to go to seed. If that happens even one year, the gardener will have a battle for a long time after, since the seeds remain alive in the soil for two or three years—even longer for some kinds.

Proper hoeing is nearly a fine art. Usually the three-pronged hoe is better for cultivation after the seeds are up in the small garden and flower beds. With it there is much less likelihood of cutting off a prize tomato or zinnia. The job is to *get* all the weeds, loosen up the surface crust so water can enter easily, and do as little damage as possible to the surface roots and soil structure. And the job needs to be done well.

Surface mulch. Mulches are discussed further in the chapter on organic matter, but they are a part of the soil skeleton. Once the small plants from seed are established, the soil may be covered with leaf mold, compost, or sawdust deeply enough to obviate the need for further cultivation. The few weeds able to get through the mulch can be pulled out by hand. Mulch protects the surface soil from beating raindrops and the hot sun, thus reducing crusting, evaporation, temperature, and losses of water from runoff.

---

[2] In dry weather when every bit of water is needed, a light sprinkling with the hose just in advance of the rain softens up such a crust and insures getting more of the shower into the soil. But one cannot always guess when the shower is coming or be there with the spray!

4

ORGANIC MATTER:
THE GARDENER'S ELIXIR

The gardener has no elixir, of course, in the complete sense of the word. But organic matter is the nearest thing to it—both fresh organic matter and humus, or partly decomposed organic matter —in the lower soil, in the surface soil, and on the surface.

Rare is the gardener who has enough organic matter. Resourcefulness in getting an abundant supply and skill in its preparation and use are the first requisites for gardening. Some soils are already well supplied, like the nearly black soils of the Middle West. But even there, mulches are necessary for the best results with many plants. Only a very few gardens are laid out on peat or muck—soils made up wholly of organic matter.

Most soils used for gardens in the eastern part of the United States and in and about the great cities are naturally too low in organic matter for good results. Where the summers are long and hot, the problem of organic matter is especially great; the soils have but little in them naturally, and that applied decomposes rapidly. The gardener cannot simply make an application or so and forget organic matter; he must add it regularly.

Important as it is and much as it has been studied, a lot remains to be learned about the nature and effects of soil organic matter. Recently speculation has increased. Some claim for it a sort of mystic power that dominates all else. Special preparations are sold and special composts recommended that are supposed to produce plants of great vigor, beauty, and health, without other fertilizer and without hazards of diseases and insect pests. Many of the composts and materials possess merit—just how much cannot always be proved. Even where scientific evidence is lacking—perhaps especially where it is lacking—one can get some testimonials.

Part of the confusion comes about because different kinds of soil vary widely in requirements and responses; different plants growing in the same soil also vary in these, although not so much. Here we cannot settle the claims of the organic-matter enthusiasts against those of the chemical-nutrition extremists. That can only be done through careful scientific research. The author believes that the truth will be found somewhere between—that both organic matter and mineral fertilizers have an essential role in gardening. He belongs to neither school, but asserts the need for research not yet begun.

KINDS OF ORGANIC MATTER IN SOILS

First of all, the soil contains living plant and animal forms. As their dead remains decompose, a great host of transitional organic compounds are produced, some very transitory, such as simple organic acids, and the more or less stable, nearly black humus. The end result of decomposition is, of course, simple gases that escape into the air, and the mineral salts.

In outline these forms might be shown as follows:

1. *Living organic matter*
   a. Plants (grasses, trees, shrubs, etc.)
   b. Micro-organisms (bacteria, fungi, protozoa, etc.)
   c. Animals (earthworms, rodents, etc.)

2. *Dead organic matter*
   a. Fresh organic matter
      (1) Very rapidly decomposable materials high in protein, such as cottonseed meal, dried blood, and meat scraps.
      (2) Succulent material high in protein and easily decomposable, such as freshly cut clover and grass.
      (3) Dry material, relatively low in protein, and moderately rapidly decomposable, such as wheat straw.
      (4) Dry material, relatively low in protein and slowly decomposable, such as oak leaves and pine needles low in bases, and maple leaves higher in bases.
      (5) Dry material, relatively low in protein and very slowly decomposable, such as sawdust and wood fragments.

b. Partially decomposed unstable organic matter. Masses of these materials contain soluble organic compounds of many sorts in small amounts.

   (1) Partially digested organic matter, high in protein and plant nutrients, such as animal manure, decomposes rapidly in the soil.

   (2) Leaf mold, lying above the mineral soil and beneath the freshly fallen leaves in the forest, decomposes in the soil at moderate rates. Generally, that under pines and spruces is acid, and that under maples is neutral. Oak-leaf mold is usually strongly to mildly acid, depending on the soil.

   (3) Compost of various sorts decomposes slowly to rapidly, depending on its origin.

   (4) Peat is a relatively stable material under conditions of poor drainage, but slowly decomposes in normal soil. It usually contains some humus.

c. Partially decomposed stable organic matter, or humus, is dark brown to black and usually granular where abundant. It is commonly most abundant in the surface layers of soil. It decomposes slowly to water, carbon dioxide, and mineral salts.

ORGANIC MATTER HAS MANY JOBS

Organic matter has several important functions in soils and in plant growth. In no soil are all these functions important at one time. And, of course, different kinds of organic matter act differently. The relationships among the functions are so complicated that it may be worth while to display the principal ones that affect soil productivity, individually, in outline form:

1. *Organic matter promotes granular structure and pore space.* This is partly a mechanical effect, like the result of mixing coarse straw and leaves into heavy massive soils in order to introduce planes of weakness and promote aggregates of small size. More important is the granulation produced by living micro-organisms that live on organic matter. The best of all kinds of organic matter for this purpose are the roots of vigorously growing grasses and legumes.[1] Under this general heading are several individual effects.

a. *Aids root extension.* In massive clay soils, the gardener may find no other way to provide a deep rooting zone for tender-rooted plants than to mix manure, compost, or leaf mold deeply in the soil.

[1] This statement may need modification as experience is gained with the newly announced synthetic organic conditioners mentioned on page 55.

b. *Reduces baking and crust formation.* Crusts form on many soils, especially those rich in clay, when they are exposed directly to beating rains and the hot sun. Such crusts reduce water intake and injure surface roots. By mixing organic matter into the surface soil, their formation is reduced or prevented.

c. *Promotes entry of water into the soil.* Often surface soils become so hard that rain water simply runs off and does not get into the lower soil for storage and for roots, especially where much of the rain comes in short hard showers. Organic matter mixed into the surface layers and mulches on the surface increase the proportion of water that soaks into the soil.

d. *Reduces soil washing.* As organic matter is used to encourage the entry of water into the soil, less runs off. Since washing, or erosion, is caused by rapidly running water passing over bare soil, the proper use of organic matter reduces it. On steeply sloping soils the use of organic matter must be supplemented with terraces, diversion channels, and other means to reduce runoff as explained elsewhere.

e. *Promotes aeration or exchange of gases.* Some of the pores in the soil must be open for air to pass into the soil and for other gases to get out. Roots and many micro-organisms important to soil productivity need air; and excessive accumulations of carbon dioxide or other gases must be dispersed else they become toxic to plants. In normal soils air passes in and out with changes in moisture content, barometric pressure, and temperature. In this sense the soil "breathes." In very compact or soggy soils the pore space can be increased by mixing organic matter with the soil in which the roots should grow.

f. *Increases water-holding capacity.* Many sandy soils, low in organic matter, allow so much water to drain away that plants suffer from drought soon after rains. By developing and maintaining a high content of humus or very fine material, such as shredded peat, the water-holding capacity of such soils may be greatly increased. This is very important to thousands of gardeners who have to use soils developed on old sand dunes, sandy coastal beaches, and outwash plains.

g. *Reduces soil blowing.* Dry sand grains or small granules of soil are likely to be blown from an unprotected soil surface by strong winds. Besides providing windbreaks the gardener can keep the

the surface soil rough and mixed with coarse, trashy organic matter that protects the fine soil while young plants are getting established.

2. *Mulches reduce the extremes of temperature, especially of high summer temperatures.* Micro-organisms and the roots of many plants in the very surface are injured by extremely high temperatures. Surface mulches reduce high temperatures greatly and, by protecting the surface soil from great heat and intense light, lower the rate of destruction of the humus in the soil. In hot regions one should avoid letting the sun beat directly on the bare soil. In cold regions, however, surface mulches must be avoided where vegetables and annuals are to be grown, since they reduce the depth of warm soil over cold or frozen subsoil. Even in New England surface mulches, in early spring especially, reduce soil temperatures too much. But mulches may be used in cold areas to protect the crowns of perennials in winter.

3. *Mulches and organic matter in the surface soil reduce evaporation losses.* By protecting the soil from the direct rays of the sun and moving air, organic matter in the surface soil, and especially mulches, reduce evaporation losses. Some shallow-rooted plants, like azaleas and blueberries, suffer great injury from drought. With these a continuous mulch is usually a necessity for good growth, but a great many other plants are benefited too. Mulches also help to maintain regular growth. They reduce the cracking of tomatoes, for example.

4. *Mulches reduce weed growth.* After plants are well established, surface mulches may be added that suppress the growth of unwanted plants, thus reducing one of the greatest losses of soil moisture—transpiration through weeds.

5. *Humus helps maintain the reaction (pH) of soil.* As explained in the section on soil acidity the acidity of soils low in organic matter, especially sandy ones, is too easily changed. With plenty of humus, reaction is more nearly stable—not easily changed. In chemistry such a substance is called a "buffer."

6. *Organic matter aids in the retention of the relatively soluble compounds of the soil.* Many of the plant nutrients are held in the soil by tiny particles, either of mineral matter (fine clay) or of organic matter (humus). Thus by maintaining a high content of humus the soil has a higher capacity to hold nutrients in forms available to plants against leaching. The nutrients in the living tissue and fresh

plant remains are also held against leaching. In permeable soils of warm, very humid regions the most important storehouse of plant nutrients is this organic matter, which gradually gives up its nutrients to plants as it decomposes. By growing winter cover crops, plant nutrients are saved in organic form that would otherwise leach out of barren soil.

7. *Part of the organic matter furnishes the food supply for micro-organisms and small animals.* Generally, soils having high populations of microbes and small animals are more productive than those with low populations. If there is to be a high population, organic matter is necessary for their food. The bacteria that fix nitrogen from the air in forms usable for plants need energy food. So do those responsible for soil granulation. Through decomposition by the organisms nutrients tied up in the organic matter are released in forms available to plants.

A few kinds of micro-organisms in the soil are harmful, pathogenic to plants. Among these are nematodes and many soil-borne disease organisms. About many there is uncertainty. The argument still waxes over earthworms, with little direct evidence that they are either greatly beneficial or harmful. Probably earthworms are beneficial under most conditions, but one cannot be certain. Where decomposition of organic matter is very rapid anyway, earthworms may do harm by a further speeding up of the process, especially where a high content of humus is essential. Then too, many other important small animals other than the slowly moving, friendly earthworms live in the soil but are not so obvious.

8. *Decomposing organic matter furnishes directly, and indirectly by promoting bacteria and fungi, complex organic compounds which may include both growth-promoting and antibiotic substances.* It is here that speculation about organic matter in soils is both interesting and uncertain. It is known that certain organic substances do promote root growth and that others do reduce or destroy pathogens. After all, some of the new antibiotics used in medicine are produced by soil organisms. Possibly some of the good influences of organic matter in soils are due to these substances. Harmful substances may also be present. How substantial these effects really are must await research not yet begun. Certainly they vary enormously in different soil types. It will be very difficult to segregate this one effect of decomposing organic matter in soils from the many others.

9. *Additions of organic matter maintain a slowly available, fairly*

well balanced supply of plant nutrients, including micro-nutrients.
This function of organic matter is very important to gardeners everywhere, but especially so to those in warm humid regions where leaching is severe. Most commonly, the gardener supplies nutrients partly
in organic matter and partly as chemical fertilizer. Organic matter as
a source of nutrients is, perhaps, most important for shrubs, naturalized flower beds, and other permanent plantings. Especially for vegetables, mineral fertilizers are usually needed also for best results.
Plants growing normally obviously are taking up all essential plant
nutrients in reasonable balance. Otherwise they would not be normal.
Leaf mold or compost made from such plant tissue releases a fair
balance of these nutrients as they decompose. Even though the gardener adds certain nutrients, such as phosphorus, potassium, nitrogen, and magnesium, in fertilizers, questions may remain about
copper, zinc, boron, iron, and the like, needed in only tiny amounts.
With generous use of leaf mold, compost, and manure from normal
plant tissue one may be reasonably certain of adequate supplies. Some
qualifications must be added, however. Certain peats, for example,
are derived from plants unusually low or high in copper, zinc, manganese, or other nutrients. If an acid leached soil is given an excess
of lime or nitrogen, the nutrient supply may become unbalanced even
with abundant organic matter present. These chemical relationships
are discussed in more detail in the section on plant nutrients.

PROBLEMS IN USING ORGANIC MATTER

The effects of organic matter in the soil are many and varied. Relatively undecomposed material is used as mulch to control temperature
and evaporation. Organic matter to supply nutrients is usually applied
in a partially decomposed form as compost or natural leaf mold. The
physical effects are quite unlike in sandy soils and in heavy clay soils,
in flat soils and in hilly ones, in dry soils and in wet ones. Coarse
fresh material acts differently from the nearly stable humus portion or
the intermediate forms like compost and leaf mold. The coarse material helps improve the structure of massive clay soils by introducing
planes of weakness or breakage; whereas it is the humus that helps
bind loose structureless sand grains into granules.

Then, too, the use of organic matter raises difficulties that should
be taken into account. Let us look at some of these.

Seed bed preparation. Most seeds require a firm, but not dense or hard, seed bed. If the soil is uneven because of unbroken clods or unmixed batches of organic matter, germination and growth are uneven. This difficulty argues against mixing coarse, undecomposed organic matter in the surface soil at seeding time. After small plants are up and well established, mulches may be added to the top, and even worked partly into the very surface soil, to hold them in place against washing or blowing and to prevent the formation of a hard crustlike surface layer just underneath the mulch.

Unless the surface 6- to 8-inch layer of garden soil is mellow and well mixed, the roots of such vegetables as parsnips, salsify, and carrots become crooked and abnormally branched.

Although the soil should be mellow and porous, not too dense, it needs to be firm and free of large air holes and cavities that dry out easily. When shrubs and trees are set out, it is very important that organic matter added to the soil, in both lower and surface layers, be thoroughly mixed with the soil so that the mixture can be pressed *firmly* about the roots with no large unfilled holes or crevices, else the roots become dry and die.

Seed beds for grass in soil of poor tilth can be greatly improved by the mixing of shredded peat or straw into the surface layer.

Tillage. Coarse organic matter in the surface soil offers handicaps to cultivation and even to hand-hoeing. The movement of little sticks, coarse straws, and large leaves often breaks or covers small plants. Where weeds are serious, some hoeing and cultivation are necessary. Here again one may wait until the plants are well established and then mulch heavily. But halfway measures are unsatisfactory: one should either mulch heavily enough to prevent weed growth or else not enough to interfere with cultivation and hoeing. For the small garden, with a good source of material, the use of mulches is an excellent practice to control weeds, provided too that the mulch is reasonably free of weed seeds. Even leaf mold from the woods is likely to have some weed seeds brought in by birds. Often, baled straw bought on the open market, or stable manure, is foul with weed seeds.

Wash of surface organic matter. If beating rains happen to fall on sloping soil with tender seedlings just emerging, loose bits of organic matter may be washed over and around them. One needs to avoid such a soil condition as much as possible before the plants are established and to be careful to inspect seedlings immediately after heavy showers in order to remove any such coverings.

Diseases and insects. Both diseases and insects can be spread by organic matter. Plants that are known to be diseased or those that wilt and die from unknown causes should be uprooted and burned. They should never be used in the compost. Probably most disease organisms and insects are killed in a well managed compost but one cannot be sure. At least there is less danger if all but diseased plant remains are composted before use.

Then too, slugs, snails, termites, and even mice are likely to be more numerous where heavy applications of organic matter and heavy mulches are used. Insects that attack seeds are attracted to them before they germinate. If such pests become bad, the gardener may need to avoid the use of much organic matter, especially mulches, until they are destroyed or brought under control.

Some go so far as to say that the use of abundant amounts of well composted organic matter gives plants of such vigor that no diseases or insects can attack them. It is true that vigorously growing plants have a better chance to remain healthy than plants struggling against too much or too little water, extremes of temperature, restrictions of root growth, or unbalanced or deficient nutrient supplies; but uncontrolled diseases and insects take their toll even of these.

Complete dependence upon organic matter in no way insures proper nutrient balance and healthy plants. There is no single rule to gardening. The wise gardener consults the plant pathologist and entomologist as well as the soil scientist and horticulturist.

THE BALANCE OF CARBOHYDRATES AND NITROGEN

Something has already been said of the differences in organic matter according to stage of decomposition—fresh, intermediate, and humus. Since plant tissue varies greatly in its content of nitrogen and other plant nutrients, so do the decomposition products. Leaf mold from pine and spruce forests is lower in nitrogen and is more acid than leaf mold from maple forests. And within each sort there are wide variations, depending on the soil in which the trees are rooted.

The ratio of carbon to nitrogen in organic matter is very important to garden soils. Roughly we can say that plant tissue contains two main groups of organic compounds: (1) the carbohydrates, such as sugar, starch, and cellulose, that furnish energy material for the soil organisms; and (2) the nitrogen-containing compounds, especially proteins, from which micro-organisms get their supply of available nitrogen for growth. A rough measure of these is the relative content of carbon and nitrogen, expressed as the ratio of carbon to nitrogen, or C/N ratio. Now, of course, proteins contain some carbon and furnish some energy to soil organisms. And waxes, resins, and other compounds are present that do not fall neatly into either group.

In a normal soil the ratio of carbon to nitrogen is a constant. The figure varies for different kinds of soil, but a ratio of about 10 carbon to 1 nitrogen, or a C/N ratio of 10, is to be expected in ordinary garden soils of temperate regions. If more organic carbon is added to the soil, say sugar or wheat straw, immediately processes are initiated within the soil to bring the ratio back to 10 (or the figure near 10 specific for the particular soil type).

By adding such energy material to a normal garden soil the micro-population is stimulated and the numbers increase—they require nitrogen for the proteins of their bodies. Thus *while the population is increasing,* the nitrogen available to plants declines; it is tied up in the bodies of the living micro-organisms. Later, when the extra energy material is used up, or when the C/N ratio returns to normal, the *population decreases* and the nitrogen available to plants *increases.* Thus, sugar added to a soil in autumn may result in an increased yield of spring-sown grass while sugar added in the spring decreases the yield.

If the organic matter added is a pure carbohydrate, such as common sugar, there is only a little more nitrogen in the soil at the end—only the amount taken from the air by the few organisms which can do that. Additions of straw and other materials that are very rich in carbon and poor in nitrogen do not increase the humus content of the soil very much because nitrogen becomes the limiting factor, since the C/N ratio of the soil tends to reach a constant. Thus to increase the humus content of a soil—to raise the percentage of stable organic matter in it—both carbon and nitrogen need to be added. Otherwise, plants suffer from a lack of nitrogen while the organic matter is decomposing in the soil and the yield of humus is low.

These relationships are very important. Repeated frequent applications of fresh organic matter, low in nitrogen, result in nitrogen-starved plants. Most materials available to the gardener, like straw and dry leaves, have a C/N ratio of about 40. That of clover hay is much lower. The roots and stubble from legume hays have a ratio of 20 to 25. In manure the ratio is about 18, or higher if it contains much straw.

Thus manure is a good source of soil organic matter because of its relatively low C/N ratio. If plant tissue is first composted, the ratio is reduced sharply with the loss of carbon from the decomposition in the compost pile. By mixing manure, dried blood, meat scraps, or other nitrogen-containing materials with leaves and straw, a much higher yield of good compost (with a low C/N ratio) is obtained.

One may add both fresh organic matter and nitrogen to the soil and let the whole decomposition process take place within it. Some advocate this practice. Most farmers handle organic matter that way; but it is often not convenient in gardening. Ordinarily, the gardener does better with compost or leaf mold—with organic matter already partially decomposed—than with fresh material, except for special mulches, such as straw or pine needles as a winter cover on strawberries and sawdust on blueberries.

The main purpose of composting is to have the initial processes of decomposition, while the C/N ratio is being reduced, take place outside the soil. This is not the only purpose, since compost is less bulky to mix into the soil and competes less with plants for the moisture in the garden soil.

The C/N ratio in good compost is not brought all the way to 10 outside the soil, but more nearly to 15 or 20, not counting easily leached nitrogen salts. For most shrubs it is best to have organic mulches with fairly high C/N ratios, up to 15 or 20, not counting easily soluble nitrogen added in the spring or early summer, which leaches into the soil with rain or irrigation.

RATIO OF PHOSPHORUS TO CARBON AND NITROGEN

Next after nitrogen, the soil micro-organisms take available phosphorus out of the soil for growth. Thus, if considerable energy material, such as sugar or straw, is added to the soil, the numbers of micro-organisms greatly increase, especially if nitrogen is also plentiful. This places a heavy demand on available phosphorus. Unless phosphatic fertilizers have been used on the soil or mixed with the added organic materials, plants may suffer a serious phosphate deficiency. Thus usually manure or compost should be reinforced with phosphorus (say superphosphate or ground rock phosphate) as well as with nitrogen.

MATERIALS TO USE

Organic materials used in gardening vary from fertilizers like cottonseed meal and dried blood, fairly rich in available plant nutrients, to peat and sawdust which are used primarily as mulches or soil conditioners and furnish only insignificant amounts of plant nutrients. Manure and compost stand between. Some forms of manure, like the dried sheep, poultry, or cow manure, sold in bags, is used chiefly as an organic fertilizer.

The materials used primarily as fertilizers are discussed in the chapter on plant nutrients. Because manure and compost are important for both plant nutrition and their physical effects, suggestions discussed there are important in determining their use. Since nutrient balance in the soil and the maintenance of organic matter are closely interrelated, practices involving fertilizer and organic matter must be decided together.

Animal manure. For most plants animal manure is an excellent source of all or part of the organic matter. It may be used directly, composted alone, or composted with leaves, straw, and other waste materials. But not nearly enough is available at reasonable cost to supply all gardens.

Manure varies in composition and quality depending upon the animal source (poultry, sheep, cow, or horse), character and amount of bedding (percentage of straw, shavings, and so on), and the degree of decomposition—whether fresh, well rotted, or composted. Poultry manure is normally highest in available plant nutrients, especially nitrogen, unless it contains plenty of bedding. Very heavy applications injure plants. At the other extreme is strawy horse manure in which all the nitrogen, and more, is needed in the decomposition of the straw.

Fresh manure, especially that containing lots of bedding, does not release much nitrogen to the soil for plant use immediately—not until after it has been at least partially decomposed. Further, the coarse straw and other materials may present difficulty in preparing a proper seed bed, especially in a small garden not equipped with machines for the purpose. For these reasons most gardeners use manure that is already well rotted, or else they compost it themselves before mixing it with the soil. Where both manure and other organic materials are scarce, composting is best. The nitrogen in the manure serves to balance the carbon in both the manure and the other materials. If the manure contains considerable straw, however, all the nitrogen in it is needed to balance the carbohydrate in the manure itself. Indeed, the very strawy manure from racing stables should have some nitrogen added to it before composting in order to balance the carbohydrate. Composting also reduces (but does not eliminate) the hazards of weed seeds and plant disease organisms.

If the garden is not subject to significant erosion and can be plowed well in advance of planting, the manure may be plowed under to advantage. In temperate regions where fall plowing is possible, heavy applications of manure can be used just in advance of plowing; then by spring a good seed bed can be prepared.

Manure that is simply rotted in an unprotected pile is apt to have lost much of its soluble nitrogen and potassium through leaching, although it may be an excellent source of humus. Generally speaking, however, fairly well rotted manure is the best source of organic matter for the kitchen garden and for most perennial and annual borders, where available at reasonable cost. For roses many gardeners prefer fresh, relatively straw-free cow manure.

For the vegetable garden and flower beds the manure may be applied in a layer some 1 to 3 inches thick, and spaded or plowed under. The same may be done in preparing soil for a lawn or for perennial borders. Generous amounts may be mixed with the soil in transplanting trees, shrubs, and other perennial plants. It may be spread on the surface of established lawns and, after a period for leaching and decomposition, the coarse remains of straw and other fibers raked off.

The amounts to use are suggested in Table 1. The rate varies with its availability and cost, soil needs, and the other fertilizers and organic materials used. For the kitchen garden or perennial beds the addition of about 2 pounds of available phosphoric acid to each 2000 pounds of manure gives a very roughly balanced nutrient supply. This would amount to 10 pounds of 20 per cent superphosphate per ton of manure or about ⅔ cupful for each tightly packed bushel. If no other phosphatic fertilizer is used, and the soil is low in phosphorus, these amounts may be increased 4 times. (See chapter on plant nutrients.) If the manure is strawy, extra nitrogen is needed for the kitchen garden.

TABLE 1. **Suggested rates for applications of manure to garden soils**

Manure	Measure [1]	APPROXIMATE AMOUNTS PER 1000 SQ. FT. FOR AN APPLICATION THAT WOULD BE		
		Light	Medium	Heavy
Well rotted horse and cow	pounds [2]	250	600	1200
or	bushels { loosely packed	8	20	40
Fresh horse and cow [3]	bushels { tightly packed	4	10	20
Fresh poultry	pounds	80	200	300
	bushels, well packed	1⅓	3	5
Dried cow [4]	pounds	35	70	140
Dried sheep [4]	pounds	25	50	100
Dried poultry [4]	pounds	20	40	60

[1] Manure is also sometimes sold by the cord of approximately 100 loosely packed bushels.

[2] A rough rule for well rotted manure is 1 pound per square foot for a fairly heavy application, suitable for the ordinary kitchen garden.

[3] If the manure is to be the only source of nitrogen in the kitchen garden, except for supplemented midseason applications to tomatoes, sweet corn, and salad crops, about 3 pounds of nitrogen should be added to each 1000 pounds of manure, roughly equivalent to 2 tablespoonfuls of ammonium sulphate for each tightly packed bushel. This is for fresh manure with a medium amount of straw. With much more straw, the amount may be increased. About equal amounts of ground limestone may be added to compensate for the acid produced by the ammonium sulphate.

[4] The application of these materials should be guided by the amount of available nitrogen in them and the suggested rates of nitrogen application.

When transplanting individual trees and shrubs, 1 to 4 bushels of well rotted manure may be used for each, depending upon the size of the plant. It should be worked into the soil to a depth of about 2 feet and well mixed with it.

Compost. Certainly no phase of gardening is more popular now than composting. Several books have been printed on the subject, especially in England. Various cults have their own formulae for making compost, including various mixtures of materials, additions of chemicals, turning, and using. Some of the claims border on the fantastic. A large part of the confusion has come about from failures to recognize that contrasting kinds of soil respond differently. Some soils need a great deal of organic matter, while others do not. But most of the enthusiasts for composts, like those for "complete" minerals and certain tillage practices, have at least some solid ground to stand on; they simply reach too far.

After manure, compost is the best source of organic matter for the gardener, at least for most uses. Even manure is commonly composted, either with the straw and other bedding contained in it or with mixed leaves and refuse from the garden and lawn.

The essential principles for producing compost include the following:

(1) The first requirement is to reduce the carbon-nitrogen ratio through partial decomposition, without loss of nitrogen and other plant nutrients by excessive leaching or heating.

(2) A reasonably compact, but aerated pile of organic matter should be built. If the pile "heats" too much, part of the nitrogen escapes in gases.

(3) Usually best results are obtained by mixing some fertile surface soil with the organic materials. The soil absorbs materials that might otherwise be lost. The surface is capped with a layer of soil, which absorbs gases that might escape. A properly made compost pile has little or no odor.

(4) Ideally, the pile should have a mixture of materials, which will give a crumbly organic matter with a balanced supply of plant nutrients, including nitrogen, phosphorus, potassium, calcium, magnesium, and the other nutrients. The organic materials to use, and especially the amount of wood ashes or lime to add, are determined in part by the plants to be grown. The compost pile should not have limestone or wood ashes added to it to make it alkaline. Burned lime or hydrated lime should not be used for best results. If the compost is made alkaline with such materials, some of the nitrogen is likely to be lost.

Most vegetables and many trees, shrubs, and flowers do best with a nearly neutral, or slightly acid mixture; but a few, like azaleas, blueberries, and mountain laurel, need strongly acid material. No wood ashes or limestone should be added to compost intended for acid-loving plants.

Although some make the compost in a pit, it is generally better to make the pile on the surface in order to be sure of good aeration. For the small garden piles may be made about 3 to 5 feet wide, 6 to 8 feet long, and 4 to 5 feet high, after being reasonably well packed. An open-work bin of bricks or boards is convenient. A portable crib can be made by using wooden pieces about 4 inches by 4 inches overlapped at the corners. Side pieces may be 6 to 8 feet long, and end pieces 3 to 5 feet long. Through holes near the end of each piece, four vertical iron rods at the corners will hold the crib in place.

With care one can do without side supports for the compost pile, but it is better to have them.

Uusually the compost is made in layers, say a layer of good garden soil or dark-colored surface soil from the woods about ½ to 1 inch thick, alternating with 6- to 12-inch layers of organic material. When finished it should be covered with 2 to 4 inches of soil.

If the pile is placed in a relatively shady place, it does not dry out badly. When first made and during periods without rain, it should be watered sufficiently to keep the material moist.

Some "organic enthusiasts" insist that chemicals should not be added; but most soil and garden specialists recommend them. If about 25 to 50 per cent of the mixture can be manure, along with leaves and other vegetable wastes, it is not necessary to add chemical fertilizers to get a fair supply of nitrogen. Young and tender plants, grass clippings, and clover hay contain considerable nitrogen. If autumn leaves are the main source of organic matter for the compost, as is so often the case, and manure is unavailable, nitrogen should be added to get a good yield of high-quality compost.

Some phosphatic fertilizer, especially superphosphate, or that in a mixed fertilizer, should be added. Wood ashes may be added for their potassium and lime content. These materials, especially the wood ashes, should be well mixed with the organic matter. Ground dolomitic limestone may be added to supply calcium and magnesium and to keep the mixture from being acid. If no limestone is used, or only calcium limestone, then Epsom salts (magnesium sulphate) should be added.

General recommendations for additions to compost, assuming that dried leaves are the main source of organic matter and that a small amount of good surface soil is mixed with the leaves, are given in Table 2.

TABLE 2.   Suggested chemicals to be added to organic materials in making compost.

Chemicals	RATE	
	Per ton of plant material (pounds)	Per bushel [1] of plant material (cups)
Combination A		
(a) Ammonium sulphate	80	1
or ammonium nitrate	50	½
or cottonseed meal	80	1 to ½
(b) Ground dolomitic limestone [2]	60	⅔
or wood ashes	80	1 to ½
(c) Superphosphate (20%)	50	½
Combination B		
(a) Mixed fertilizer 5–10–5	300	3
(b) Ground dolomitic limestone [2]	60	⅔
or wood ashes	80	1 to ½

[1] Tightly packed. A bushel of dry straw or leaves, packed tightly with the hands, weighs about 12½ pounds; moist packed manure, about 60 pounds; moist loose manure, about 30 pounds.

[2] Epsom salts is added if no lime is used, or if ordinary ground limestone is used instead of dolomitic limestone, at the rate of 8 pounds per ton or one tablespoon per bushel. The ashes and ground limestone should be omitted from compost for acid-loving plants.

This table is only suggestive. Any one of a number of nitrogen-containing materials, such as fish scrap, dried blood, and the like, may be used instead of ammonium sulphate. Ground rock phosphate at 3 or 4 times the rate suggested for superphosphate may be used. Burned or hydrated lime should be avoided because these materials are so strongly alkaline that any unevenness in mixing results in some spots being too alkaline and in losses of nitrogen. Coal ashes should not be used.

Some gardeners recommend larger amounts of chemicals, but these have no beneficial influence on the composting process. Additions of lime or ashes should not be high enough to produce an alkaline reaction in the compost. When additional fertilizers are needed (as they often are), they should be applied to the soil, as explained in the section on plant nutrients.

Some recommend frequent turning of the compost, say three, five, and twelve weeks after making. Such turnings help produce a more mixed and crumbly material, although a fairly good compost can be had with no turning at all. In temperate regions it is the usual good practice to make the main compost pile in autumn from the fallen leaves and to turn it once or twice in late spring or early summer, about May 15 and July 1. In the small garden another supplementary compost pile may be made from plant remains as they accumulate during the summer. It is usually most convenient to incorporate this material into the main compost pile made later in autumn. Usually one will need to hold part of the compost made during the previous year over the winter for use in the spring.

Good material for general use as a mulch on shrubs and flowers, all or part of which may be acid-loving, may be made by simply piling up leaves in a shady place, keeping them moist, and turning them two or three times during the season. Such compost made from leaves piled up in the autumn in warm temperate regions can be used the next summer and autumn; but better results are had with two seasons rather than with one.

Leaves and straw. These may be added directly to the soil in order to increase the amount of organic matter. In autumn, leaves or straw may be mixed in the upper surface of the soil or laid on top of the soil in a thin layer and held down in firm contact with the moist soil by brush or poles. In this way the materials protect the soil from beating rains and wash during the winter. They become partially decomposed for spading under in the spring. Somewhat more nitrogen should be added to the soil when this is done, since these materials are so high in carbohydrates. Ordinarily about 1 pound of nitrogen, equivalent to 4 pounds of ammonium sulphate, should be added for each 100 pounds of dry straw or leaves. Generally speaking, composting is preferable to this method although many gardeners have good results with it.

Straw, especially when chopped, makes a satisfactory mulch for strawberries, raspberries, and other plants. Many use it under tomatoes to help keep the fruit clean and to protect the soil from rain and sun. Straw makes a good protective cover for strawberries in winter. In the spring this may be worked under the plants and left on the soil between the rows. One should cover the soil to a depth of 3 to 4 inches with straw or use approximately 100 to 150 pounds per 1000 square feet. Such mulches suppress weeds if they are clean to begin with. As with manure, one can introduce serious weeds through unclean straw.

Straw mulches may become very dry and present a serious fire hazard. For this reason it is dangerous to have large continuous areas of valuable plants mulched with straw.

Sawdust. Although sawdust has no significant value as a fertilizer, it is increasingly appreciated by gardeners as a mulch and as an organic conditioner of the soil. It can be used on acid-loving plants and on the lime lovers. It is practical because it is more easily worked around the plants and under the low leaves than leaf mold or straw. Of course it does furnish the soil micro-organisms with a very slowly available source of carbohydrates. When used by itself, especially if fresh, it can thus depress the amount of available nitrogen. In order to counteract this effect on the available nitrogen in the soil 1 to 2 per cent of nitrogen may be added to the sawdust—say about 5 to 10 pounds of ammonium sulphate or sodium nitrate, to each 100 pounds of dry sawdust, or one to two cupfuls to a bushel.

On acid-loving plants requiring a heavy mulch one may use sawdust to a depth of 1 to 3 inches with good results. As a more general application, a layer one-half to one inch thick is satisfactory.

Peat. Peat is a good soil conditioner and useful as a mulch, but it is ordinarily too expensive for wide use in the garden. That is, most gardeners find it more economical to make compost out of the available leaves and other materials for mixing with the soil. Leaf mold and sawdust are generally available more cheaply for use as mulches. For tiny city gardens peat materials are relatively convenient to purchase and to use, especially for small plantings of azaleas or other fine plants and as a conditioner prior to seeding grass. For general use over an area 100 pounds per 1000 square feet is a reasonable rate. It needs to be much deeper when used as a mulch for acid-loving shrubs, say 3 to 4 inches. Only the acid peats, such as moss peat, should be used on the acid-loving plants.

Peat is commonly used to prepare soils of poor tilth and low in organic matter, for grass seeding. About 500 to 700 pounds of dry peat are mixed with the upper 3- or 4-inch layer of soil over an area of 1000 square feet.

Peat varies widely in its content of nitrogen. Some kinds are quite high, up to 3 per cent. But this becomes available to plants so slowly that its fertilizer value is usually insignificant.

Leaf mold. Often the gardener finds it possible to get leaf mold conveniently from the woods. This is the partially decomposed material beneath the freshly fallen leaves and above the mineral soil. That under the pine and oak forest is usually quite acid and makes a good mulch for the acid-loving plants. That under the maples is not quite so acid. The material is excellent for mulching and for soil conditioning. High quality leaf mold is nearly as good as compost. The leaf mold from pine needles is especially good for acid-loving plants. Many gardeners use nearly fresh pine needles as mulch for winter protection on their strawberries.

In collecting leaf mold it is best to remove as many of the small twigs as possible, partly because they are a nuisance in cultivation and partly because they are inclined to harbor insects and slugs. One may also get weed seeds in leaf mold, partly from the plants in the woods and more from the droppings of birds roosting in the woods.

Other materials. Many other organic materials are available to the resourceful gardener for mulching. Lawn clippings can be used as mulch, although ordinarily they should be mixed with the less succulent things that go into the compost pile. In the garden they get slimy and smelly in humid hot weather. Cornstalks are too coarse for use in the garden, but the stalks of young sweet corn are all right. Excellent compost can be made with cornstalks as a principal ingredient. Peanut hulls can be used, although these too are improved by composting first.

Special organic conditioners. Many special organic compounds are offered for sale to use in the garden. These vary all the way from peat, which has almost no fertilizing value but is used for soil conditioning and mulch, to cottonseed meal and soybean meal, which are primarily organic nitrogen fertilizers. Those organic materials, valuable chiefly as fertilizers, are listed in the section on plant nutrients. Between these two extremes are a great many special products that have some value as conditioners and some value as fertilizer. Most of them are necessarily very expensive because of the costs involved in their preparation, bagging, and delivery. Many of them are good, but much more expensive than the other materials described for mulching and as fertilizers.

Synthetic Organic Conditioners. A very promising new material for improving soil structure was announced at the Philadelphia Meeting of the American Association for the Advancement of Science, December 29, 1951, while this book was in press. Dramatic effects on the development of lasting good granular structure in clayey and clay soils were reported from the use of small amounts (0.1 per cent or less) of synthetic organic compounds. Although much more research and testing remain to be done the preliminary results are exceedingly promising for far-reaching improvements in the structure of massive soils for both gardening and farming.

The early experience thus far reported indicates that the powdered material should be mixed with the soil to be modified. So far, no direct effects of the material have been observed on the chemical and biological properties of the soil. It seems to act wholly to improve soil structure with excellent effects on water penetration, root growth, and the maintenance of a proper balance between air and water in the soil.

It is expected that the Monsanto Chemical Company will soon have this synthetic soil conditioner for sale under the trade name of "Krilium."

GROWING PLANTS

Live plants are good sources of organic matter for vegetable gardens and annual flower gardens. According to the purpose to be served and the growing season, we refer to them as green manuring crops or cover crops.

Green manuring crops are grown for the primary purpose of improving the soil. Such crops are very useful in helping to recondition an area that is about to be used for a lawn or garden. They are grown occasionally on the vegetable garden; that is, one may rotate the use of the land so that each year a part of it is devoted to a green manuring crop.

The legumes are best as green manuring crops because the bacteria on their roots fix atmospheric nitrogen; so one has this extra nitrogen as well as the organic matter to spade under for following crops of vegetables or flowers. Any of the ordinary climatically adapted clovers may be used, such as red clover, crimson clover, or sweet clover. Cowpeas are often used and so is vetch. Some use a mixture of grass along with the vetch. Others dislike the grass because it may persist and cause some difficulty in weeding the following year.

Ordinarily, true green manuring crops do not have an important place in the small garden except at the very beginning when one is trying to develop a good garden soil from a soil of poor tilth.

Cover crops are exceedingly useful. These protect the soil during periods when no crops are being grown, as in winter. In northern areas, where the soil is frozen and protected by snow in winter, cover crops are not commonly used. But in the middle and southern parts of eastern United States they have an important place in the vegetable garden. If planted early in the fall, so they get a good start, cover crops protect the soil from the beating rains during winter. Of equal importance is their retention of the soluble plant nutrients in the soil that would otherwise be leached out of it and gone forever. This is especially important on sandy soils. The nitrates and some of the other ions [1] that would leach out with the drainage water are taken up by these plants and wrought into their composition. Thus they are held against leaching. Then in the spring the cover crop may be plowed or spaded into the garden. The fresh organic matter decomposes rapidly, releasing the stored nutrients for the regular crops. Here, also, it is best to grow legumes or at least to have legumes in the mixture along with ryegrass, or wheat, or rye.

The use of cover crops in this way also adds a bit of organic matter to the soil—but only a bit. The plants are so succulent when they are incorporated into the soil that the organic matter decomposes very rapidly. Thus it is a mistake to assume that the growing of cover crops significantly reduces the need for compost or other sources of organic matter.

Some recommended cover crops for various areas are shown in Table 3.

The seed of the legumes used as cover and as green manuring crops, or the soil, should be inoculated with the appropriate legume bacteria that fix nitrogen. Otherwise nitrogen may not be fixed on the plant roots. Growth may be poor. Once established in a soil, the organisms persist for some time. A few pounds of soil from a well inoculated soil area may be spread over the garden soil to inoculate it. A better way is to buy the proper commercial culture from a reliable dealer in garden supplies and treat the seed just prior to sowing.

Like mulches, cover crops may delay too much the early warming of northern soils. In these soils the losses of nutrients by winter leaching are small anyway because the soil is frozen.

[1] See page 91.

TABLE 3. Some suggested cover crops for the garden

Kind of crop	Seeding rate (pounds per 1000 sq. ft.)	General region of adaptation
Ryegrass	1	Pacific Coast, Gulf States, Middle Atlantic States, and lower Middle West
Ryegrass and hairy vetch	½ ¾	
Ryegrass and crimson clover	½ ¼	Pacific Coast, Middle Atlantic, and Gulf States
Crimson clover	½	
Rye	4	Wherever moisture is available
Hairy vetch	1 to 1½	
Rye and hairy vetch	3 ¾ to 1	
Winter wheat	4	Middle Atlantic States, Middle West, southern Great Plains, Intermountain States, and Pacific Coast
Winter wheat and hairy vetch	3 ¾ to 1	
Winter oats and crimson clover	1½ ¼	Southern States and Pacific Coast

5

PLENTY OF WELL-BEHAVED WATER

Either too little or too much water at some time during the year is the most common cause of poor garden plants. Water will become increasingly the limiting factor for excellent results in the garden because methods for improving soil fertility are getting better all the time. Then too, it is generally easier to improve soil fertility than to improve soil structure. Although some gardeners spend money freely for new plants, fertilizers, manure, and the like, they avoid the hard work of deep spading to get organic matter, fertilizers, lime, sand, or other materials into the deep subsoil. Most gardeners need to give relatively more attention to soil structure and water if they are to get the benefits of fertilizers and composts.

The amount of water available to plants in the garden is, of course, partly a matter of climate. But within any one climatic zone a great deal depends on the kind of soil and how it is managed. Unless given special management more water runs off from hilly soils than from level ones, and more soaks into open sandy soils than into massive clays. Anything that confines the root system reduces the soil-root contacts for the intake of water. The gardener can do many things to change the natural soil, to overcome the natural handicaps, and to control the water in his soil—many practices besides drainage at one extreme and irrigation at the other. What he can or should do also depends upon the kind of soil he has to work with.

Soils generally have the ability of holding water so that plants can get what they need. Different kinds of soil vary widely in the amounts they are able to hold and in the length of time they can hold it. The good garden soil allows the rain to enter freely, allows the excess water to drain away, and holds enough for growing plants between rains. Many that do not fulfill these conditions can be made to do so. Through his art in water control a gardener can often change a poor soil into a good one.

Any ordinary soil contains some water; it is always moving in or out. The less water in the soil, the more tightly it is held. Even soil too dry for plants to grow holds some water very tightly—water that does not evaporate or freeze under ordinary conditions in the garden. At the other extreme, excess water, unable to drain away, fills the pore spaces and crowds out air essential for the roots of land plants.

When plants wilt. Starting with moist garden soil, water is lost by evaporation and transpiration through the leaves and stems of plants until the plant can get no more. The plant wilts. The percentage of water in the soil when plants wilt from the lack of it is called the *wilting coefficient.* In very sandy soils this value may be as low as 1 per cent and in very heavy clays as much as 30 per cent; that is, depending upon the character of the soil material, one must have 1 to 30 pounds of water for each 100 pounds of dry soil before any is available to plants. Thus a mere measure of the amount of water in the soil does not tell us how much is available to plants until we subtract this overhead, which is specific for each kind of soil.

The wilting coefficient is nearly constant for any kind of soil. Interestingly, the values vary scarcely at all for different kinds of plants. This means that as a soil becomes dry, different kinds of plants cease to remove water from it at about the same percentage of water in the soil. But it does not follow that they wilt at the same time.

First of all, some plants are shallow-rooted and begin to wilt as soon as the surface soil has reached the wilting coefficient; whereas more deeply rooted ones continue to get water through the lower roots. This is why the gardener should maintain good structure and a good nutrient supply deep in the soil in order to to encourage deep rooting. On such deep pervious soils plants can resist drought much longer than on those permitting only shallow rooting. A difference of only a few inches can be very important.

Secondly, some plants can store water within their own cells for long periods. They may grow little or none during drought; yet they remain more or less static, unwilted, and are able to grow again with the next rain. Many cacti and other desert plants can thus remain nearly dormant under the hot sun for long periods. Such plants are said to have *drought resistance*. Most of the vegetable crops have little drought resistance, but a great many of the ornamentals do have. By selecting plants with drought resistance one may have a beautiful flower garden on a dry droughty slope where ordinary plants would die. The several kinds of grasses vary greatly in this respect. *Zoysia*, for example, has a higher drought resistance than Kentucky bluegrass. Many of the grasses native to the western Great Plains are highly drought resistant.

People commonly associate drought with warm weather—too much so. During hot days, we watch for wilting, expect it; yet plants may suffer almost as much in cold weather. Evergreen shrubs and trees can exhaust the soil water to the wilting coefficient in cold weather and die without the gardener's being aware of the trouble. During warm days in winter, evergreens, epecially those in the sun, require significant amounts of water that must be supplied by irrigation during drought, even in winter. The careful gardener sees that such plants have moist soil as they go into the winter. Even deciduous trees and shrubs need to take in considerable water just before the autumn leaf-falls.

Where the soil freezes deeply, trees and shrubs may die from lack of water in the spring if warm weather comes abruptly, before the soil has thawed enough for the roots to get water. It is primarily the air temperature rather than the soil temperature that starts the buds of plants. Such difficulties can be avoided by using enough mulch to prevent deep freezing, and then removing it in early spring to hasten thawing of the soil.

The moist soil. In an ordinary moist soil the water is held closely as films around the grains and in the fine pores, like water in a wet blanket or oil in a lamp wick. It moves through the soil in the fine pores, as the oil goes up the wick of the lamp. In very heavy clays the small pores become plugged, and in light sands they are too large for much movement. Thus at these extremes the upward movement of water from a water table is not very great; but in silty, very fine sandy soils, water can move up several feet in this fashion.

Freezing of the soil at the surface intensifies these movements of film or capillary water. If a flat stone or board is left lying on the moist soil, a concentration of ice crystals is nearly always found just under it after heavy freezing. Even though the surface soil is dry before a hard freeze, it is usually moist after thawing. As the ice crystals form in the surface, they attract moisture to them. They grow. This growth of ice crystals pulls water out of the fine capillaries and sets up a movement of water in the direction of the crystal. Under cement walks and pavements that are not constructed with a well drained subgrade or base of gravel or crushed stones, ice crystals several inches thick are sometimes built up in this way, heaving and smashing the pavement. Such growing ice crystals may wedge plants upward. With repeated freezing and thawing, plants may be forced out of the ground several inches, especially if their root systems are shallow or weak. After periods of much freezing and thawing the gardener needs to examine his plants carefully and to press back into the soil any that have been heaved before they dry out and die. Rock gardens need special attention because so many spots are shallow.

During cold periods water moves out of the soil rapidly as a vapor because of the low vapor pressure of the water in the cold surface soil as compared to that in the warmer substratum. Thus uncovered soil may dry out severely in winter if the temperature falls very low. Even in summer great losses of water may occur in this way during a very cool period without rain immediately following a very hot period and while the lower soil is warmer than the surface soil.

An examination of a block of ordinary garden soil shows that about 35 to 65 per cent of the volume is solid matter—sand grains, clay, and the like. The other 35 to 65 per cent is pore space. Most of the values for different kinds of soil fall within these limits. When garden soil is in its best productive state for ordinary plants, say vegetables, about one half of this pore space is filled with air and about one half with water.

Plants may drown. When still more water is added to a permeable moist soil (water beyond that which can be held in the capillaries), it passes down through the lower part of the soil under the force of gravity as *gravitational* water. This is like the extra water that drips from a wet blanket hung up to dry. In a soil productive for most plants, this extra water should drain out. It should not remain, to fill up the part of the pore space that should contain air. Soils from which water drains out very slowly are called poorly drained. If a soil hardly loses water at all and collects it from surrounding land, it is ponded. Between well drained soils and poorly drained ones are the imperfectly drained soils: in the rainy season they may be very wet indeed, but in dry periods they are not. Steeply sloping soils, on which runoff is very rapid, or very porous soils are said to be excessively drained.

In humid forested regions where the well drained soils are brown, grayish brown, or reddish brown, poorly drained soils are commonly dark gray or perhaps nearly black on the surface and gray beneath. Imperfectly drained soils are likely to be gray on the surface and mottled gray, reddish brown, and yellow beneath.

Plants vary widely in their adaptability to poorly drained soils. At one extreme are plants, like water lilies, that need ponded soil. Other fine ornamentals grow well only in water-saturated soil. Most vegetables need moist but well drained soils. Some of the shallow-rooted plants that like well drained soil grow also on the imperfectly drained soils. Some annuals, for example, may be planted after the wet season and grow to maturity before the soil is again saturated. Thus soils with intermediate drainage can be used for annuals but not for ordinary perennials. Other plants, like some of the heathers, can go into resting stages during very wet and very dry periods and receive enough nutrition from shallow roots during the rest of the time.

By thoughtful selection of plants one may have a good garden with flowers and shrubs on either very wet or very dry soils. By artificial drainage, with tile or ditches, or by bedding, garden plants requiring good drainage may be grown on naturally poorly or imperfectly drained soils.

A GOOD SOIL SPENDS ITS WATER WISELY

The importance of keeping the soil in a moist condition—neither too dry nor too wet—can scarcely be emphasized enough. Many failures could be avoided by better water control.

Of the water that falls as rain or snow, a part is lost in each of four ways—runoff, leaching, evaporation, and transpiration through plants. A good soil loses water in each way, but not too much in any one.

Runoff. This is the part of the water that falls on the soil but fails to enter it, and flows off the surface instead. If runoff is rapid, the water may carry away some soil and even small plants with it. This is called soil *washing* or *accelerated soil erosion.* Some washing, or normal soil erosion, is necessary for the maintenance of good productivity in many soils. As the surface of the soil is gradually worn away, the uppermost part of the second horizon just below gradually takes on the properties of the one above it and becomes a part of it. In turn, the soil materials of the successively deeper horizons gradually take on the properties of those immediately above them. Finally, fresh minerals are incorporated into the lower horizon from the rock beneath. In this way soils are rejuvenated through additions of fresh rock material to the lower part of the rooting zone. But normal erosion is a *very* gradual process.

Accelerated erosion—erosion more than that normal for the kind of soil—can be very harmful, especially where relatively impervious soil on strong slopes is left bare and exposed directly to sharp showers. A granular surface soil may be moved away, leaving heavy plastic clay or other soil material difficult to put into good tilth for plants. In fact, this harm that accelerated erosion does to the physical condition or structure of the soil is far more important than the nutrient losses. It is true that organic matter and plant nutrients are usually most abundant in the surface soil. Still, these can be easily replaced in garden soil. But the problem of developing a deep rooting zone with good soil structure from hard layers exposed by erosion may be extremely difficult to solve.

Some of the bad effects of excess runoff that are laid to erosion are really due to other causes. Of first importance is the loss of water—water that plants should have but fail to get because it is not stored in the deeper soil for use between rains. The lack of deep moistening leads to shallow rooting and a low content of organic matter deep in the soil. The thinness of the granular surface soil on strongly sloping natural soils is more generally due to this lack of water in the soil than to excessive erosion.

When a sloping soil becomes fully saturated with water, additional water must run off the surface. The amount that can be held by a soil depends on its depth and porosity—on the total volume of pores. The rate at which the water can enter—its permeability—depends upon the size of the pores. If the soil is packed and hard, the pores are so small that water penetrates the soil too slowly for it all to enter unless rains are very gentle indeed. In this respect most of western Europe has an advantage over most of the United States. In Europe the rains are gentle; in the United States many of our rains are short and hard. Unless soils are very permeable, runoff is great even though the soil has a high capacity for water.

The gardener should aim for combinations of plants and soil management practices that maintain a high rate of water infiltration into his soil. Dense vegetation or such mechanical devices as terraces, which slow down the water, increase its penetration by giving it more time to enter.

Less soil is carried away by slowly moving water than by rapidly moving water. The carrying capacity of water increases with the sixth power of its velocity. The amount of erosion is only partly related to the amount and rate of the runoff, however. Soil exposed to the splash of raindrops and to the direct effect of little rivulets is more erodible than that protected by thickly growing plants and mulch.

Thus ideally as much water as is necessary for plants should enter the soil, and the excess water that cannot be stored in the soil without sacrificing needed air space in the pores should run off the surface slowly without erosion.

Leaching. Except in deserts and semi-deserts, most normal soils have some water pass through them into the deep substratum. In dry regions this happens infrequently—only once during several years when the rainfall is especially high. Then, of course, little or no water can move through wet soils already saturated with water, such as a swampy soil with a ground water table at the surface. Little water passes down through thin soils over solid rocks like granite; whereas a great deal of water finds its way through the cracks in limestone and basalt. That is, simply because a soil is thin over rock, one cannot conclude that there is no leaching. Indeed, some soils formed from limestone, like the red soils from limestone (Terra Rossa) around the Mediterranean Sea, are thin partly because the fine clay itself has moved down into the cracks with the water as weathering and soil formation have gone forward over the centuries.

In a highly productive soil some water moves through the profile into the substratum beneath. Any excess of soluble salts is thus removed. In very dry regions many soils have too little leaching to remove the excess soluble salts accumulated through the processes of rock weathering and soil formation. When such soils are irrigated, unless there is good drainage and considerable leaching, the salts accumulate in the rooting zone and prevent good plant growth. Most common vegetables and flowering plants do not grow well with much salt in the soil. Amounts over about 0.15 per cent are harmful. Some salts are more toxic than others, and many wild plants, a few of which may be grown as ornamentals, tolerate much more salt than vegetables. Beets and especially asparagus grow well on soils a bit too salty for other vegetables.

In very porous soils, like the common sands or highly granular soils of the tropics, too much of the water moves through the soil. This causes excessive leaching with the removal of nitrates and other soluble plant nutrients beyond the reach of roots. Further, such soils hold too little water for plants between rains.

To increase leaching, drainage must be improved with tile or ditches, or by opening up the lower soils with deep tillage or spading and the addition of organic matter or coarse materials. Where soils are permeable and well drained, leaching can be increased by increasing the water supply.

Some reduction in leaching can be had by increasing the water-holding capacity of the soil through increasing the content of clay or humus. Perhaps of greatest significance in garden soils is to use plants to take out both water and nutrients during periods of excessive leaching. A rank growth of ryegrass and crimson clover during the winter months on the sandy soils of the southeastern part of the United States, for example, greatly reduces losses by leaching. If the fresh growth is plowed or spaded into the garden in the spring, nutrients that would have been completely lost are available for plants.

Evaporation. The evaporation of water from the surface of the soil cools it. In the bright sun of summer both leaves and soil would become terribly hot were it not for this essential cooling. Because of the enormous surface exposed to the air by the countless soil grains, evaporation from a square yard of moist soil is even greater than from a square yard of free-water surface as in a lake. When the sun is bright, evaporation is higher. The level of water in some lakes goes up and down with cloudy and sunny days. Wind at the surface, especially of dry air, hastens evaporation.

It was once held generally that frequent tillage reduces water losses from evaporation. The idea is simple. By maintaining a surface layer of loose dry soil—called a "dust mulch"—the water connections of the films and capillaries are broken so water cannot rise to the very surface. Of course, this is true. But actually not much water moves as film or capillary water into the surface 6-inch layer of garden soils with ordinary summer moisture contents. The water moves into the surface chiefly as a vapor over which the dust mulch has little if any influence.

We know now that the chief effects of tillage on soil water are (1) the reduction of weeds and hence losses of water by their transpiration, and (2) the breaking of crusts and the maintenance of a soil surface receptive of water when the rain comes.

The gardener can reduce evaporation by providing shade and by using mulch. Even the partial shade of trees is beneficial to many plants, provided the tree roots are pruned and do not pull more water out of the soil than is saved.

Mulches are of first importance. From central United States south to the equator they can almost always be used to advantage except when the soil is being reworked and when seedlings are just coming through the ground. In warm areas even a light mulch of coarse grass, pine needles, sawdust, or straw has an enormous influence to reduce temperatures and evaporation at the surface. This is one reason why the gardener never has enough organic matter. As soon as his plants, including vegetables, are well established, mulches can usually be added to advantage.

In northern areas mulches are less useful, at least in the spring and especially on short-season annuals, because of the need to have the full direct sun on the soil to warm it. In north central Alaska, for example, it is amazing how well many vegetables and flowers grow with permanently frozen soil only 30 to 40 inches beneath the surface. Yet, even though the soil is not frozen, the roots of most plants do not grow in soil colder than about 42° F. In these northern areas days are very long in summer, so the exposed surface of the soil becomes warm, almost hot. Then with a gentle rain the water is warmed and carries heat to the lower soil. Where this warming is necessary, mulches must be avoided.

Transpiration and weeds. The fourth major loss of water from soil is by transpiration through plants. Generally, the gardener needs to control the other moisture losses in order to provide ample water for his plants. But transpiration through weeds and competing trees is a serious loss well within the gardener's control.

Weeds are one of the worst enemies of the garden. If the gardener starts with clean land, the weed problem may be avoided or kept simple by rigidly keeping out the few weeds that are brought in by the birds and wind and by allowing none to go to seed. But once they get out of hand, nothing short of a lot of work will control them. Care must be taken that bad weeds are not introduced through manure, straw, topsoil, or poorly cleaned grass seed. In lawns, some of the weed killers may be used—those like 2, 4-D that kill the broad-leaved plants, but not the grass. Yet none of these is sufficiently selective to be practical for the small garden, especially in perennial borders of mixed culture.

For bad weed infestations pulling by hand is often essential. Many deep-rooted weeds need to be kept pulled and cut from the perennial borders, rock gardens, and other areas of mixed culture until the plant food reserves in the roots are exhausted. If they are kept in hand and not allowed to gain any size, the job is not so great as it looks. But if they are allowed to develop to considerable size, they will have rebuilt the food reserves in their roots and one must begin the process of cutting and starvation all over again.

Once the crabgrass, for example, is removed from a lawn and the soil properly fertilized, it is fairly easy to keep it out. Crabgrass and other weeds come into lawns mostly where the grass is weakened because of disease, excess shade, excess heat, drought, low fertility, acidity, very short clipping, grubs, dog urine, or some similar cause. Once established these weeds may persist even after the soil conditions have been corrected. The chemical weed killers can be very useful on some of these weeds. But once a good turf of adapted species is established on properly prepared soil, it is an easy matter to keep out the few weeds that come in. Bad spots that appear because of injuries to the turf may be seeded in off-seasons to some suitable temporary cover, like ryegrass or lespedeza, until time for seeding the regular cover.

In the garden thick clean mulches help a great deal to keep the weeds down. Once the annual flowers and vegetables are well established, a thick mulch prevents the growth of weeds.

The nearest approach to a single rule about weeds is: Never let them go to seed. Seeds of many weeds remain viable in the soil for a long time. Like several other aspects of gardening there is not much room for compromise between a good job and a poor one, between a clean garden and a weedy one. The chances are that any garden will be definitely the one or the other. Unfortunately, many folks get a kind of short-lived spring enthusiasm for their garden that fails to last long enough to prevent weeds from going to seed in the late summer and autumn.

In mixed cultures, as in perennial beds, the gardener must watch the strong growers as well as the weeds. In most mixtures of plants there are weak ones and strong ones. Unless the strong ones are cut and the new plants pulled out, the weaker ones are destroyed as they are by weeds.

In semiarid regions, like the American Great Plains, one cannot expect enough water for a vegetable garden on the same area of soil each year. Where irrigation is not feasible, one must resort to *fallowing*. By keeping the soil in fallow is meant keeping it cultivated— entirely free of plants. Of course, this prevents all losses by transpiration and allows water to accumulate in the soil. In such places where the rainfall is low, one should plant only one half or one third of the garden area for vegetables and annual flowers in any one year. The other part is kept in fallow, either one or two years, so that water may accumulate. With such a system the gardener may have good plants on soils where little could be expected from consecutive plantings every year.

LET IN THE WATER

On naturally permeable soils rain water or irrigation water goes in easily. Some soils are not naturally permeable and others lose their receptability to water if exposed to the sun and cultivated without special practices to keep them granular and porous. These practices include the use of organic matter, both within the soil and on the surface as a mulch; tillage at the proper moisture content to avoid puddling and subsequent baking to a crust or mass; use of planned walks or stepping stones on clayey soils to avoid treading on them when moist; additions of sand, cinders, or the like to keep the pores large; breaking of temporary surface crusts; and methods to insure slow movement of surface runoff.

Each of these points needs to be discussed in more detail. What should be done in any spot depends upon the soil and the kind of plants. With thick-growing grass or naturalized plantings of shrubs and trees, the problem may be quite simple. But in the kitchen garden, in the annual flower beds, and in other cultivated areas, the maintenance of permeability is commonly a serious problem if any layer of the soil is rich in clay and the soil has much slope.

MAKE THE EXCESS WATER CRAWL AWAY

Even with the garden soil properly prepared for the maximum amount of water to enter it, some water runs off the slopes during heavy storms or during periods of rain and snow-melt when the soil is already saturated. This excess should flow away slowly so no harm will be done.

Rows curve with the soil. Square and rectangular garden plots and beds are not well fitted to curving slopes. Beds often can be made to fit the surface of the soil and at the same time give a more pleasing appearance. On comparatively gentle slopes all that may be necessary to prevent rapid runoff is to have the rows of cultivated plants, say in the kitchen garden, across the slopes rather than up and down the slopes. On complex slopes the rows need to be curved rather than straight in order to follow the contour.[1] Then tillage and irrigation furrows, if any, serve to hold the water. Once the plants are established, they also serve as barriers.

With rows up and down the slope, on the other hand, little rills are apt to start that carry the water away rapidly before it has had a chance to soak into the soil. Once started on erodible soil such rills lead to deep destructive gullies. The longer the slope, the more water accumulates in each rill and the greater its speed. Even with similar grades, or percentages of slope, a greater erosion hazard exists on

---

[1] A contour is an imaginary line on the ground connecting all points of equal elevation. The contour lines may be established by using a surveyor's level or hand level to set stakes along the slope at nearby points of equal elevations. In a small garden or for short distances one may use a straight board on edge, and an ordinary carpenter's level. By choosing one stake as a starting point others can be set at the same level in a properly curved contour line. Another line, say 1, 2, or 3 feet lower, may be started by setting the board down the slope, keeping it level, and setting the stake where the lower edge is the required distance—1, 2, or 3 feet —above the ground level. In this way one may lay out the contour lines with sufficient accuracy for ordinary purposes.

convex (outward curving) slopes than on concave (inward curving) slopes. For example, the strongly convex slopes or "noses" between two tiny valleys merging into a larger one present a more difficult runoff-control problem than concave side-slopes of the same gradient.

Even in laying out perennial beds and other plantings care should be taken to avoid placing cultivated strips up and down slopes. Even paths in naturalized plantings may be subject to serious erosion on strong slopes. Usually, attractive curving margins and paths can be accommodated to the contour.

Strips. Where the runoff problem is somewhat greater because of strong slopes or relatively impervious soil, it is not enough simply to put the rows and edgings on the contour. In the kitchen garden groups of rows can be separated by strips of permanent vegetation like grass. A slope may be laid out in strips 5 to 20 feet wide on the contour, with alternate ones cultivated and in grass. Thus, any rapidly flowing water that begins on the cultivated strip is stopped in the grass strip. Although this is a very common practice on farms with relatively sloping soil, such strips are not used much in gardens.

Terraces. A wide variety of terraces are used in the garden, not only to hold the water and prevent erosion, but also to add color and charm. A great many houses are built on sloping and hilly soils. Then too, many garden plantings show up to much better advantage on a hillside than on smooth land. Rock gardens and rocky hill gardens are really complex systems of terracing.

A terrace, in the sense used here, varies from a simple low ridge of earth to a stone wall. Usually they are placed at a very slight angle to the contour in order to hold the water on the ground long enough for maximum entrance into the soil and yet to allow the excess to flow away slowly without causing damage to soil or plants.

On soils permeable to water the terraces can be level—can be placed directly on the contour lines. To avoid excess water in the sub-soil drain tile are often laid about three feet deep on the lower slope, just back of permanent terraces, for drainage. In this way the terrace blocks the surface runoff and the tile carries away the excess water. Although relatively expensive to install, such a scheme avoids poorly drained soils just back of level terraces or flowing surface water back of terraces laid at an angle to the contour.

Unless the soil is quite permeable terraces should be made at a little angle to the contour—with some side slope—so that the excess water gradually runs off the surface just back of the terrace. Otherwise it accumulates back of the terrace during heavy rains and finally breaks over it in a waterfall that may cause great damage, and even cause a deep gully if much water becomes concentrated in a single narrow place. All terraces, and earth terraces especially, need to be watched for such breaks. In fact, an unwatched terrace may lead to much worse erosion than no terrace at all. Instead of having some water loss and relatively uniform erosion, or sheet wash, over the whole slope water may be concentrated at a break in the terrace and cause serious irreparable gullying.

This leads directly to the problem of what to do with the excess water flowing back of the terraces or from tile underneath them. Such water must be guided into open drainageways carefully protected from deepening by grass, trees, or linings of masonry, or into catchment basins that lead by large tile into natural streams, canals, or storm sewer systems. Otherwise one may protect one slope by terraces only to stimulate serious gullying or flooding at the margins where the water pours out from the terraces. In other words, terraces must be thought of as part of a water disposal system.

What is needed beyond the terraces depends upon the porosity of the soil and the severity of the rainfall. On many soils a few low-level earth terraces are all that is needed to get all the water into the soil and there is no other soil-water disposal problem. On other soils the excess water—excess beyond that which soaks in—can be allowed to run safely into a border of dense shrubs and trees without doing damage. Yet on strong sloping, thin soils of low capacities to take in water, rather elaborate precautions must be taken to handle the excess storm water at the margins through prepared drainageways.

If the soil freezes deeply in winter, a serious water-disposal problem arises in the spring, especially with combinations of rapid snow-melt and heavy spring rains. Even though the soil is normally permeable, most of the water runs off until the lower soil thaws. In fact, terraces may be needed primarily to protect the soil during such spring thaws. One needs to keep a close watch of terraces during this period and break up any ice that may block the flow back of the terraces and cause the water to break over in waterfalls and to start gullies. This sort of problem is intensified on soils of the far north with ever-frozen subsoils.

Stone and brick walls are commonly used on the hilly soils in countries with comparatively cheap labor. They are not used nearly so much in the United States because of their cost, except as retaining walls at the margin of a sidewalk or on a property line. In southern France, for example, good gardens with flowers, fruits, and vegetables are grown on steeply sloping soil by building strong walls of masonry approximately on the contour. The gardens appear to be laid out in long curving stairsteps of variable width, depending on the shape of the slope. The soil areas between the walls are nearly level. Usually shrubs and vines are trained on the walls, especially on the south-facing ones. Fruit trees are often trained in espalier fashion—flat against the wall with all the branches pruned away except those in the one plane with the wall.

In addition to the high cost of such walls the plots of soil often need to be connected by stone stairways in order to pass conveniently from one to another. Then too, the plots between them are quite narrow on strong slopes. Thus, only small light tools are practical. This is another great disadvantage of stone-wall terraces to the American gardener who uses machines for tillage, grass clipping, and spraying that are too heavy to move about over such terraces. Still the stone terraces have a place where stones are plentiful and the soil is otherwise productive.

Usually lower ridges of earth at a slight angle to the contour, sloping gently on both the up-slope and down-slope sides, are most practical in the American garden for water control where needed. To make these, do not level the soil between the terraces, but only move enough soil to the center of a narrow strip to make the low ridge. The distance between terraces depends upon the local situation. On strongly sloping, relatively impervious soil they should be 5 or 6 feet apart; on gentler slopes they may be 12 to 20 feet apart. The steeper the slope, the less pervious the soil, the more intensely the soil is cultivated, and the greater the hazard of excess water, the closer together should the terraces be made.

In a great many small sloping gardens one really needs but one of these ridges or low earth terraces placed on the upper edge of the garden to catch water from still higher land and direct it away from the garden. Such low ridges are called *diversion terraces* since their purpose is to divert the water away from the garden plot. With well prepared soil and proper attention to mulching, the water that falls on the garden may all soak in, or at least enough of it, so there is no serious problem of runoff control. Frequently with small gardens the trouble is caused by excess water flowing over the garden from steeper slopes in the background, perhaps from a neighbor's land; if this can be diverted no other terraces are needed. Such a diversion terrace should be seeded to lawn grass or other permanent cover and care taken to dispose of the water from it in a safe place, well protected with natural cover, or to a storm sewer.

After these earth terraces are made, they need some repair, especially at first. Some may not have been placed exactly right at first and need to be moved a bit. Commonly, the soil settles unequally after they are made. The gardener can post himself in a good place to watch the terraces during a hard rain to see any low or high places in the ridge or in the channel just back of it. These may be adjusted easily with a shovel until the water moves slowly along the back of the ridge without breaking over anywhere and without leaving any pools of water for more than a few hours after the rain has ceased. In case a break does occur during a hard rain it may be repaired temporarily with some small boards set against stakes or with bags of earth.

After the terrace has been established and the water system works properly, it is a good plan to cover the ridge with a permanent cover unless the garden is very tiny and space is at a great premium. Grass or a mixture of lawn grass and white clover makes excellent cover but requires too much hand clipping. English ivy, pachysandra, trailing myrtle, and so on may be used if kept pruned at the margins. Iris is a fine ornamental to hold the soil, especially on the down-slope side of the ridge. The gardener may use a combination of such plants and stepping stones to good advantage.

As an excellent alternative to the low earth ridges, especially in the small intimate garden, the gardener may set fairly heavy stones a little way down in the soil to give, in effect, a very small stone wall some 6 to 12 inches high. These rows of stone take less space than the low earth terraces, but the rows usually need to be put closer together than the earth ridges. These stone ridges are much nicer than the earth ridges for the flower and shrub gardens. But they are rather a nuisance in a large kitchen garden. If the lines of stones are set fairly close in the perennial garden where the soil is not often respaded, they do not need to follow the contour exactly but can be set in interesting curves with occasional cross lines of stones between the main lines. These serve to check water that might flow too rapidly back of the main stone line and to give the effect of individual beds. Plants like creeping phlox, ivy, and trailing myrtle, which fall over the stones gracefully, can be set along the upper sides. Where soil is well prepared to begin with and kept properly mulched, these low stone terraces serve to control runoff even in very bad places, especially if the garden is protected against overflow from higher slopes by a proper diversion terrace.

Individual terraces may be used for perennial plants, including shrubs and trees, grown on a slope. On the lower side of the plant ridges of earth or, better still, ridges of flat stone set edgeways may be made in a half circle or slightly more. These hold the water long enough for it to soak into the soil around the plant. Such individual terraces may be used separately—one for each plant—or they may amount to a broadening of the regular ridge or stone type of terrace, which is laid out at a slight angle to the contour. Often fruit or nut trees are planted this way in curving rows along a terrace.

Hillside drains. If the land is not overcultivated, water enters the surface layer of many soils satisfactorily, but does not pass on through the subsoil properly. Thus the slope is likely to have wet spots or "seepy" spots where such water accumulates. With long periods of wet weather the whole soil may become saturated; then a sharp shower is likely to do a great deal of harm. It is a very old practice, and still a good one, to place tile about 3 feet deep to tap such accumulations and to remove the water, provided care is taken that the soil above the tile is pervious. That is, after the tile are laid to tap the wet places sufficiently, cinders or gravel may be mixed with the soil above to be sure that it will not become packed and impervious.

In southern European vineyards, the vines are often planted directly over the tile, which are laid out at a slight angle to the contours. No other structures for runoff control may be needed except those required for protection of the soil at the end of the tile line where it discharges into a stream or gully, and some small stone dams to prevent deepening of the natural drainageways.

Some people dig little surface ditches, called hillside ditches, at a slight angle to the contour. These are simply a modification of the low earth terraces already described. Neither the hillside ditches nor the low earth terraces work very well if the lower soil is impervious to water. Where such soils are to be cultivated, tile, as described above, should be used along with the low earth ridges where needed. More is said about drainage a little later.

Gullies. Even the gardener must occasionally deal with gullies— deep U-shaped or V-shaped intermittent streams. These form when the soil has had to take care of more runoff than is normal for the soil type, and the water is concentrated. Gullies may result from the removal of protective natural vegetation through cutting, clearing, excessive grazing, fire, or unusual drought. Often they have been started from an unusual concentration of water from poorly planned road drainage, at the outlet of a terrace or storm-water pipe, or from some other disturbance. Gullies may be started in the natural land-scape as a result of great earth movements or climatic changes. The deepening of a stream causes all the little side streams to deepen their channels, if the earth is soft and yielding; and these push back into the uplands as new gullies.

The first step in gully control is to remove the cause, if possible. Often the amount of extra water to be handled is so small that heavy plantings of vigorous plants, especially if well fertilized, stop the flow. Vines, like kudzu, ivy, and honeysuckle, may be used. To be most effective, the stems need to be tipped into the soil as they grow. One may see lots of soil washing on steep vine-covered slopes if the crowns are widely spaced. Gardeners often fail to stop erosion with English ivy that covers the slope, simply because it is not tipped in enough to give a good root mat.

Various trees like locust and eucalyptus may be planted. But with some grading and smoothing to reduce the grades and with careful fertilization, good stands of grasses can sometimes be established. If the excess water is too great for plantings alone to get started, a series of dams may be made from sticks or brush set between stout stakes or from bags of earth. More permanent little dams can be built from stones, or even from concrete. Such little dams must have good foundations else the water will cut through the soil material at the margins. Where the soil material is soft and yielding, the individual dams cannot be very large and be expected to remain in place.

These little dams can be depended upon only to slow down the water and give the vegetation a chance to get well started in properly prepared soil. In extreme cases a substantial masonry dam, with good foundation, including deep wings into the soil at the side, is required, along with buried culvert pipes to carry the water away from the slope to a suitable outlet. The planning and construction of such dams require engineering services beyond the resources of the usual gardener.

Rock gardens. In a proper rock garden stones are set so they interrupt the flow of the water down the slope and guide it into the soil. The soil must be well prepared and the stones set deeply and thickly. A good way is to prepare a grade some 8 to 15 inches below the final grade line of the completed garden. Then the stones may be set into the lower soil, roughly edgeways, at approximately right angles to the slope. They should be deep enough, large enough, and numerous enough to give the effect of a network of intricate terraces. Then the surface soil may be placed between them. The water, as it falls and begins to flow, strikes the upper surface of a stone and is guided deeply into the soil.

Snow traps. In the semiarid regions and in some humid regions that have winter snow, snow fences or, better still, tree plantings that serve also as windbreaks can be used to trap the snow over the garden area. To say the same thing in reverse, one must avoid conditions where the garden is swept clean of snow in winter. The snow is needed not only for the moisture it contributes to the soil, but also for the protection it gives to both soil and plants during bitter cold weather. Careful selection of land in the first place, proper tree plantings, and the use of snow fences will give the benefit of deep snow for the garden. Where practicable, the gardener should look over his land area in winter and spot the places where the wind sweeps away the snow. Then in his planting, he may seek to change the wind currents or avoid these places for all but the most hardy plants.

Cover crops. Plants are best for slowing down the excess runoff. In fact, terraces and the other devices are primarily to aid the vegetation. In areas with a long winter season the soil is frozen and protected with snow during the winter. In warm areas without frost plants can be grown easily all of the time, provided they are irrigated during dry seasons. Most gardens are between these extremes. Many are used for annual flowers and vegetables in the summer and are then bare for long periods between harvesting and planting—periods too cold for most garden plants, but yet with much rain. These winter rains can do serious damage to bare garden soil.

Such garden soils should be protected during the winter months with cover crops. These must be sown early enough to become well established in late autumn—strong enough to slow down runoff and to protect the soil from erosion. The plants take up soluble plant nutrients like nitrates and hold them in their cells against leaching. Then in spring the green fresh organic matter can be plowed or spaded into the soil. Both roots and tops furnish organic matter that gradually decomposes, releasing the nutrients for the new garden plants.

As explained in the chapter on organic matter the actual crops to be grown depend upon location of the garden. Ryegrass is one of the best, especially in combination with crimson clover. Winter wheat or rye may be used alone or mixed with vetch or crimson clover. Generally, it is best to have a legume or a mixture of a grass and a legume. (See Table 3.)

KEEP THEIR FEET MOIST BUT NOT WET

Most vegetables and ordinary flowering plants require well drained soils. Their roots require both water and good supplies of oxygen that are maintained in the soil through the exchange of gases between the soil-air and the air above the soil. The excess water that accumulates in poorly drained soils fills the pore spaces and excludes the air.

Some soils are wet most of the time. These usually have a dark mucky surface underlain by wet gray soil. Others are wet only occasionally, say in the spring, but long enough to kill roots or prevent their growth. These are often mottled gray, yellow, and reddish brown beneath the surface. Such imperfectly drained soils may be found on fairly sloping land as well as on nearly level land. Often water moving down through the soil reaches a compact or hardpan layer and then seeps along the surface of it and appears in the surface soil down the slope as a seepy spot.

Open ditches. Excess surface water can be removed through shallow open ditches. Such drainage may help some—enough to grow shallow-rooted plants tolerant of some excess water. Of course, ditches some 2 to 4 feet deep may be prepared for drainage, but rarely are these practicable in the garden. They are usually very unsightly and inconvenient, to say nothing of being dangerous hazards. Especially for wet areas or seepy spots on slopes, ditches are usually not good. They may even be the forerunners of gullies. For deep peat and muck, which settle greatly and unevenly with drainage, ditches are usually better than tile.

Tile drains. Tile drains are ordinarily best for improving the drainage of an imperfectly or poorly drained garden soil. One must have a well protected outlet into a natural stream, a canal, or a storm sewer of some sort.

The tile must have sufficient grade (or slope) for the water to flow well. If the tile line is nearly level, it becomes clogged with fine mud settling out of the water. The amount of grade required depends partly on how evenly the tile is laid. That is, water flows satisfactorily in a perfectly straight tile line of low gradient, while with any unevenness the low spots in the line become clogged. The minimum gradient with ditches dug by hand is about 4 to 5 inches fall for every 100 feet. With machine ditching and grading a more nearly flat tile line will work, say as low as 2 inches fall per 100 feet of line. But only if the soil is practically level will the gardener need to approach these minima.

The depth to place the tile depends somewhat upon the plants to be grown, the kind of soil, and the spacing of the lines. In cool regions it is best to have the tile below the frost line, which means 3 to 4 feet. If deep-rooted plants are grown, the tile should be around 3 to 4 feet deep. For the ordinary plants grown in vegetable and flower gardens, 2½ feet may be deep enough if frost is not a hazard. With soils pervious to water, like many loams and sandy loams, tile lines can be some 200 feet apart, but ordinarily 100 feet is better. With clay soils or very wet soils a spacing of 75 feet is better, down to 15 feet in extreme cases. The wider the spacing, the deeper the tile need to be, other things being equal. That is, tile spaced 100 feet apart may need to be 3½ feet deep in a soil to have proper drainage everywhere, whereas 2½ feet would be sufficiently deep with 50-foot spacing.

In a comparatively uniform area of nearly level, poorly drained soil the tile are laid in a grid pattern, with laterals at right angles to the main drain, or in a herringbone pattern with laterals laid out at 45° angles from a central main drain. For small plots ordinarily the first method—the grid pattern—requires somewhat less tile than the herringbone pattern. The laterals should have tile about 4 inches in diameter with mains somewhat larger if an area of considerable size is to be drained.

For wet spots or seepy areas on slopes the tile need to be laid out to intercept the water seeping into the surface soil from deeper layers higher on the slope. Definite rules cannot be laid down; each situation must be studied individually. Ordinarily, the tile may be laid across the slope, at a slight angle to the contour and about 15 feet above the wet place. Some trial digging is necessary to locate any water-bearing strata of sand or gravel that may need to be tapped in order to capture the water and carry it off. If the water-bearing stratum is very coarse and permeable, the tile line needs to have a strong gradient—a rather wide angle to the contour—so the water will flow in it and not find it easier to flow on through the gravel. Once the tile line has tapped the sources of water, it may be laid directly down the slope to an outlet.

If a tile line leads up a slope to drain a spring, small pond, or seepy spot, some laterals are usually necessary to capture all the water.

Tile drainage is often combined with runoff control to take care of the excess water causing a gully. Short laterals across the head of a gully, or just above it, can be led down the slope along the side of the gully itself. It is best not to put the tile line in the very bottom of the gully since it may be washed out in a heavy storm before the drainage system gets to working well and before the earth is well compacted over the line.

Ditches for tile lines need to be even and straight, except for slow easy curves where changes in direction are needed. The gradient should be as uniform as possible to prevent low places where mud may settle and plug the tile. The bottom of the ditch needs to be smooth and firm so individual tile do not settle. Formerly, some followed the practice of leaving a narrow space between individual tile, but it is better to fit them tightly one against another to avoid fine sand or silt seeping into the line. Tough sod or sphagnum peat packed around the joints helps to prevent clogging.

Many gardeners may find all of this a little difficult. For a small garden it is not a very big job. For a large area, one should lay out a plan with a good surveyor's level. But in a small area a hand level or straight board and ordinary carpenter's level can be used. The main thing is to be careful—to take pains to lay the lines at an even grade well above the minimum if possible, to have a firm foundation and to lay the tile evenly, and to be certain of a protected outlet. If well laid with good quality tile, the system should last indefinitely. Especially in heavy soil the system may function imperfectly for two or three years—until natural channels through cracks in the clay to the tile become established. The gardener needs to avoid trees, like elms and poplars, near his tile drains, since the roots of such trees often find their way into the tile line and expand into a fibrous mat that plugs it.

On level or nearly level, highly permeable soil, especially very sandy soil, closely laid tile may be used for both drainage and irrigation. During wet periods the water drains out through the tile as described. During dry periods the drainage outlets are closed and water is added to the tile system by irrigation canals into which the tile also open. In this way the water table may be controlled within very narrow limits so that plants have optimum water and air for growth at all times. Many of the famous gardens, orchards, and pastures of Holland and Belgium are managed in this way. So are some in Florida.

Mole drains. Machines are available for pulling a cylinder, bell, or ball through the subsoil to produce an artificial channel for drainage in place of tile. Although such lines may work for several years if well made, they are not recommended for the gardener who has any permanent vegetation. They are most commonly used in clay soils.

Bedding. On soils that are too wet in summer for vegetables or other annuals but are otherwise productive, success can be had by bedding, with surface drainage. In effect, the gardener lays out a pattern of surface ditches about 8 to 10 inches deep, 12 to 14 inches wide, and 3 to 6 feet apart. The soil is thrown into small beds—say 3 to 6 feet wide and 6 to 12 feet long. In this way the surface between the ditches is raised. When completed, the surface of the beds should be about 1 foot or more above the bottom of the ditches.

Such a pattern of ditches and beds is often used in low lands, including those along streams that are flooded in winter or spring. In the spring the soil is worked up into beds as soon as possible. Where good sources of water are available, the ditches may be used also for irrigation during dry periods. If water can be directed into the area from a stream or spring, it may be guided about and held as needed by small earth dams across the ditches. A skillful operator can control the water table near the optimum for his plants while they are growing.

A low earthen ridge or diversion terrace or dike may be needed along the sides to prevent flooding from adjacent slopes or from the stream itself after sudden showers.

Some put sweetpotatoes and other plants on ridges, or single-row beds, so they will not suffer from excess water during and immediately after heavy rains.

WATER THOROUGHLY BUT GENTLY

Some gardens always need irrigation, like those in arid and semi-arid regions. But most gardens need some irrigation for the best results during dry periods or when transplants are getting established. Of course, ornamentals that do not require irrigation may be selected for steep slopes or for dry places almost anywhere. In fact, some would even be injured by much extra water.

Thus, even in humid regions, vegetable and flower gardens should be laid out near a good source of water. In some years the gardener may get along very well without irrigation. But there are likely to be many years when he will have poor results despite all of his other careful treatments—deep spading, fertilization, and so on—because of drought. Through careful tillage, weed eradication, mulching, and the proper selection of plants, he can greatly minimize the effects of drought.

One inch of water in rain or irrigation keeps the soil moist for five to fifteen days, depending upon the temperature and humidity, the kind of soil, the kind and stage of development of the plants, and how well the gardener controls water losses. Simply enormous contrasts may be seen among unirrigated gardens during drought because of differences in these practices. The well managed garden may not even need irrigation during a drought that severely injures other gardens. Still, for the best results, the soil should not become dry in the root zone. For many ornamentals, especially the evergreens, watering may be necessary in cold weather as well as in warm.

When plants are watered they should be well watered. Light sprinklings of the garden and the lawn with a hose are really worse than no watering at all. A very thin layer of moist soil over very dry soil is harmful. It encourages the formation of surface roots that soon perish. It is much better to water less frequently but well. Then, of course, one must avoid excessive soaking that gives the soil the effects of poor drainage just because a large supply of water is at hand.

In fact, irrigation and drainage go hand in hand, especially in dry regions. We must remember that by irrigating soil in semiarid and desert regions we are really producing a humid climate in the soil. Deep hardpans or other layers that do not cause the soil to be poorly drained under natural conditions may lead to swamping under irrigation. Such soils must be drained along with irrigation so that excess water may leach through the soil and take the salts away with it.

At the beginning of the garden season, before planting, the soil should be moist for a depth of 3 to 5 feet. In humid regions the soil is normally moist in the spring, but in arid regions a thorough soaking by flooding may be necessary at the start before seeding. The soil should not be too wet at first, else plants produce only shallow roots and suffer from drought later.

Subsequent needs of irrigation vary with soil and weather. For vegetables, and for flowering plants of somewhat similar requirements, in arid regions the layer of soil between 2 inches from the surface and 10 inches should be continually moist, and 15 inches is better than 10. In humid regions, where the subsoils are normally moist most of the time, it is best to have no layers of soil too dry for root growth below the surface soil. Sandy soils need more frequent irrigation than clayey soils. Care must be taken not to irrigate clay soils too much and reduce the air in the soil. If this happens, plants appear weak, stunted, and yellowish, as they do on poorly drained spots. Generally, properly moistened soil holds its shape when squeezed in the hand without being so wet that it is sticky or so dry that it readily crumbles and does not hold together when squeezed.

Soils vary, of course, in the rate at which they take up irrigation water. Clay soils with poor structure can be irrigated only slowly. A flow of 1 gallon per minute adds to 1000 square feet of soil an inch of water in about 10½ hours. If the soil can take water faster, the time may be reduced. Ordinarily, 1 inch is about enough to use at one watering.

Except for root crops like carrots, most vegetables are comparatively shallow-rooted and require more frequent watering than farm crops or orchards. Under warm semidesert conditions one should count on 4 to 6 acre-feet of water, or 30 to 50 gallons per square foot, for the year. For a seasonal garden less is needed. With cooler temperatures and more rainfall the amount needed gradually decreases to perhaps only 2 or 3 gallons per square foot added during dry periods.

Vegetables vary in their irrigation requirements for best results. Onions, for example, should have frequent light irrigation, and so should cabbage. Carrots need frequent watering until they are established; but after the roots are about ¼ inch in diameter they should be irrigated only sparingly, else the roots are liable to crack. Beets are intermediate, between onions and carrots. Celery needs frequent watering at first and less later, with special care to keep mud off the crowns of the young plants. Cucumbers need plenty of water. They may be trained on standards or to the middles between furrows so they are not injured by the water. Mellons may also be trained to the middles between furrows. Potatoes are often planted in 3-foot rows. The soil is worked toward the row, leaving the plants in the middle of low ridges with irrigation furrows between. They should have frequent light watering. Tomatoes are often handled somewhat the same way, but in wider rows. By having them in the middle of a broad ridge, with irrigation furrows 5 or 6 feet apart, the leaves and fruits are not likely to get muddy. They need a good supply of water.

Furrows. Where plants are in rows, as in the kitchen garden, irrigation water is easily applied to the soil in furrows between the plant rows. Where practicable, the soil may be leveled so that the surface has only a very gentle slope. Otherwise the furrows may be laid out on the slopes at a very slight angle to the contour. The slope of the furrows should not exceed about 2 inches to 100 feet, and less is better, else the water flows so rapidly that it fails to moisten the soil and may even cause erosion. The water spreads out laterally into the plant beds between the furrows as well as downward.

In flat soil in dry areas, or on the contour of gently sloping soil, it is convenient to lay out a small kitchen garden or annual flower garden in low flat-topped ridges about 15 inches across the top and 30 to 40 inches from the center of one to the center of the next one. Lettuce, beets, carrots, onions, and the like may be planted in double rows 12 inches apart on the ridge, with each row 1½ inches from the edge. The furrows can be filled with water, which will soak the soil around the seed. The gardener can, instead, plant single rows near the center of narrower ridges 18 inches apart.

Other things being equal, the rows, especially double rows, or two-row beds, are run approximately north and south or, better still, northeast by southwest, so both sides of the ridges have about equal temperature and evaporation.

If the local situation is favorable, one may be able to trap runoff water from higher land with earth-ridge terraces, store it in a small man-made pond, and let it down through a gate into the irrigation furrows as needed.

Planting on flat soil and watering by flood irrigation is used for grasses, but is not good for cultivated plants. Most common garden plants do not stand flooding. The soil is likely to puddle and then to bake in the sun, and the lower leaves of plants are apt to get covered with mud.

With soils that are periodically wet and dry, say along a stream that overflows in spring and becomes low in summer, or in a region with a wet-dry climate, one may bed the soil between ditches, as explained under drainage, and use the system for drainage during wet seasons and for irrigation during dry seasons. Some commercial vegetable growers use dikes along the margins of such a pattern of furrows or ditches and beds, and pump water out of the area during wet seasons and into the area in dry seasons, thus maintaining the water table at the optimum level for the plants grown.

In the humid region where irrigation is needed only occasionally, small furrows may be prepared between the rows after the plants are well established so that the water soaks into the soil; then the surface is covered with a mulch. Such small furrows promote water penetration on gentle slopes in soils of low permeability, say soils having silt loam or clay loam surface layers and plastic clay subsoils. Such furrows should be supplemented by low earth terraces or stone lines on slopes above 3½ per cent (3½ feet fall for each 100 feet). Such little furrows under a loose mulch are helpful in watering, even though the water is supplied through a porous hose or in sprays.

Porous hoses. For the small garden porous hoses are ordinarily better for irrigating the kitchen garden, flower beds, and lawns than sprinklers, especially in areas where the air is both hot and humid. Excessive moistening of the foliage of plants increases their susceptibility to diseases. If the land is exceedingly uneven, of course neither furrows nor porous hoses can be used conveniently. If the slopes are regular, the porous hose can be laid out on the contour of sloping soils easily. The water can be applied gently through the hose with the very minimum of disturbance to soil or plants.

If little furrows between rows of plants or small individual terraces around shrubs and perennials in the beds have been prepared, the porous hose may be laid over the organic mulch; the water finds its way to the soil most in need of water with the very minimum of loss through runoff and evaporation.

Many gardeners with small areas to irrigate can well use the inexpensive porous hoses attached to the ordinary garden hose in preference to set sprinklers or mere hand sprinkling. In this way the gardener avoids wetting the plants, keeps losses of water to a minimum, and generally gets a better job done. Few people have the necessary patience to hold an ordinary hose long enough in one place to do a thorough job of watering.

Sprinklers. Sprinkling is a popular way to irrigate the soil, perhaps partly because it seems more like natural rain. Where proper furrows are difficult to prepare, sprinkling is an easy way to irrigate. Some use permanent installations of overhead pipe. More commonly now, movable pipe is laid out temporarily for a season or for part of a season after the plants are established. These may be laid on the ground or on blocks a few inches above the ground.

In many gardens pipes are laid out permanently just under the surface of the soil with openings for sprinkler heads, so that all or part of the lawn and garden may be irrigated as needed. These should be arranged so that they may be drained in autumn before freezing. Some lay out the pipes so that either a hose or a sprinkler head may be attached as needed according to soil moisture conditions and plant needs during the year. On lawns, one may arrange in this way a pattern of sprinkler heads so that all of the area is properly moistened. The sprinkler heads can be set in specially designed receptacles placed just at the soil level and thus not interfere with mowing.

Without proper terraces, either as continuous ridges of stone or earth, or on the lower side of individual plants, much of the water may run off and not get into the soil around the plants unless the sprays are fine and gentle. If the air is very hot and dry, a large part of the water thrown out in a fine spray evaporates before it even reaches the ground and considerably more evaporates off the foliage without ever getting into the soil. Under such conditions it may take more water to accomplish the same result, as in furrows or with the porous hose. On very permeable soils, however, much water is lost in the furrows; water soaks down beyond the reach of plant roots before sufficient water has spread laterally to moisten the soil properly between the furrows.

With sprinklers, one cannot avoid wetting the plants. This does not matter much unless the air is hot and humid. Then such wetting may encourage disease, especially the fungi. On the other hand, where rains are uncommon, sprinkling washes the dust from the plants and improves their appearance. Then too, plants adsorb some of the water directly into their leaves.

It is somewhat better to use sprinklers in the late afternoon, evening, or very early morning, than during the heat of the day.

If the soil is rather hard and dry, it is wise to sprinkle with a fine spray just before a heavy rain. The spray softens up the surface and more of the rain enters the soil instead of running off in the first few (and often only) minutes of the shower. Unfortunately, the author has no precise suggestion on how the gardener may tell exactly when it is about to rain.

Underground irrigation. In favorable locations many gardeners have had success with tile or porous pipe laid under the surface of the soil in such a way that water seeps out into the soil and moistens it. As already explained under the use of tile drains, such systems for sub-irrigation and drainage are often combined to control the water table within narrow limits. Another scheme for irrigation is mentioned in the discussion of furrow irrigation. By having a pattern of ditches and soil beds surrounded by dikes to hold the water one may control the water table, either by opening gates in the dikes where it will flow out, or by pumping it out. When water is needed, the dikes may be closed often simply by closing the drainage ditches, and water may be added to the ditches so it soaks laterally into the soil of the beds.

This same situation is occasionally found in nature where the water of streams soaks laterally through rather porous strata, which lie above impervious ones and beneath good surface soils. The water in these pervious strata supplies water to the soil lying just above them. This accounts for the bright green patches one occasionally sees along a low stream terrace in semidesert regions.

WATER AND SALTS

In arid and semiarid regions excess salts often give the gardener trouble. These may be carried into the soil by the irrigation water itself, if it is salty. Assuming that good irrigation water is used, poor drainage is the most likely fundamental source of trouble. In dry regions salty soils are found in places that have boggy and swampy soils in the humid regions. Salty water often seeps into low places from higher land above. If the water cannot leach on through the soil, the salts are left behind as the water evaporates. Salts can be carried up in ascending water from a salty water table. These accumulate at the surface or in a layer beneath the surface where the water ceases to move up by capillary action and continues out as a vapor. Even a soil that is not salty in the root zone may soon become so after irrigation; the irrigation water goes down into the soil from the furrows and then up again by capillary action, bringing salts with it from the deeper layers.

The gardener with salty soils should install proper drainage. Then with flooding, ordinary salts may be leached out. If the soil contains large amounts of sodium salts, like sodium chloride (common table salt) or sodium sulphate, or is very strongly alkaline, the clay is likely to "run together" badly when wet and the soil "freezes"— that is, becomes impervious to water. Such soils are often called "black alkali" locally in parts of western United States. They may be improved by adding gypsum or calcium sulphate along with manure. If a soil of this character contains a fair amount of calcium carbonate, and most of them do, a combination of sulphur and manure is often more effective. It should always be emphasized that these treatments are of no avail unless the soil has been properly drained so that excess salts may be leached out, plus the products resulting from the reactions of these chemicals with the soil.

The amount of these materials to use depends upon the intensity of the alkali condition. Applications of gypsum or calcium sulphate usually run between 50 to 200 pounds per 1000 square feet, although they may run up to 800 pounds per 1000 square feet under extreme conditions. Generally speaking, the gypsum is less effective than the sulphur. Recommended applications of sulphur vary from around 40 to 140 pounds per 1000 square feet. With good applications of manure somewhat less of the chemical is required. Good results have been had by combined applications, using manure and half dosage each of gypsum and sulphur.

If the soil has very bad structure, the manure should be worked into the surface along with the chemicals, and the soil irrigated heavily sometime in advance of seeding. To improve alkali soil it is usually worth while to grow an ordinary green manuring crop for the first year after treatment before using the soil for vegetables or ornamentals.

Often ideal drainage is impossible to arrange, or too expensive. Here again, bedding helps. The soil may be thrown up into rather narrow beds about 2 to 4 feet wide between irrigation furrows. The two sides of the beds can be made some 2 to 3 inches higher than the center and some 8 to 10 inches above the furrow bottom. Parallel rows of plants may be grown on each side of the bed with each row 3 or 4 inches in from the margin of the furrow. In this way the plants are on the margins of two low ridges. The excess salts tend to concentrate along the tops of the ridges and the sides. If some water is guided into the slightly lower strip between the two rows, salts can be flushed back into the furrows. Thus there will be less salts around the plants themselves. In this way one may be able to have fairly good crops of vegetables and other annuals on soil a little too salty if handled in the ordinary way.

6

SOIL ACIDITY AND
HOW TO CHANGE IT

Soils vary widely in acidity and alkalinity, primarily according to the natural conditions under which they have developed and, secondarily, according to how they have been managed. Some are very acid indeed, while others are strongly alkaline. In the older literature, those that were not acid were called sweet.

Plants vary as widely in their tolerance of acid or alkaline conditions, or nearly so, as the natural soils. In semiarid regions a few soils are so strongly alkaline that no plants will grow, not even wild ones. Then too, in many soils great differences exist in the acidity of the several horizons; that is, two soils may be acid in the surface, but one may be alkaline beneath and the other acid.

Most of the ordinary vegetables and cultivated flowers do poorly on garden soils having either extreme acidity or alkalinity. The great bulk of cultivated plants does best on soils that are nearly neutral—neither acid nor alkaline, or at least only slightly acid. Yet there are very important exceptions among the ornamental plants and even among the fruits and vegetables. The gardener needs to find out how acid or alkaline his soil is in the surface, in the subsoil, and in the lower subsoil. Then he can select plants adapted to the conditions he finds or change the soil to make it receptive of plants needing a different condition.

WHAT SOIL ACIDITY MEANS

The acids in soils may be thought of as weak acids like those of certain fruits rather than strong acids like concentrated sulphuric or hydrochloric acid. Generally soil acids are only weakly soluble. Soils vary in both the *intensity* of the acidity and the *amount* of acidity in a unit volume.

In normal garden soils the salts dissolved in the water are in dilute solutions. In such solutions many of the salts are thought to be present as ions; [1] that is, a dilute solution of common table salt, or sodium chloride (NaCl), is thought to exist partly as molecules of the salt (NaCl) and partly as chloride ions (Cl) and sodium ions (Na).

Many of the important plant nutrients, and other substances that influence plants, are thought to exist in the soil as ions. These include, for example, the anions, carbonate (CO_3), bicarbonate (HCO_3), sulphate (SO_4), chloride (Cl), nitrate (NO_3), nitrite (NO_2), phosphate (PO_4), and hydroxyl (OH), and the cations, potassium (K), ammonium (NH_4), calcium (Ca), sodium (Na), magnesium (Mg), and hydrogen (H).

The degree of acidity depends upon the relative amounts of the H-ions and OH-ions. In absolutely pure water only a very small part of the water molecules (HOH) ionize to form H-ions and OH-ions. In pure water these balance, and the solution is neutral. But pure water exposed to ordinary air absorbs a little carbon dioxide (CO_2) to form a bit of carbonic acid(H_2CO_3), and the H-ions exceed the OH-ions, and the water is acid. As the concentration of either OH-ions or H-ions increases, that of the other decreases.

A mathematical notation, called pH, has been established to indicate the relative acidity of solutions. This expression is a very com-

[1] For this discussion we may think of an ion as an electrically charged atom or group of atoms in solution. Pure water is a poor conductor of electricity but if some salt, like common table salt, is added it becomes a good conductor. The current is carried by the Na-ion and the Cl-ion as the salt NaCl splits into these two parts in water. One atom, the Cl, gains an electron, while the Na loses one. These separate particles that carry the current are also called electrolytes and, by an extension of meaning, any substance that gives ions when dissolved in water is an electrolyte. If we pass an electric current through the salty water, the Na-ions move to the negative pole, while the Cl-ions move to the positive one. Those that move to the positive pole, or anode, are called *anions*, while those that move to the negative pole, or cathode, are called *cations*.

mon one in writing about soils and fertilizers because the relative degree of acidity is so important and can be much more briefly and precisely stated in figures than in words.

The following table shows how words describing soil acidity and alkalinity relate to these pH values.

	pH		*pH*
Extremely acid	Below 4.5	Neutral [2]	6.6–7.3
Very strongly acid	4.5–5.0	Mildly alkaline	7.4–7.8
Strongly acid	5.1–5.5	Moderately alkaline	7.9–8.4
Medium acid	5.6–6.0	Strongly alkaline	8.5–9.0
Slightly acid	6.1–6.5	Very strongly alkaline	9.1 and higher

pH is a measure of the intensity of acidity, but soils having the same pH vary in the *amount* of acidity—in the potential supply of H-ions. As the active H-ions are removed from a soil by adding some neutralizer, like ground limestone, other H-ions take their place by ionization from reserve acids. In some soils this reserve is small, in others very large. Thus the amounts of lime needed to change different acid soils from pH 5 to pH 6.5 vary with the total amount of acidity.

Sandy soils, low in clay and organic matter, have low reserves of acidity. Clay soils rich in organic matter have high reserves. Peats and mucks have very high reserves. Thus these three general kinds of surface soil, likely to be found in New York or Indiana, may require about 80, 200, and 400 pounds, respectively, of finely ground limestone per 1000 square feet to change the upper 7 inches of soil from about pH 5.2 to pH 7.0. The kind of clay minerals is also important. Thus acid soils developed in warm regions generally require less limestone to neutralize them than do soils of the same pH in cool-temperate regions. For a vegetable garden on strongly acid soils of medium texture in New York, one should use around 150 pounds of ground limestone per 1000 square feet, but only about 90 pounds on a strongly acid soil of medium texture in Alabama.

In thinking about the soil as a medium for plant roots we are especially concerned with pH—the intenseness of the acidity. In

[2] Strict neutrality is precisely pH 7.0. Very few actual soil samples have this value and those having pH values between 6.6 and 7.3 are considered, for all practical purposes, neutral. For more precise identification those between 6.6 and 7.0 are described as very slightly acid, and those between 7.0 and 7.3 as very mildly alkaline.

undertaking to change the environment by changing the pH of the soil we have to consider also the total amount that must be neutralized—the capacity factor.

WHAT ACIDITY DOES

The good effects of adding some sort of liming materials to acid soils have been known for centuries. Of course early European gardeners did not know that their soils were acid. They knew only that crops were greatly benefited by adding marl, wood ashes, or some other liming material to certain kinds of soil. It is not easy even now to explain just why these effects are good in every case because there are many reasons that apply unequally to different kinds of acid soils. The solubility of nearly all compounds in the soil varies with the pH. Thus, when lime (CaO) or limestone ($CaCO_3$) is added to neutralize an acid soil, many other things happen besides simply changing the ratio of H-ions to OH-ions and the addition of calcium. For example, plants that grow well in soils that have naturally a pH of 7.5, or even higher, do poorly on naturally acid soils that have been changed to a similar pH by liming.

First of all, an excess of H-ions or of OH-ions seems to be toxic to many plants. Yet some plants that grow well in acid solution cultures of pH 3.5 to 4.0 scarcely grow at all in soils with the same acidity. So reasons must be found for the effects other than simply the abundance of H-ions.

Calcium supply. The common liming materials used to neutralize acid soils contain calcium primarily or calcium and magnesium together. Both are essential plant nutrients. Most acid soils are relatively low in calcium, and often in both calcium and magnesium, in forms available to plants. Thus liming increases the supply of these. Certainly, this accounts for some of the benefit, but not all. One may add other forms of available calcium and magnesium to acid soils, say gypsum and Epsom salts, without getting the good effects of limestone on the growth of plants characteristically not tolerant of acid soils.

Other nutrients. pH has a pronounced effect on the solubility of several other compounds in the soil and thus upon the availability of several other essential plant nutrients. As the soil becomes more acid iron and aluminum become more soluble; and they are more able to react with the phosphates to form iron and aluminum phosphates that are not available to plants. On the other hand phosphates become relatively unavailable at pH levels between 8.0 and 8.5, especially if plenty of calcium is present.

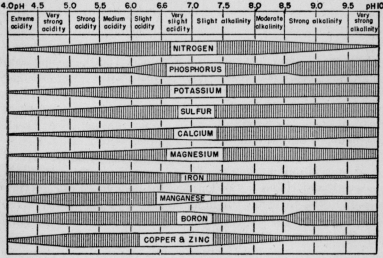

Figure 1.—In this group of diagrams, Professor E. Truog suggests the usual relations between degrees of soil acidity and alkalinity, or pH, and the availability of plant nutrients in the soil. The width of each labeled band is proportional to the availability of that nutrient element. Since only general relationships are suggested, the bands indicate *relative* availability, not the total amount, which varies from soil type to soil type. Then too, some of the effects are indirect, through the relation of pH to the growth of micro-organisms. (Not enough is known about molybdenum to add it to this chart; probably its availability increases on the alkaline side.) The chart shows graphically why pH 6.5 is in the optimum range for so many plants.

Professor Emil Truog has summarized some of these important relationships on the chart shown in Figure 1. The wider the bands, the more favorable the pH for the availability of the particular plant nutrient to ordinary vegetable and flowering plants. Now, of course, there are other factors that influence the actual amounts of any nutrient present besides pH. First of all, if the amount of phosphorus is very low in the soil, as is true of a great many soils used for gardens, plants do not have enough phosphorus no matter what the pH. Or one may maintain a high content of available phosphorus or nitrogen, let us say, in acid soils through special fertilization. Then too, some plants require an acid soil for good growth. Blueberries, azaleas, rhododendrons, mountain laurel, and many others thrive best in soils between pH 4.5 and 5.5.

This chart gives a good idea of the effects of pH on plant nutrients and can help the gardener see what nutrient deficiencies are most likely at various pH values. One sees that iron, manganese, copper, and zinc, for example, are all likely to be inadequate for good plant growth in soils of pH 8 and higher. Fertilization of the soil or plant sprays containing small amounts of these nutrients are often needed for fruit trees on alkaline soils. The chart shows why most vegetable crops and ordinary flowering plants grown in the garden find their best conditions for growth at about pH 6.5. But we must repeat: there are many exceptions.

The chart also shows why overliming can depress the availability of many plant nutrients. Although many gardeners need to use lime, there are certainly a great many that use more than they should— especially more of the ordinary burned lime (CaO), which is an active chemical that is harmful in excess. It not only may raise the pH too high, where used in abundance, but also may raise the concentration of calcium too high in respect to magnesium, phosphorus, and potassium, thus making it impossible for plants to get adequate supplies of these nutrients.

Toxic effects. Besides excessive H-ions at low pH values, aluminum becomes soluble. High amounts of soluble aluminum are known to be toxic to many plants. Apparently they are not so toxic to the acid-loving plants, although this point is not entirely clear. Generally one may counteract this effect on garden soil being prepared for plants like azaleas and blueberries, and reduce the soluble aluminum by adding good supplies of a phosphatic fertilizer. Also soluble manganese may be abundant enough to be toxic in very acid soils.

Then too, in very acid soils many of the bacteria that decompose organic matter in normal garden soils cannot thrive. Some people hold that toxic organic compounds resulting from the partial decomposition of organic matter—toxic compounds that are decomposed as rapidly as they form in ordinary neutral garden soils—accumulate in very acid soils, especially if they are swampy.

Effects on micro-organisms. The most favorable range for most soil micro-organisms lies between pH 6 and pH 8. Within this range, the bacteria that attach themselves to the roots of legumes and fix atmospheric nitrogen usually grow best. This is especially important to cover crops of clover for the kitchen garden and for white clover in the lawn. Yet these plants can grow and support the bacteria in somewhat more acid soils if they are furnished adequate calcium.

The fungi that change the nitrogen compounds in the soil organic matter to ammonia can grow in strongly acid soil. Different plants vary greatly in their ability to use this form of nitrogen. At least a great many, including the common vegetable crops and fruits, need much of their nitrogen in the nitrate form (NO_3-ion). The organisms that change ammonia to nitrates in soils do best in the range from about pH 6 to pH 8.

Neutralizing acid soils has its effect on the micro-organisms that maintain a good supply of available nitrates in garden soil. The whole micro-population is more active in decomposing organic matter and in releasing all of its plant nutrients in neutral soils than in very acid or very alkaline ones. One of the great benefits to the gardener from using abundant compost and other organic matter in the soil is the steady supply of plant nutrients released as it decomposes. This process is slow in strongly acid soils.

Tilth. The structure or tilth of the garden soil depends both directly and indirectly on pH. The clay in very acid, and especially in very alkaline, soils is likely to be sticky, plastic, and easily puddled when wet, and to bake hard when dry. A good crumb structure is most easily maintained in soils, particularly clayey soils, with pH's between about 6.5 and 8.0, especially with abundant calcium present. The gardener must always remember that this is true of the deeper soil as well as the surface. Thus, in order to put acid soils in the best possible shape for vegetables and other plants that require a pH around 6.5, lime needs to be incorporated into the deep soil as well as spaded into the surface. Good garden soils have excellent tilth and fertility to at least 18 inches.

Possibly the indirect effects of liming acid soils on tilth are more important than the direct effects. A large active population of bacteria is very helpful to the formation of crumb structure in clay soils—in fact, probably essential. Thus the maintenance of a proper pH in the plant-rooting zone is necessary in order to have the bacteria. Now the bacteria also need food material—organic matter. Organic matter can be incorporated into the lower soil by deep spading. It gets there naturally from the remains of deeply rooted plants. Thus, once we have the soil in such shape that plant roots grow deeply, the remains of these roots help to maintain good structure. Partly for this reason most acid-loving plants grow well only in rather sandy soils, loams, or sandy loams. In clays the soil is likely to be too compact for good root growth; and it is difficult to improve the structure of clay without raising the pH.

PLANTS HAVE DIFFERENT TASTES

Soils vary in pH from a little below pH 3.5 to a bit above pH 9.5. Although some plants grow over a wide range of soil pH, I cannot think of any that cover the whole range. Other plants are quite specific and grow well within only a narrow range of pH.

If we look at Professor Truog's chart again, we shall see that pH 6.5 is most favorable for plant nutrients. For an amazing number of plants pH 6.5 is somewhere within their optimum pH range—perhaps near the top or the bottom; for most garden plants it is near the middle of their optimum range. But we may have said too much: there are many important exceptions.

Professor Spurway compiled the values for the optimum pH ranges for a great list of plants from an extensive survey of scientific literature.[3] Many of the values he gives are included in the soil notes on individual plants in Appendix II. These values can be very helpful to the gardener. By testing his own soil he can select adapted plants, as far as pH is concerned, or he can make his soil more acid or more alkaline to meet the requirements of the plant he wants to grow. Gardeners are likely to do some of both—some selection and some changing—but often more of the latter than necessary. After all, if one has a strongly acid sandy soil with partial shade, it may be much better to plant azaleas, if they are otherwise adapted, than to go to the trouble of preparing from it a clayey, slightly acid soil in full sun for roses. Lists like those in the Appendix can be especially helpful in selecting plants for combination plantings. Acid-loving ground covers and edgings need to go with the blueberries and rhododendrons, for example.

[3] "Soil Reaction (pH) Preferences of Plants," by C. H. Spurway, (Michigan Agricultural Experiment Station Special Bulletin 306, 1941).

But such figures are not precise, in general. The optimum pH for a plant depends in part on the kind of soil. As we have already seen, a soil is a mixture of things. Two soils may have the same pH, but yet be quite different mixtures. That is, one surface soil at pH 5.5 may contain tiny spots ranging from pH 3.5 to pH 7.0, whereas in another surface soil of pH 5.5, no part is below 4.5 nor above 6.0. For example, climatically-adapted plants grow well in many of the soils in the northern part of New England, in the northern Lake States, in the Pacific Northwest, and in Alaska at somewhat lower values for soil pH than indicated in this and other usual tables of pH preferences. Further, if all factors except one favor the growth of a plant, it may do fairly well even when this one is far from ideal. Thus, with good supplies of plant nutrients and with a thick mulch of acid-forming organic matter one may do quite well with acid-loving plants on nearly neutral soils. On the other hand, daffodils can be grown successfully along with the acid-lovers in moist fertile soil at pH 4.5 —well below their optimum range—with a little superphosphate placed an inch or so beneath the bulb. Thus by careful attention to all the other factors, including nutrient supply, structure, mulch, moisture, shade and sunlight, plant competition, and winter protection, plants may be grown outside their usual optimum pH ranges.

A disease hazard may force the gardener to crowd a few plants to one end of their pH range. Potatoes are an excellent example. For the plants themselves the optimum range is about 5.0 to 6.5. Considering only the ease of maintaining a supply of plant nutrients, and the needs of other plants that one may want to grow in rotation with the potatoes on the same area, the soil should be prepared at about pH 6.2 to 6.5. But potato scab, a serious disease of the tubers, grows easily in this part of the pH range, but not in the lower part. Thus one prepares soil for potatoes to have a pH of about 5.5, not above 5.6. For similar reasons, the pH of soil for eggplant or tobacco should be below 6.0.

Then too, by keeping the pH of a soil near one end of the range for a plant, certain weeds that require a different pH may be kept out or at least partially suppressed. Thus, by keeping the soil quite acid one may grow pine seedlings without weed trouble. Many say that liming lawns on acid soils encourages the growth of dandelions more than it does the lawn grasses, but this has not been my experience except where excessive amounts of lime are applied. Dandelions grow in mildly to strongly alkaline soil—above the optimum range for many lawn grasses. But they also grow in soils too acid for the very best nutrition and growth of good lawn mixtures. Few exceptions can be found to the rule that the best way to keep weeds out of a lawn is to make the soil as productive as possible for the lawn grasses themselves.

TESTS FOR ACIDITY

Despite the fact that pH measures only intensity of the acidity, nearly all reliable and convenient field and garden tests measure pH. Most of these are based on the use of "indicators"—complex organic compounds in solution that change color at specific pH values—or a combination of such compounds. There are several good field kits that may be used. On the whole, these colorimetric field tests are not entirely dependable at the extremes—say below pH 4.0 or above pH 8.5—nor in very salty or peaty soils.

Electro-chemical apparatus is used in the laboratory for more precise measurements and some field kits based upon the same principle are available; but most of these are too expensive and too exacting for the gardener unless he has a flair for physical chemistry. Nor is the greater precision ordinarily significant.

The gardener should equip himself with a simple soil acidity tester or have his soils tested. Several state agricultural colleges make tests of soil samples sent to them according to their directions. In some states special local laboratories have been established for making soil tests. It is a good plan for a gardener to have a few tests made in order to check his own results, but it is not difficult for most gardeners to make the tests themselves with these simple kits. Tests should be made of the surface 5 to 8 inches that is moved in surface spading, and of the lower layers. Then, of course, tests should be made of the various kinds of soil—of which there may be several even on one city lot. (See page 139 *et seq.*)

It is a good plan to follow through after treatments for changing the pH have been made to see the results achieved. Where there is danger of overliming one should proceed cautiously, and add repeated light applications to reach the optimum value rather than run the hazard of going over it. Once a soil is overlimed, it is difficult to bring the pH down again.

LIME FOR CORRECTING ACIDITY

Forms of lime. Strictly speaking, lime is calcium oxide, but in ordinary practice all the common materials used to correct soil acidity are called lime. These include ground limestone, mainly calcium carbonate, ground dolomitic limestone, containing both calcium carbonate and magnesium carbonate, burned lime, or calcium oxide, and hydrated or slaked lime, calcium hydroxide. Locally, marl, chiefly an earthy calcium carbonate, is used. So are ground oyster shells. Wood ashes are a good source of lime and also contain significant amounts of potash and some other plant nutrients. Slags left over from blast furnace operations are used for liming materials.

Since ground limestone is most commonly used, recommendations are now generally given in terms of that material. If finely ground, it is much more quickly available than if coarsely ground. A good material should all pass a 10-mesh (to the inch) screen and one half of it should pass a 100-mesh screen, or at least a 60-mesh screen. Pure calcium carbonate is said to have 100 per cent neutralizing ability as a standard. Of course no limestones are completely pure calcium carbonate. Because molecules of magnesium carbonate weigh a little less than molecules of calcium carbonate, there are more of them in a pound of material. Yet each has the same neutralizing effect. Thus a dolomitic limestone having 60 per cent calcium carbonate and 30 per cent magnesium carbonate would have a neutralizing power of 97.5 per cent, not 90 per cent.

It requires only about 55 pounds of burned lime or 74 pounds of hydrated lime to equal in neutralizing power 100 pounds of high quality ground limestone. Further, both of these compounds are much more finely divided and active than ground limestone. Where used, either should be applied in small quantities more frequently, whereas ground limestone may be applied in larger amounts at one time. Marl or wood ashes may be used at about the same rate as limestone. One should not use wood ashes simply because they are available—not unless the soil actually needs them.

Of the principal sorts of lime, ground dolomitic limestone is by all odds the best for gardeners. For one thing, it contains magnesium—an essential plant nutrient often too low in garden soils for best plant growth. This is especially true of acid soils in the eastern and southern parts of the United States. This deficiency of magnesium is also aggravated by the general use of the low-analysis or "ordinary" super-phosphate, which contains a large amount of calcium sulphate. By adding quantities of sulphates in this and other fertilizers some of the magnesium present in soils is changed to the very soluble magnesium sulphate (Epsom salts), which is, as a result, lost from the soil through leaching. By the addition of a relatively pure calcium limestone or other liming material and the use of the low-analysis super-phosphate with abundant calcium sulphate in it, many soils acquire too high a ratio of soluble calcium to soluble magnesium for plants to get all the magnesium they require. This condition is especially common in very fertile garden soils where all the other nutrients are abundant. These relationships among the individual plant nutrients are explained in the next chapter.

Another reason for favoring dolomitic limestone is its low solubility in neutral or alkaline soil. It is much less soluble than burned lime or slaked lime—less caustic—and even less soluble than finely ground pure calcium limestone. In strongly acid soils dolomitic limestone is soluble enough to neutralize the acidity, slowly to be sure, but fast enough. Then as the pH rises, the remaining material becomes less and less soluble until at pH 7.0 to pH 7.5 it becomes very slightly soluble indeed. Thus there is practically no danger of overliming with any reasonable application of dolomitic limestone.

This is not true with burned lime or hydrated lime. With an excess of these materials the pH of the soil can be raised to 8.5, which is generally too high and may cause serious shortages of phosphorus, potassium, magnesium, and the minor elements. If the material used is lumpy or for any reason an extra heavy dose hits some spot, the soil under that spot will likely be too alkaline for most garden plants.

Next best after dolomitic limestone is ordinary limestone. If this is used, some magnesium should be added as magnesium sulphate mixed with the limestone, the fertilizer, or the compost. Unless one has a reliable chemical test to indicate a slightly lower or a slightly higher rate, about 2 to 5 pounds may be used per 1000 square feet.

I strongly advise against the use of burned lime or slaked (hydrated) lime in the garden unless ground limestone, marl, and ground oyster shells are all unavailable. These materials should be spread at pro-portionately lower rates—55 per cent for burned lime and 74 per cent for slaked lime—than the rates given for finely ground limestone. Further, the application should be split into two or three separate applications over a period of about two years and not put on all at one time, as can be done with dolomitic limestone. Care should be taken to break up any lumps and to spread it as evenly as possible. Nor should the dust from these materials get onto the foliage of acid-loving plants nor even onto the soil near their roots.

Time to apply. In the garden the lime should be applied a little while before spading so it is mixed with the soil. When double spading, the lime should also be worked into the subsoil, if acid, along with compost or manure and fertilizer.

For shrubs and trees lime may be mixed with the soil as needed [4] at planting time; for established lawns the application is ordinarily made in the early spring, but ground limestone can be put on any time.

Ordinarily, one may expect a proper application of ground limestone to last four or five years where there is a fair amount of leaching. Tests of soil acidity can be used to check the gradual change.

Amounts of lime to apply. So many factors influence the amount of lime to apply that it is difficult to lay down rules. In warm-temperate regions like the southern part of the United States one may say about 25 to 50 pounds of finely ground limestone for 1000 square feet on sandy soils and 75 to 125 pounds on clayey soils. Corresponding figures for the Northern states are roughly 50 to 75 and 100 to 200. But, of course, the rate depends upon the texture of the soil, the content of organic matter, the plants to be grown, and especially the degree of acidity. Somewhat more specific recommendations are set forth in Table 4.

Ordinarily one should not attempt to change the pH of a soil more than one pH unit by one application of lime. The pH may be checked between applications. That is, if the soil for the garden or lawn is at pH 4.5, it is better to change it to pH 5.5 one year and to pH 6.5 the following year, or even two years later. This is especially true of strongly leached sandy soils in warm regions, or where burned or hydrated lime is used instead of ground dolomitic limestone as recommended.

Overliming. Many gardeners use too much lime either in single applications or in too frequent light applications, especially of

---

[4] Tables 9a and 9b, pages 142–44, can be used to calculate the amounts needed for individual plants, depending on their spacing, by converting the recommendations per 1000 square feet given in Table 4.

TABLE 4. Approximate amounts of finely ground limestone [1] to raise the pH of a 7-inch layer of several classes of acid soils as indicated

	POUNDS PER 1000 SQUARE FEET [2]		
	pH 3.5 to pH 4.5	pH 4.5 to pH 5.5	pH 5.5 to pH 6.5
Soils in southern Gulf States			
Sands and loamy sands	15	15	20
Sandy loams	—	25	35
Loams	—	40	50
Silt loams	—	60	75
Clay loams	—	80	100
Muck	130	175	200
Soils in northern Central States			
Sands and loamy sands	20	25	30
Sandy loams	—	45	55
Loams	—	60	85
Silt loams	—	80	105
Clay loams	—	100	120
Muck	150	200	225

[1] All through a 10-mesh screen and at least one half through a 100-mesh screen. With coarser materials, the amounts need to be higher.

[2] The suggestions for muck soils are for those essentially free of sand and clay. For those containing significant amounts of sand and clay the recommendations are reduced to a value midway between that given for muck and the corresponding class of mineral soil. If the other soils are unusually low in organic matter, the amounts should be reduced by about 25 per cent, and if unusually high, increased by about 25 per cent, or perhaps a little more. One should use about one half the amounts given in this table with burned lime and about three quarters with hydrated lime.

burned lime. The hazard of overliming is greatest on light sandy soils developed in humid forested regions like the eastern part of the United States. Such soils have been long leached under acid conditions. As a result their supply of plant nutrients is already low. If the pH is raised too high, much above pH 6.5, and especially if it goes above pH 7.0 and free lime accumulates, many of the compounds containing plant nutrients become so insoluble that serious plant-nutrient deficiencies develop. This hazard exists in temperate regions, and increases as one goes toward the equator.

Some sandy garden soils in the southeastern part of the United States have been placed in poor fertility by excessive use of lime. Although the hazard is worse on sandy soils, some of the loamy garden soils have been injured too.

Once this overliming has occurred, the gardener may need to apply rather large amounts of fertilizer, including the minor nutrients, and organic matter. In extreme cases sulphur may need to be added to bring down the pH, followed by heavy applications of organic matter and fertilizers.

MAINTAINING AND INCREASING SOIL ACIDITY

The gardener often wants to grow blueberries, azaleas, rhododendrons, mountain laurel, trailing arbutus, or other acid-loving plants in soils naturally too high in pH for their best growth. For a few of these plants in a small garden, it is often most practicable to remove the existing soil to a depth of 18 to 24 inches and replace it with a mixture of acid sandy loam and acid peat or leaf mold. In doing this one wants to be sure that the underdrainage is good. Although many of these plants need moist soil, most of them cannot endure wet soggy conditions. Holes in deep massive clays filled with sandy soil may become, in effect, cisterns or catchment basins that are too wet. When making these holes for special plants they should be filled with water and tested for drainage. Small-diameter test holes can be made first; that is, the water should disappear through natural drainage in an hour or two. If it does not, some provision for adequate drainage needs to be made or another site should be chosen.

If the surrounding soil has a pH above 7.0 and contains free lime, a little of this lime may seep into the acid soil in the refilled hole. Except on rather strong slopes where surface or underground water seeps from one kind of soil to another, there is comparatively little lateral movement of lime or salts in the soil. But often the water used in watering plants during dry periods is alkaline—hard water. If so, it may be necessary to add acid to the water to counteract it, or sulphur to the soil. Thus, after the soil has been prepared to the proper pH, occasional tests need to be made to check its condition.

This method of preparing soil for specimen plants or for small beds is generally more practicable than trying to change the pH of the natural soil. It works all right if there is no difficulty with drainage, if there is good material for refilling the holes, and if the underlying soil is not very high in pH or in its content of free lime. A good material for making the beds is leaf mold and the upper 4 or 5 inches of acid mineral soil that may be found under a good growth of trees on a soil with a sandy loam surface.

For larger areas of plantings, where the drainage is good, one may add chemicals to acidify the soil. Aluminum sulphate and sulphur are most commonly used. The latter is much preferred, partly because it takes about 6 pounds of aluminum sulphate to have the effect of one pound of sulphur and partly because much soluble aluminum is toxic to plants. The soil should be prepared in advance and set for a considerable time so that the reactions may take place and the most soluble materials leach out before planting.

TABLE 5. The approximate amounts of sulphur to change the surface 8 inches of soils with various pH values to stated lower pH values [1]

Original pH of Soil	APPROXIMATE POUNDS OF SULPHUR PER 100 SQUARE FEET TO REACH pH OF											
	4.0		4.5		5.0		5.5		6.0		6.5	
	Sand	Loam	Sand	Loam	Sand	Loam	Sand	Loam	Sand	Loam	Sand	Loam
4.5	0.4	1.2										
5.0	0.8	2.4	0.4	1.2								
5.5	1.2	3.5	0.8	2.4	0.4	1.2						
6.0	1.5	4.6	1.2	3.5	0.8	2.4	0.4	1.2				
6.5	1.9	5.8	1.5	4.6	1.2	3.5	0.8	2.4	0.4	1.2		
7.0	2.3	6.9	1.9	5.8	1.5	4.6	1.2	3.5	0.8	2.4	0.4	1.2
7.5 [2]	2.7	8.0	2.3	6.9	1.9	5.8	1.5	4.6	1.2	3.5	0.8	2.4

[1] Adapted from "The Blueberry in New York" by G. L. Slater and R. C. Collison, New York State Agricultural Experiment Station Circular No. 189, 29 pp. illus., Geneva, 1942.
[2] Figures in this row do not include amounts necessary for extra reserves of free lime in the soil.

Table 5 shows the approximate amounts of sulphur to use in order to make pH changes of sands (or loamy sands) and loams. Sandy loams are intermediate. Somewhat higher amounts would be required for clayey soils; but it is not usually practicable to make drastic decreases in the acidity of clayey or clay soils. If a soil having a pH higher than 7 contains significant amounts of free lime or calcium carbonate in the surface or in the lower soil, additional amounts of sulphur are needed; but it is usually impracticable to acidify soils rich in free lime. As with the limestone recommendations these figures are not precise because the other characteristics of the soil, especially the kind of clay minerals and the amount of organic matter, influence the effectiveness of the treatment.

Suppose it is desired to reduce the pH of a sandy loam from pH 5.5 to pH 5.0 for azaleas. From the Table a value .8 is intermediate between 0.4 for sand and 1.2 for loam. Table 9a, page 142, makes it possible to convert this from pounds per 100 square feet to liquid measures. It turns out to be 3⅕ cups. For plants set 5 feet by 5 feet, we see from Table 9*b* that about 13 tablespoons are needed per plant. For this purpose, odd pH values lying between those given in the table may be treated proportionately. Thus in going from pH 5.7 to pH 4.5 with a loam soil for blueberries, 2.4 (the value for pH 5.5 to pH 4.5) plus ⅖ of the difference between 2.4 and 3.5 (the value for pH 6.0 to pH 4.5) or about .45, gives a total of 2.85 pounds or about 4¾ pints per 100 square feet. This works out, from Table 9b, to about 2¼ cups per plant, spaced 5 feet by 5 feet.

After the soil has been prepared and the appropriate amount of sulphur (or aluminum sulphate at 6 times the rate in pounds for sulphur) thoroughly mixed with it, the whole should be allowed to stand for 2 to 6 weeks before planting, under occasional wetting with rain or irrigation.

Once the pH has been thus reduced to the appropriate level by sulphur and the incorporation of abundant amounts of acid compost, peat, leaf mold, pine needles, or sawdust, good mulches of these organic materials help in keeping it there. The pH of a moist mulch of sawdust is about 4.5, which is just about ideal for blueberries and satisfactory for azaleas and rhododendrons.

Some gardeners have reported plants dying in soils treated with sulphur in this way. Quite likely the troubles have resulted from poor drainage. In the presence of decomposing organic matter, and in the absence of air due to poor drainage, some hydrogen sulphide or other toxic substances may be formed that injure plant roots. It should be emphasized that this use of sulphur is recommended only if the soil is well drained, either naturally, or by the use of tile or other equally effective means. Even in sandy soils the water table should never be nearer the surface than 15 inches and preferably somewhat deeper. The upper 15 inches of soil should not be saturated for more than a very few hours after a rain.

One should not attempt a drastic increase of acidity, or decrease in pH, after the plants are established in a soil. But gradual changes can be made through small additions of sulphur, say a tablespoonful for an area of some 5 square feet once a year. Although some use aluminum sulphate, this chemical is not recommended for use around growing plants. Soluble aluminum is toxic to plants and it is very easy to apply too much.

By using the kinds of fertilizer that leave an acid residue in soils, such as cottonseed meal or ammonium sulphate, the pH of the soil is gradually lowered. In fact, one needs to be careful that long continued use of such materials does not lower too much the pH of garden soils used for most plants.

Because iron is often a limiting plant nutrient in soils with a pH a bit too high for acid-loving plants, a little ferrous sulphate may be used when preparing the soil, say a tablespoonful for about 5 to 10 square feet. This material adds available iron and somewhat lowers the pH. Such treatments will not immediately cure a case of chlorosis (yellowing of the leaves) due to iron deficiency. For immediate effects the plants need to be sprayed with a dilute solution of ferrous sulphate, about 2 teaspoonfuls in a quart of water.

Finally, it must be emphasized that a continuous deep mulch of acid-organic matter is most important for acid-loving plants. Many of them do quite well in soils considerably above their optimum range of soil pH, provided no free lime is present or added and that a deep acid-organic mulch is maintained at all times.

7

BALANCING THE PLANT NUTRIENTS

Many successful gardeners have not taken the trouble to study plant nutrients. By following a few general guides, success can usually be had with vegetables, for example, by using heavy applications of farm manure along with superphosphate and a little extra nitrogen. Or one may use compost or a little manure along with a generous application of mixed fertilizer.

Nevertheless, such general recommendations do not insure success in many gardens. For one thing manure is usually very expensive for the suburban or city gardener, if indeed he can obtain it at all. Besides, much of the manure delivered in cities is of poor quality—strawy, leached, and foul with weed seeds. To have good gardens on soil not naturally suited to them, their special management requirements, which lie outside the application of "general recommendations," must be reasonably met.

Plants vary in their needs. Although the principal plants in a kitchen garden have roughly similar nutrient requirements, the ornamentals vary so widely that individual treatment is necessary.

The study of plant nutrition is very rewarding, mainly in better plants, but also in the satisfaction of knowing why plants grow as they do and in the sense of freedom it gives from complete dependence upon outside recommendations. Gardeners are continually subjected to propaganda and to overstatements about fertilizers, manures, and composts—especially by those with things to sell.

To review all that is known would fill many volumes.[1] Even then, there are many uncertainties that scientific research has not yet removed. In what follows, the main principles are reviewed with a minimum of technical language. Both soils and plants vary too much to allow many recommendations to be given that apply generally. Tables are used to bring out the major differences among kinds of soil and kinds of plants. By using these tables and applying the principles given in the text, it is hoped that the gardener will be able to fit his management to the particular combinations of soils and plants in his own garden. With both skill and luck he may hit a nearly perfect combination.

Plants must have a reasonably well balanced supply of nutrients for normal growth. Green plants manufacture foods from the nutrients taken from the soil, air, and water. These foods made by plants include a wide variety of organic compounds that nourish the cells of plants and provide the materials for leaves, stems, roots, flowers, and fruits.[2]

Plants can take in some organic compounds in small amounts. Much remains to be learned about the effects of the new insecticides and hormones. Some varieties of beans and squash are especially sensitive to DDT, while other vegetables are fairly tolerant. Tolerance also varies with the kind of soil. Benzene hexachloride (BHC) is an effective control agent for certain soil-inhabiting insects. Yet potatoes, carrots, and other root and tuber crops grown in soil treated with it pick up undesirable flavors and odors. Effective as many of these new organic pesticides are, they should be used only where truly needed

[1] Two very good recent books may be cited in this field. For the reader with a working knowledge of chemical principles: "Soil Conditions and Plant Growth," by Sir E. John Russell, 8th ed., rewritten by E. W. Russell (635 pp., illus., Longmans, London and New York, 1950). Russell's book contains many technical details about soils besides those concerned directly with plant nutrients. A less technical and smaller book, dealing mainly with fertilizers, is: "Efficient Use of Fertilizers," ed. by Vladimir Ignatieff (183 pp., illus., Food and Agriculture Organization of the United Nations, Washington, 1949). Editions of this are also available in French and Spanish.

[2] Unfortunately, this important distinction between plant nutrients and plant food is confused as a result of the incorrect early use of "plant food" (sometimes written "plantfood") as a catch word in the advertising and sales talk of the fertilizer trade. "Plant food" is still used incorrectly by some in one of three different senses: as a synonym for "commercial fertilizer," for the plant-nutrient part of a fertilizer or manure, or for all the plant nutrients in a soil, either in the surface soil alone or in the whole rooting zone.

and without excess. For most of the ornamentals, no specific information on the effects of residues left in the soil following treatments with the various organic pesticides is yet available.

Plants need fifteen elements for growth. They take carbon, oxygen, and hydrogen from the air and water. From the soil they take phosphorus, potassium, nitrogen, calcium, magnesium, and sulphur in relatively large amounts and iron, boron, manganese, zinc, copper, and molybdenum in relatively small amounts. Besides these, plants take in several other elements. Sodium, for example, stimulates the growth of some plants besides being able to substitute for part of the potassium. Silicon is used in the cell walls and spicules of some plants, horsetails, for example. Some plants even take in substantial amounts of gold if it is present in the soil. Chlorine is almost always contained in plants, often in large amounts. Several other elements, if abundant in the soil in soluble form, enter plants, including even poisonous ones like arsenic and selenium.

In general, nitrogen, phosphorus, and potassium are the most commonly deficient nutrients in soils. The mixed fertilizers sold to gardeners nearly always contain them, along with some calcium, sulphur, and other elements—as impurities, or as additions to provide supplies of the so-called "minor" or "trace" elements, iron, manganese, zinc, boron, copper, and molybdenum. Although these "minor" elements are usually present in most soils reasonably well supplied with organic matter, they may not be. Each is used importantly as a fertilizer in several kinds of soil in the world. Acid soils are nearly always low in calcium and magnesium, and calcium is commonly supplied as lime to decrease the acidity or as dolomitic lime, which contains both calcium and magnesium. Many fertilizers contain magnesium also, added as dolomite partly as a neutralizer of an otherwise acid fertilizer, or as make-weight "filler," or as both. Several compounds of the elements used in fertilizer contain calcium and sulphur, especially the low-analysis or "ordinary" superphosphate. Yet a few soils need special applications of sulphur as a plant nutrient and to increase soil acidity.

Each of the essential nutrients has one or more functions in the plant. Yet some of these are still imperfectly known. Besides, plants take in other elements that have no known function (including iodine and cobalt) but which are essential to foods of certain animals.

FORM AND AVAILABILITY

The elements used by plants do not exist in the soil or move into plants in pure form as such. The bulk of the supplies exists in relatively insoluble mineral and organic forms and comes into solution very slowly. This ability of a soil to maintain a small supply of the nutrients in soluble form so that plant roots can get them and to keep the supply replenished from a storehouse of nearly insoluble compounds is one of its most important qualities.

Generally speaking, very sandy soils, rich in quartz and low in nutrient-containing clays and other minerals, and low in organic matter, have the smallest storehouse. With them, small but repeated additions of nutrients as organic and chemical fertilizers are necessary for high fertility. If large amounts are added, especially of the soluble chemicals, the plant roots are injured by too high a concentration of soluble materials and a high proportion is lost by leaching before the plants can use them. Highly weathered clay soils of the tropics have a low storehouse except for the organic matter in them. Soils pervious to water and roots, yet fairly rich in clay and naturally well enough supplied with lime to be about neutral in reaction (neither acid nor alkaline), and containing abundant organic matter, have an enormous storehouse of plant nutrients. The nearly black loam and silt loam Prairie soils of the Middle West corn belt are examples of these.

Most of the nitrogen in a soil and up to one half of the phosphorus are tied up in the organic matter. A significant part of the other nutrients is also slowly released from decomposing organic matter, but still a good deal comes from the gradual solution of mineral particles and by release from the clay.

The relative importance of all these sources varies widely from soil to soil and even among the several layers within the rooting zone of the same soil.

Total chemical analysis of a soil tells us little about the amounts of nutrients actively available to plants. A soil may have a relatively large amount of total phosphorus and still very little in soluble form that plant roots can get. Indeed, many soils even fix phosphorus added to the soil so tightly that only a small part of the fertilizer ever gets into the plants. With such soils it is best to localize the phosphatic fertilizer in spots or bands near the plant roots rather than to mix it with the whole soil, so it will need to satisfy the fixing power of as little soil as possible and still be available to some of the roots.

The relative availability of the plant nutrients in soil is greatly influenced by the degree of acidity or alkalinity as already explained (page 93 *et seq.*). The ideal condition of reaction for most plant nutrients is very slightly acid. In Figure 1, one may see what happens to their solubility with increasing acidity or alkalinity.

Several general methods are used to determine the availability of a plant nutrient in the soil:

(1) Plants, like rye or some grass, may be grown under standard conditions in pots within the greenhouse on a weighed sample of the soil, and the amount of nutrient extracted by the rye determined by total analyses of the plants and subtracting the amount contained in the same number of comparable seeds. This is an expensive, time-consuming procedure that requires elaborate laboratory equipment. Then too, soils do not necessarily furnish nutrients in the greenhouse as they do out of doors. Nor do other plants behave in the same way as rye or some other test crop.

(2) Bits of tissue from growing plants may be removed and tested for various nutrients. By comparing these results to established standards, one can tell whether the plant has a normal or subnormal amount of the nutrient. The use of this method is rapidly increasing, especially for expensive plantation crops like sugar cane. It also requires some laboratory facilities and skills unavailable to nearly all gardeners. Then too, for short-season plants one gets the information too late for the plants tested.

(3) Plants suffering from deficiencies show characteristic symptoms in coloring and leaf form. A skillful person can identify the characteristics and associate them with particular nutrient deficiencies. To do this accurately for all nutrients takes rather more skill than the ordinary gardener can expect to acquire. But many gardeners are able to recognize iron, magnesium, and nitrogen deficiency readily. Here too, with short-season crops, the information comes a bit too late. Plants respond with deficiency symptoms more quickly than they recover when the missing nutrient is added. Then too, nutrient deficiency symptoms often become confused with the effects of diseases and insects. Sometimes two or more

nutrient deficiencies occur together, or there is an excess of one and a deficiency of another. That is, an excess of nitrogen and phosphorus may cause or worsen an iron deficiency.

Under the discussion of the individual nutrients, some of the deficiency symptoms are described. Several books deal with the symptoms of important groups of plants.[3]

(4) Chemical tests of soil samples are used to approximate the amount of nutrients that are available to plants. By standardizing such tests according to kinds of soil against plot tests showing the response of various plants to fertilizer use, good predictions of fertilizer needs may be made by a skilled soil scientist or horticulturist. He needs to take account of the kind of soil, previous management, proposed management, and the kind of plant to be grown. *The test results by themselves are not safe guides to fertilizer use.* Yet, if considered with the other factors they can be very helpful indeed. A skilled and careful gardener can learn to use the tests in this way if he wants to. Certainly he can test for acidity and probably for phosphorus. Several test kits are on the market. Their use is adapted to somewhat different kinds of soil, and the advice of a competent local soil scientist should be sought before deciding upon the one to use. In the United States many of the state agricultural colleges examine soil samples with such chemical tests and make recommendations for a nominal fee. Some states have several laboratories for this purpose.

(5) The most reliable method of determining fertilizer needs is probably by the field plot test. On a given kind of soil, one may fertilize comparable groups of plants in different ways and note the results. Here too, great care is needed to be sure that the results from plants treated differently are not due to soil variability, differences in plant species, or some other factor.

---

[3] "The Diagnosis of Mineral Deficiencies in Plants by Visual Symptoms," by T. Wallace. 2nd ed. (107 pp. + 312 colored plates. His Majesty's Stationary Office, London, 1951). This is an excellent handbook—the best for both the serious gardener and the professional expert.

"Hunger Signs in Crops: a Symposium," ed. by Gove Hambidge (327 pp., illus., American Society of Agronomy and National Fertilizer Association, Washington, 1947).

"Diagnostic Techniques for Soils and Crops," ed. by H. B. Kitchen (308 pp., illus., American Potash Institute, Washington, 1948).

BALANCE

Plants grow well over a rather wide range of nutrient conditions if enough of each nutrient is available to the roots and none is in excess. If one nutrient is deficient, applications of the others will not do much good even though they are low.

In many soils used for gardens, several or even most of the plant nutrients are low. On such soils plants may grow nearly normally, but slowly, and with low total yields. If one or two nutrients only are supplied in abundance, the nutritional balance may be so upset that plants grow abnormally. Heavy nitrogen dressings alone, for example, may give weak and flabby plants, low in fruit or flowers, and especially subject to disease. An excess of either calcium or potassium may depress the intake of magnesium so that plants become chlorotic or suffer from phosphorous deficiency because magnesium is necessary for its movement within the plant. As soils that are naturally low in fertility are built up in phosphorus, potassium, and nitrogen, one may expect deficiencies in the other nutrients, because of the higher balance level. As already explained, heavy dressings of lime on acid soils are likely to cause deficiencies of some of the other elements.

INDIVIDUAL PLANT NUTRIENTS

Some of the principal points about each nutrient are summarized in the following paragraphs.

Nitrogen. Nitrogen is an essential element in all proteins. It is obviously needed in all the growing parts where new cells are forming. As nitrogen is increased from a low supply, plant leaves become larger and the area for photosynthesis is increased. With increasing nitrogen the plant cells are larger and their walls thinner. Leaves become more juicy and tender. But if too much nitrogen is added, this process of cell-wall thinning makes the plants more subject to disease or drought and to lodging (falling down) by the wind. Then too, abundant nitrogen causes the leaves to be a rich dark green and to stay green for a long time. Too much nitrogen may seriously delay maturity and prevent flowering or ripening before frost, and delay the hardening off of perennial plants before winter. For this reason one needs to fertilize azaleas in temperate regions lightly with nitrogen in spring or early summer so that it will be low by autumn. Soft, juicy stems are likely to freeze and to be killed in winter.

Large amounts of nitrogen added to a quickly growing plant tend to increase the ratio of leaves to roots. With long-season plants, the extra carbohydrate produced by the larger leaves is stored in the fruits or roots. Thus very high nitrogen tends to give low yields of short-season root crops and high yields of long-season ones.

The nitrogen goes into plants mainly as the nitrate (NO_3) ion or the ammonium (NH_4) ion. Most plants can use either. Plants that grow in very moist soils likely use the ammonium, while those growing in well drained soils use mostly the nitrate. Even if an ammonium-containing fertilizer, such as ammonium sulphate, is used, probably most of the ammonium is changed to nitrate in a well drained soil before it goes into the plant. Organic forms of nitrogen, such as those in manure and compost, must first be changed to ammonia before they are used by plants. This, in turn, largely goes to nitrates in well drained soils.

Deficiencies in nitrogen result in reduced plant vigor and small plants with smallish light green, yellowish-green, or reddish-green tough leaves. The yellowing of the leaves is more nearly uniform than in iron or magnesium deficiencies. Trees shed their leaves too soon. On many plants the older and lower leaves quickly turn yellow and die. Grasses have a yellowish-green color, slender leaves, and an early dying of the older leaves. Many confuse these symptoms of nitrogen deficiency with the effects of drought. If other plant nutrients are high, nitrogen-deficient plants may go into maturity early with small abnormal flowers and fruits.

Nitrogen deficiencies may be expected in any light colored soil low in organic matter and especially in the sandy ones subject to much leaching. Soils that have lost surface soil by washing or grading are likely to be low in nitrogen. Most soils are low in nitrogen if they have been repeatedly burned or cultivated without compensating additions of manure or compost or without occasional periods with legume green-manuring crops. Soil in permanent grass, without clover, that has been cut or grazed is commonly low in nitrogen. The addition of fresh organic materials, high in carbon in relation to nitrogen, causes a deficiency in nitrogen available to growing plants. Most well drained soils recently cleared from a pine or oak-pine forest are too low in nitrogen for lawns or gardens.

Most soils rich in organic matter contain abundant nitrogen, although a few developed under high rainfall do not. With excess nitrogen, in relation to the other nutrients, plants are rank and spindly; they have a high ratio of leaves and stems to fruits and flowers; and they are likely to be more than usually subject to injury from diseases, drought, cold, and transplanting.

Although the air contains abundant nitrogen as the elemental gas, plants cannot use it in that form. A few bacteria can, including some "free-living" sorts that live in the soil and, more importantly, several that grow on the roots of legumes—plants like peas, beans, clover, and alfalfa.

Sources of nitrogen for the gardener include the protein-containing waste materials of plants and animals, such as those in manure and good compost, and the various nitrogen-containing chemical fertilizers. Some of these, like sodium nitrate, are naturally occurring salts found in desert regions while others are made by chemical-fixation processes from the nitrogen in the air—processes perhaps not altogether different from those that go on in soil organisms at much lower temperatures. Years ago the amount of nitrogen in a fertilizer was expressed as per cent of ammonia (NH_3); now it is expressed as nitrogen (N) regardless of the form.

Phosphorus. Phosphorus is essential for protoplasm and for many of the enzymes in plants. In contrast to plants growing on phosphorus-poor soils, those well supplied with phosphorus have strong deep roots, sturdy stems, early maturity, and good yields of seeds, flowers, and fruits. Besides stunted growth and delayed ripening, the leaves of many plants deficient in phosphorus show a purplish tinge, especially on the margins. Unlike nitrogen there is little hazard of excess phosphorus in the soil, except for very large amounts where iron is low.

Phosphorus deficiency in soils is widespread and most unfertilized soils are too low in available phosphorus for the best results in the garden, especially those in warm-humid regions that are low in organic matter. Highly acid soils are usually low in phosphorus. The effectiveness of phosphatic fertilizer in them is increased by liming. Very alkaline soils are also usually low in available phosphorus.

Unless the gardener knows that the natural soil—for example, in the blue-grass region of Kentucky—is rich in phosphorus, or that abundant supplies have been used before, he might as well assume that his soil is low in it. Since phosphatic fertilizers do not leach down into the soil, simple surface applications are not adequate; the phosphorus should be worked deeply into the soil as well.

Because manures and composts are relatively low in phosphorus, some mineral source is generally essential for good results. The gardener can get nitrogen from good compost, from manure, and by growing legumes. Composts or manure, supplemented with wood ashes, supply potassium. But even with these practices, the soil will be low in phosphorus. Generally, superphosphate is used, either alone or in a mixed fertilizer; rock phosphate can be used on acid soils, and there are many new kinds of materials on the market that are as good as superphosphate. (Descriptions of the fertilizer materials are given on pages 127 to 131.)

The chemistry of phosphorus compounds is rather complicated. Probably most of the phosphorus goes into plants as the complex ion, H_2PO_4. Unfortunately, the amounts in soils and fertilizers are still usually expressed as "phosphoric acid" (P_2O_5) and not as phosphorus (P), although several leading soil chemists are beginning to use the simpler form. On the containers of most fertilizers sold in the United States, the percentage of available phosphorus is shown as phosphoric acid. Thus, if a fertilizer is guaranteed to contain 20 per cent available phosphoric acid, it is really just under 9 per cent available phosphorus (as P).

Potassium. Although not an important constituent of the plant body like carbon and nitrogen, potassium is essential for the living processes.

Deficiencies of potassium may be expected in most long-cultivated soils in humid regions that have received little manure or fertilizer. Sandy soils, and especially peaty and mucky soils, are generally low. Plants growing on potassium-deficient soils are likely to be stunted, grayish in color, poor in flowers and fruit, and premature if nitrogen and phosphorus are also low. Deficiencies of potassium show up most strikingly where nitrogen and phosphorus are relatively abundant. The plants are likely to have weak stems and to lodge (fall over) easily. In some plants the leaves are abnormally dark green in the early stages and then show a brown scorching later. In many plants potassium deficiency leads to small gray, reddish-brown, or yellow spots on the leaves. Later the edges or tips may turn brown. Sometimes these brown margins fall off. Potassium deficiency worsens iron deficiency. With low potassium and high nitrogen plant leaves are especially subject to fungus diseases. This is usual in gardens where lots of manure and nitrogen fertilizer are used without potassium fertilizer.

Excessive application of potassium can upset plant nutrition by reducing the intake of other nutrients, such as calcium and especially magnesium. Here again the gardener using naturally infertile soil must guard against magnesium deficiency, which may become very serious if he uses pure calcium limestone and large amounts of a mixed fertilizer containing nitrogen, phosphorus, and potash; although some mixed fertilizers now contain significant amounts of magnesium.

The analyses of fertilizer containing potassium are still expressed in terms of water-soluble potash (K_2O) and not as potassium (K), regardless of the form. Most of these potassium fertilizers are naturally occurring salts. Many have been processed to increase their concentration. A 60 per cent potash (K_2O) fertilizer contains only about 50 per cent potassium (K).

Calcium. Calcium is an essential part of cell walls and is needed in the young growing tissues. Doubtless it has other functions, such as helping to control the acidity of plant cells.

Generally, calcium is lacking in very acid soils, and abundant in neutral and alkaline soils (see page 93 *et seq.*). There are exceptions: one may add calcium sulphate to a very acid soil, for example, and have abundant calcium without reducing the acidity. Some alkaline soils owe their high alkalinity to sodium carbonate and sodium-clay rather than to calcium carbonate and calcium-clay. Most gardeners are not concerned with these extremes and, if the soils are brought from an acid condition to the proper pH by lime, calcium is sufficient. Possible exceptions are soils kept acid for blueberries, azaleas, rhododendrons, and the like. These plants need only a little calcium, and a small application of gypsum, or calcium sulphate, or low analysis (ordinary) superphosphate, which contains a lot of calcium sulphate, will suffice.

Calcium deficiency causes a stunting of the root system and distortion of new leaves. The margins and the areas between veins of the leaves may turn yellow or brown. Commonly, deficiencies of calcium are associated with excesses of other elements, such as magnesium or manganese.

Excesses of calcium are likely to reduce the intake of potassium and magnesium. Although these effects are often noticeable in soils naturally rich in calcium, they are much more so in naturally acid soils that have been given large additions of calcium in the form of calcium oxide or calcium carbonate. It is, therefore, best to use dolomitic limestone, which contains both calcium carbonate and magnesium carbonate, and be sure that the potassium supply is adequate.

Magnesium. Magnesium is an essential part of chlorophyll—the green coloring matter of plants responsible for photosynthesis—the basic process in plant food formation. It also helps to transport the phosphorus in the plant and is especially important to plants with oily seeds. Thus a magnesium deficiency may be confused with a phosphorus deficiency if enough magnesium is present to form chlorophyll, but not enough to transport the phosphorus.

Plants on magnesium-deficient soils are likely to have badly colored leaves. Tips and margins are usually first affected. The veins may remain green, while other parts become yellowish red or purplish. This chlorosis of plants due to magnesium deficiency is sometimes called "sand-drown." In corn, for example, yellowish-white streaks run the length of the leaf while the veins remain green. Usually, old leaves are first affected and the coloring extends to the younger ones. This important generalization applies to many plants and serves as one basis for distinguishing yellowing (or chlorosis) due to magnesium deficiency and yellowing due to iron deficiency, which starts with the young leaves and gradually progresses to the older ones.

Acid soils are likely to be low in magnesium as well as in calcium, especially sandy ones. These should be treated with dolomitic limestone. If soils are low in both magnesium and calcium, the use of nearly pure calcium oxide or limestone as a liming material to decrease the acidity worsens the magnesium deficiency. Then additions of potassium or sodium salts still further emphasize the magnesium deficiency. Magnesium deficiency is especially serious on acid soils where both ordinary limestone and superphosphate have been used for a long period of years.

If the soil does not require liming to decrease acidity and is low in magnesium, magnesium sulphate (Epsom salts), or the double salt of magnesium and potassium if both are needed, may be used. Small applications of magnesium sulphate are often needed on acid-loving plants, especially if they have been fertilized with calcium, phosphorus, and potassium. It may be added in light applications directly to the soil or mixed into the compost used on the plants. Some phosphatic fertilizers that contain substantial amounts of magnesium are made especially for soils deficient in both these nutrients.

Once magnesium deficiency appears in woody plants, such as fruit trees, it is usually necessary to spray them with a weak solution (one per cent) of magnesium sulphate from time to time to overcome the yellowing of the leaves. Applications of magnesium sulphate to the soil after the trees are fairly well grown are not usually sufficient. Thus one should do his best to have the soil properly prepared in advance, before the trees or shrubs are planted. Because magnesium sulphate is so soluble one would suppose that additions of it to the soil would immediately enter fruit trees and cure the deficiency. Yet after trees are once well established, such corrections are exceedingly slow.

A few soils developed from rocks very rich in magnesium have an excess. Here again, the matter of balance is important. An excess of magnesium may reduce the intake of calcium and especially of potassium into the plant if these are in short supply.

Sulphur. Many proteins and oils in plants contain sulphur. If lacking, growth is reduced and leaves turn yellow, especially the new ones.

Few gardeners need to be concerned much about sulphur. Near industrial areas, large amounts are absorbed from the air by rain and moist soil. Many of the compounds used in fertilizers to correct other nutrient deficiencies have some sulphur, and considerable amounts are contained in good compost. Where there is little smoke in the atmosphere and the rain clouds originate over the sea or other places with essentially no sulphur fumes in the air, soils may be deficient. Usually the sulphur in low-analysis (ordinary) superphosphate is sufficient. If this is not used, sulphur may be added at the rate of 200 or 300 pounds per acre.

Iron. Iron plays an important role in the leaves of green plants. It must be present in soluble form. Iron chlorosis is a troublesome physiological disease in many gardens. The upper or new leaves lose their green color, except for the principal veins. As the chlorosis worsens, even the veins of the new leaves may turn yellow too, the new leaves die, and the yellowing between veins extends to older leaves. The growing points are stunted or even die altogether. Yellowing due to nitrogen deficiency is more nearly uniform and that due to magnesium deficiency generally starts with the older leaves and spreads toward the new ones.

Characteristically, iron chlorosis occurs on calcareous or lime-rich soils, but not on all of them. It often affects trees and shrubs irrigated with very hard lime-containing water. It is commonly induced by excessive overliming, especially with calcium oxide. It often goes along with potash deficiency. It can be induced by the excessive use of phosphorus, and even more by excess phosphorus and nitrogen together, especially on neutral or limy soils and where potassium is low. A high content of zinc induces iron chlorosis and possibly excesses of manganese, lead, copper, and other metals.

Plants vary a great deal in their susceptibility to iron deficiency. Generally, most trouble is had with such plants as azaleas, rhododendrons, and mountain laurel, requiring acid soils, but fruit trees are commonly affected and sometimes other plants. Iron chlorosis is hard to cure. Plants may even take in enough total iron, but still not in such a form that it can perform its functions. The reasons are not clear.

For plants requiring acid conditions for best growth, one should avoid planting them on neutral or alkaline soil. If acid soil is unavailable, then the soil may be made acid with sulphur, as already explained (see page 104 *et seq.*). The maintenance of a deep mulch of acid organic matter, such as acid leaf mold or sawdust, is helpful. In addition, localized applications of iron (ferrous) sulphate or iron silicate in the soil may be helpful, but these take some time to become effective. Thus, when symptoms appear, one needs to spray the plants with a 1 to 2 per cent water solution of iron (ferrous) sulphate, as well as to improve the soil conditions. With woody plants, spraying may need to be continued occasionally for several years. Fortunately this is a simple procedure and quickly effective. Some have had success by putting tablets of iron citrate or iron tartrate under the bark of woody plants.

As with magnesium deficiency the gardener will find it easier to prepare his soil properly in advance than to attempt to correct iron deficiency after it appears in his shrubs or fruit trees.

Boron. At least a little boron is needed by all plants. Without it, the young tissues fail to form, the upper leaves become distorted, and the terminal buds die. The edges and tips of leaves may turn brown or reddish yellow and die. Root systems are weakened. Several plants have special symptoms of boron deficiency, such as the cracked stem of celery, the browning of cauliflower, the internal cork of apples, and the heart rot of beets. Tomatoes may be more susceptible to end rot. Some plants are far more susceptible to boron deficiency than others. Alfalfa and beets need a relatively abundant supply, for example, whereas beans are injured by relatively small amounts. Thus, the gardener must be very careful not to use too much borax and to spread it evenly. To correct deficiencies, borax is used at rates of about 10 pounds to the acre for sandy soils, up to 25 or 30 pounds for clay soils. The gardener will usually find it convenient to calculate the amounts needed for his area and mix them with some bulkier material, such as superphosphate or a mixed fertilizer.

On naturally fertile soils and where manure and compost are used, the gardener does not need to worry about boron. On strongly leached soils, like many of those in the eastern part of the United States, boron is likely to be deficient, especially if little or no manure is used. On such soils gardeners should by all means use borax, especially for tomatoes, beets, and celery. For safety, the whole garden and lawn may be given a light application, say about ½ tablespoon per 100 square feet, every two or three years, but excesses must be avoided.

Manganese. Small amounts of manganese are essential for the synthesis of enzymes and other compounds in plants. Leaves of manganese-deficient plants have yellow, light green, or gray spots, and the tissue may die. Some show a light green color between the veins that later spreads to the whole leaf.

This deficiency is mostly limited to naturally limy soils, especially peaty or mucky soils, or to those given an excess of lime. It is not a common problem in gardens, although some fruit trees and shrubs may be affected. Where a deficiency is suspected, a 1 or 2 per cent spray of manganese sulphate may be used. If naturally infertile acid soils have been limed and brought to a high level of other nutrients without the use of abundant compost and manure, for safety, manganese sulphate should be applied occasionally with the other fertilizers at rates of about 10 pounds to 15 pounds per acre. Heavier applications may be detrimental.

Zinc. Although all plants need small amounts of zinc, deficiencies are most common on citrus, pecans, tung, and other fruits in very sunny areas. Corn also is quite susceptible and shows a characteristic "white bud," so-called from the whitish appearance of the new leaves. Leaves of zinc-deficient plants have yellow and brown splotches on them and dark colored veins.

Where a deficiency is suspected, zinc sulphate may be sprayed on the trees or added to the soil in light applications as suggested for manganese. If abundant compost is used, deficiencies are quite unlikely in most gardens.

Excesses of zinc are occasionally caused by seepage from mine tailings or by inheritance from zinc-rich rocks or waters. Such excesses may cause iron chlorosis.

Copper. Copper is essential for some plant enzymes. It seems to need to be reasonably in balance with the zinc and manganese of the soil. Deficiencies are most likely in newly developed peat soil but are also known on old leached soils, especially sandy and gravelly ones that are now or were once under a humid tropical climate. In southwestern Australia, for example, "copperized" superphosphate is regularly used on certain soil types.

In copper-deficient plants the upper leaves wilt and the tops die, often with little or no change in color. If manure and compost are used, few gardeners need to worry about copper, but if they are not and the soil is naturally infertile, copper sulphate may be added to the fertilizer at a rate not to exceed about 5 pounds to the acre on a sandy soil or around 50 pounds on a peat soil. Although higher amounts are helpful on a very few soil types, they should not be used without the guidance of specific experimental results.

Molybdenum. At one time it was thought that molybdenum was essential only to clovers, but now it seems that at least very tiny amounts are needed by all plants. In a few soils clovers make a great response to as little as ½ pound of sodium molybdate per acre. Never should more than 2 pounds per acre be used on the garden. It is highly unlikely that more than one garden in ten thousand needs any molybdenum added to it.

Sodium. Although not regarded as a plant nutrient, sodium can replace a small part of the potassium needed by plants. A few plants respond to additions of common salt (sodium chloride) over and above normal fertilizer applications. Dressings of agricultural salt up to 500 pounds to the acre on leached soils in humid regions have given increases in yields of sugarbeets, celery, swiss chard, beets, and turnips. Common salt, however, probably has little place in the ordinary garden.

In arid regions soils generally contain considerable sodium—often too much. A great deal is brought to some soils by wind-blown sea spray.

Chlorine. Although most plants take up chlorine as the chloride ion, there is no evidence that it fulfills any specific function in plants. Chlorides are present in many fertilizers, especially potassium fertilizers (muriate of potash), and in varying amounts, from a few pounds to 2 or 3 tons annually, come into some soils near the coast from wind-carried sea spray.

In arid regions, chlorides and other soluble salts are abundant to excessive in soils.

A WORD ABOUT QUALITY

In discussing the individual nutrients, something was said about their effects on plants. Generally, vegetables growing on fertile soil are higher in quality than those grown on nutrient-deficient soils. Especially are they more tender, less woody and stringy. Although not necessarily higher in nutritive value, they may be. Vegetables growing on phosphorus-rich and calcium-rich soils are likely to be higher in phosphorus and calcium than those growing on soils deficient in these nutrients, other things being equal. Excessive nitrogen tends to reduce the mineral content. The plant nutrients seem to have little, if any, direct effect on the vitamin content of the vegetables.

The relationship between food quality and soil conditions is a very complicated one. Generally, one may say that the influence of the natural soil type is greater than that of management practices. Research in this field is growing rapidly. Yet the many claims for good effects of various fertilizers on plant quality are much exaggerated.[4]

Still, soil management and fertilizers do have a very great influence on crop quality—not a direct one on a specific kind of plant, except in a few instances. Their effect is indirect by widening the gardener's choice of crops. Many thousands of homes are built on such poor soils that few vegetables can be grown on them as they are; but with

[4] The interested reader with inquiries should write to the Director of the United States Plant, Soil, and Nutrition Laboratory, Ithaca, New York, for such specific and reliable results as are available.

proper management, including fertilizers, excellent crops of soybeans, tomatoes, cabbage, kale, turnip greens, and other health-protecting foods may be grown well. In fact, without fertilizer, the great vegetable-producing area along the eastern coast of the United States would scarcely exist.

Perhaps the most absurd current idea that a few people are pushing is that chemical fertilizers are harmful to crop quality. The origin of the notion that the nitrogen in organic matter, for example, is more "natural" or somehow different from that in fertilizer is obscure. No thoughtful person should deny the importance of either organic matter or mineral fertilizer in garden management. An excess of chemical fertilizer, especially one rich in nitrogen, can be harmful. So can complete dependence on compost where phosphorus, potassium, or other elements are badly lacking. Applications of such trace elements as boron, manganese, zinc, copper, or molybdenum, should be light. Excesses of these are harmful. The gardener may cause unbalance by exclusive dependence on calcium limestone, as contrasted to dolomitic limestone, or by overdoses of chemical fertilizer. He can also cause serious unbalance by depending upon organic matter to build up the productivity of a soil very deficient in one or more of the mineral elements.

Not all advertising is bad, of course, but the gardener should be wary of those with "special" routines and products for his use. The promoters may have books or materials to sell at handsome profits that will do him little good.

THE MATERIALS FOR FERTILIZING

Four general classes of materials are used that add plant nutrients to the soil:

(1) Soil amendments like limestone, sulphur, and gypsum, discussed in the previous chapter, and used primarily to change the reaction of the soil—to reduce acidity or alkalinity—but that also add calcium, magnesium, or sulphur;

(2) Green manures, or plants that are grown to take up nutrients from the rooting zone and that are then plowed or spaded into the soil to improve its structure and furnish a source of nutrients as the organic matter decays;

(3) Manures and composts that add organic matter for several

purposes already described, besides furnishing some plant nutrients; and

(4) Commercial fertilizer, including both natural materials and manufactured chemicals.

It is this last group that concerns us here. A very long list would be needed to include all the materials that are used in the world as fertilizer. Further, new compounds are continually becoming available. Here we shall look at only the common kinds and the principles governing their use with the thought that the gardener can see for himself how any other material fits into the scheme. Because nitrogen, phosphorus, and potassium are by far the most commonly needed, these are given the most attention.

It is a common practice in the United States, encouraged by the fertilizer trade, to use mixed [5] fertilizers containing all three of the major nutrients and sometimes others, such as calcium, magnesium, and sulphur added as parts of the chemical compounds containing the primary nutrients, directly as plant nutrients, or to make weight. Then too, the trace elements are sometimes included in small amounts, especially boron. A few commercial fertilizers are special mixtures of the trace elements, to be used in addition to the main fertilizer where deficiencies are suspected.

In contrast to mixed fertilizers are the simple nutrient-carrying fertilizers, called "straight goods" in the fertilizer trade. An example is superphosphate, which has only phosphorus. Some natural materials and some manufactured ones contain two or more nutrients within the compound, such as diammonium phosphate, which carries both nitrogen and phosphorus.

As the gardener gains experience and learns to fertilize his soil according to its specific needs in relation to the kind of plant, the manure and compost used, and the previous treatments, he should buy supplies of the "straight goods" and mix his own fertilizers just before using them or else add them separately. For large areas of lawn or for the kitchen garden, it is often more convenient to use a mixed

[5] Sometimes fertilizers containing nitrogen, phosphorus, and potassium are called "complete" fertilizers. Such a term has an incorrect connotation, because a truly complete fertilizer could only be one so adjusted to the specific soil that any deficiencies were corrected to produce a soil having the needed nutrients in proper balance *after* reaction with the soil. Thus a complete fertilizer for one soil-plant situation might have an entirely different combination of nutrients than a complete fertilizer for another soil-plant situation.

fertilizer, at least as the base, with any other materials added to change the ratio of nutrients significantly.

The approximate composition of several materials is given in the following lists.[6] The organic materials may vary in composition from the average figures given. Laws governing the sale of fertilizers generally require that a guaranteed statement be placed prominently on the bags or other containers giving the plant nutrient content in terms of total nitrogen (N), available phosphoric acid (P_2O_5), and water-soluble potash (K_2O). In a mixed fertilizer, the figures are given as a formula in the form "5-10-10," for example, meaning 5 per cent total nitrogen, 10 per cent available phosphoric acid, and 10 per cent water-soluble potash.

COMPOSITION OF SELECTED CHEMICAL FERTILIZERS

Nitrogen materials

Ammonium nitrate. This material, sometimes called "nitrate of ammonia," contains 32.5 to 34 per cent nitrogen. Like the other nitrogen fertilizers in this list it is highly soluble. Unless carefully granulated and packed in moistureproof bags it cakes into hard lumps. Unless stored where ventilation is good it can burn or even explode. It is acid-forming, but less so than ammonium sulphate, and can be used on acid-loving plants. The gardener must remember its relatively high nitrogen content and use it sparingly.

Ammonium sulphate. Commonly called "sulphate of ammonia," this is, perhaps, the most easily available of any chemical nitrogen fertilizer to most gardeners. It contains about 20.5 per cent nitrogen and is acid-forming. It is especially good on limy soils or on acid-loving plants, such as blueberries, azaleas, mountain laurel, and rhododendrons. Where much is used on lawns and kitchen gardens, slightly more lime is needed to correct the acidity.

Calcium cyanamide. Often known simply as "cyanamid," this material contains 21.0 per cent nitrogen and is basic. It is toxic when applied on many plants. It can be applied as a dust on lawns if used lightly and spread evenly. It can be used a few weeks in advance of planting because the toxic effects are soon lost in moist soils. Generally, however, it is not a safe material in the perennial garden.

[6] For more complete lists, the reader may see some standard reference book on fertilizers and especially "Efficient Use of Fertilizers," published by FAO, *op. cit.*

Calcium nitrate. Calcium nitrate or "nitrate of lime" has 15.5 per cent nitrogen and is a little basic.

Cal-Nitro. This runs about 20.5 per cent nitrogen, although some brands are as low as 16 per cent. A similar material called "Nitro-Chalk" has 15.5 per cent nitrogen. These are somewhat basic.

Sodium nitrate. Next to ammonium sulphate, this is the most common nitrogen fertilizer for the American gardener to buy. It contains 16 per cent nitrogen and is slightly basic. Some evidence exists that long continued use of it may injure the structure of moderately sandy soils, making them more sticky because of the sodium in it. This and other basic fertilizers should not be used on acid-loving plants; they are suitable for the lawn, for the kitchen garden, and for most trees and flowers. It is often called "nitrate of soda." The naturally occurring material from Chile is known as Chilean nitrate or Chile saltpeter.

Urea (or Uramon). This is a relatively concentrated material that runs about 42 per cent nitrogen. Since it is somewhat acid-forming, it can be used on acid-loving plants in place of ammonium sulphate. Experimental work is under way to develop combinations of this material with other compounds to reduce its solubility. When perfected, such compounds will make excellent nitrogen fertilizers for lawns where a slow continuous supply of nitrogen is needed during the whole season.

Phosphorus materials

Basic slag. These by-products of the steel industry vary from about 6 to 17.5 per cent total and from 2 to 16 per cent available phosphoric acid. The higher grade is also called Thomas slag or Thomas meal. These slags also contain calcium and a little magnesium. They are basic.

Calcium metaphosphate. This is a relatively new material of high analysis—about 64 per cent total and 53 per cent available phosphoric acid. It is neither acid nor basic and is a very good material for the gardener.

Defluorinated phosphate rock. This material is called by various other names, including "fused phosphate rock," "fused tricalcium phosphate," and "alpha phosphate." It runs 20 to 30 per cent total and 8 to 24 per cent available phosphoric acid. It is slightly basic.

Dicalcium phosphate. Dicalcium phosphate runs about 40 per cent total and 39 per cent available phosphoric acid and is slightly basic.

Phosphate rock-magnesium silicate glass. Although containing only about 17 per cent available phosphoric acid this fertilizer also has considerable magnesium (17 per cent as the oxide). It is slightly basic. Sometimes it is called "calcium-magnesium phosphate" or "Thermo-Phos."

Rock phosphate. The other phosphatic fertilizers listed here have been heated or otherwise treated in order to make the phosphorus more available to plants, but the raw untreated rock can be ground very fine and used directly. Large applications are required because of its low availability, but once applied, it continues to give a slow supply in many soils. Rock phosphate gives much better results on naturally acid soils than on neutral or alkaline ones. In fact, there is little use in applying it to soils of pH 6.2 or higher. Legumes can use it far better than grasses. In a lawn, for example, clovers can use it and then grasses may feed on the organic remains of the clovers. Mixing rock phosphate with the organic materials in making compost seems to increase its availability somewhat. The rock phosphates from North Africa are more available than the American sorts. Thus some good European experience with them cannot be duplicated in the United States. Generally, however, gardeners can expect better results from superphosphate or the other manufactured sorts. The composition of rock phosphate varies from about 20 to 30 per cent total phosphoric acid, depending upon the local mine.

Superphosphate (ordinary). Low analysis or ordinary superphosphate is still the commonest phosphatic fertilizer. It is made by treating the raw rock phosphate with sulphuric acid. It contains around 14 to 20 per cent available phosphoric acid and over 50 per cent calcium sulphate. It is neither acid nor basic. This is a good material except for its low analysis.

Superphosphate (double). High analysis or double superphosphate is similar to the ordinary superphosphate, except for a much higher content of available phosphoric acid—about 43 to 49 per cent—and a low amount of calcium sulphate. It is neither acid nor basic and is an excellent material for the gardener. It is called a number of other names, including "triple superphosphate," "treble superphosphate," and "concentrated superphosphate."

Potassium materials

Kainite. Kainite varies from 12 to 22 per cent water-soluble potash (K_2O) and contains varying amounts of magnesium.

Manure salts. This material runs 25 to 40 per cent soluble potash but has little or no magnesium.

Potassium chloride. Commonly called "muriate of potash," it contains 48 to 62 per cent of water-soluble potash and minor quantities of magnesium. It is better to use potassium sulphate on acid-loving plants like blueberries.

Potassium sulphate. This is also called "sulphate of potash." It contains about 48 to 52 per cent of soluble potash. Potassium sulphate and potassium chloride are the potassium fertilizers most commonly available to gardeners.

Potassium-magnesium sulphate. This material contains about 21 to 30 per cent of water-soluble potash and somewhat higher amounts, up to 56 per cent, of magnesia (as MgO). It is sometimes known as "double manure salts." It is excellent for leached soils deficient in both potassium and magnesium.

Compound materials

Several special compounds are manufactured that contain both nitrogen and phosphorus, such as ammoniated superphosphate (2 to 4 per cent nitrogen and 14 to 49 per cent phosphoric acid) and diammonium phosphate (21 per cent nitrogen and 53 per cent available phosphoric acid). A few, like potassium metaphosphate, contain both potassium and phosphorus. Nitrate of potash contains 13 per cent nitrogen and 44 per cent soluble potash. Nitrophoska contains around 12 per cent of nitrogen, 12 per cent of phosphoric acid, and 21 per cent of soluble potash. Rarely, however, does the ordinary gardener have an opportunity to use these compound materials.

Materials for trace elements

Ordinary borax is used to supply boron. Copper, iron, zinc, and manganese are applied mainly as their sulphate salts.

COMPOSITION OF SELECTED NATURAL ORGANIC FERTILIZERS [7]

A great many organic materials are used as fertilizers, both directly and in mixtures. Some of them are added to mixed fertilizers partly

[7] See footnote, page 127.

to keep them loose and free from caking into lumps. For the plant nutrients contained, most of the organics are relatively expensive, especially those that are useful also as stock feeds.

The natural organic fertilizers give up their nitrogen somewhat more slowly than the soluble chemicals and so last a bit longer in soils. Larger amounts can be applied safely because of the very small salt effect. These materials also contain small amounts of many of the "trace" elements. Naturally, the composition of any particular sample of material may vary considerably from the average values given in Table 6.

TABLE 6. Approximate composition of a few selected organic fertilizers

Material	Total Nitrogen (N) (Per cent)	Total Phosphoric acid (P₂O₅) (Per cent)	Total Potash (K₂O) (Per cent)	Reaction with soil	Remarks
Ash, Wood	—	2.0	5.0	basic	
Blood, dried	13.0	2.0	1.0	acidic	Nitrogen readily available
Bone ash	—	35.0	—	basic	
Bone meal, raw	4.0	22.5	—	basic	Only slowly available
Bone meal, steamed	2.5	25.0	—	basic	
Cottonseed meal	7.0	3.0	2.0	acidic	Fairly rapidly available
Fish scrap or meal, dried	9.5	7.0	—		
Guano, Peruvian	13.0	12.0	2.5		
Garbage tankage	2.5	3.0	1.0		
Horn and hoof meal	14.0	1.0	—		Very slowly available
Kelp, Pacific, dried	2.5	1.5	15.0		
Linseed meal	5.5	2.0	1.5		
Manure, cattle, dried	2.0	1.5	2.0		
Manure, horse, dried	2.0	1.5	1.5		
Manure, poultry, dried	5.0	3.0	1.5		
Manure, sheep, dried	2.0	1.5	3.0		
Peat, dry	2.0	—	—		Little available nitrogen
Sewage sludge, dried	2.0	2.0	—		
Sewage sludge, activated	6.0	3.0	0.5		
Soybean meal	7.0	1.5	2.5	acidic	Fairly rapidly available
Tankage, animal	7.0	10.0	0.5	basic	
Tankage, process	9.0	0.5	—	acidic	
Tobacco stems	2.0	0.5	6.0	basic	

Other materials, like hair and wool waste, not included in the table, also contain some nitrogen, but it becomes available only very, very slowly.

Materials like cottonseed meal and soybean meal are among the best for use in the spring on acid-loving shrubs. About one half of the nitrogen becomes available almost at once. The rest comes more slowly. Normally it is essentially gone by the time the plants should harden off in autumn. Generally, however, these organic materials are much lower in analysis than the chemicals. Most gardeners will find it far cheaper to buy chemicals to supplement local sources of organic matter, especially manure and compost, than to use these organics. Prices must be compared not on the basis of pound per pound gross weight in the bag, but on the basis of the cost per pound of available plant nutrients.

HOW TO FERTILIZE

If his soil is deficient in phosphorus—and most are for the best results—the gardener will do well to fertilize rather liberally with phosphorus when he first works the soil for a lawn or garden. Because phosphates do not leach into the soil significantly, the only practical way to get them down into the rooting zone is to put them there. The addition of phosphatic fertilizer during double spading of highly phosphorus-deficient soils is strongly recommended. Compost and lime, if needed, can be added at the same time to produce a deep layer of fertile soil. When trees and shrubs are planted, phosphorus can be added to the deep soil and mixed with that replaced, avoiding direct contact between the fertilizer and the live roots of tender plants.

Except with very sandy soils, substantial applications of potassium and magnesium may also be made in advance because these are held fairly well by the clays. But soluble forms added to the surface will, in time, leach down into the soil, in contrast to phosphorus. On very sandy soils, however, one must add light applications of potassium and magnesium salts, as required. The danger of getting unbalance from heavy applications is great and losses by leaching are large.

With the soil first well supplied with phosphorus, the other things can be spread on the surface. With soils fairly rich in clay—loams, silt loams, clay loams, and clay—it is also an advantage to build up the soil to some depth in potassium, magnesium, calcium, and organic matter. Then one may apply nitrogen and light applications of the other nutrients when plants are seeded or set out and from time to time as they are growing.

The amounts of fertilizer needed depend upon the soil and plant requirements. This book includes several tables and lists to help the gardener estimate his own situation. Let us take a common situation in the east-central part of the United States. Suppose the soil is fairly rich in clay, say a silt loam, strongly acid, very low in phosphorus, and deficient generally in the other plant nutrients.

To prepare it for a kitchen garden, about 100 pounds of finely ground dolomitic limestone, about 30 pounds of 20 per cent superphosphate, around 10 pounds of potassium chloride, and about ½ pound of borax (not more) per 1000 square feet should be spaded into the soil along with 10 to 20 bushels of manure or good compost. If only calcium limestone is available, not the dolomitic limestone, then about 5 pounds of magnesium sulphate (Epsom salts) should be added at the same time with the limestone. After the soil has been spaded and prepared for seeding, a V-shaped trench about 2 inches deep is made next to the row marker in which a mixed fertilizer is sprinkled, say about 2 pounds (or pints) of a 10-20-10 or 4 pounds (or pints) of a 5-10-5 for each 100 feet of row if the rows are 2 feet apart. A little more is used with wider spacing and a little less with narrower. This trench is filled and a smaller one made directly under the seed marker. After the seeds are planted, the local band of fertilizer should be about 1½ inches beneath and 1½ inches to the side of the seed. The fertilizer should not be placed directly with the seeds.

With transplants, like cabbage, tomatoes, and peppers, the mixed fertilizer may be put under and around the plant, say an inch or so from the roots. Tomatoes, for example, do well if large plants are set quite deeply. A hole may be made about 8 to 10 inches deep and 2 tablespoonfuls of a 5-10-5, or its equivalent, placed in the bottom and a little sprinkled around the sides of the hole. That in the bottom is covered with 2 inches of soil and the plant set down 6 to 8 inches with a slight depression left at the surface. After the tomatoes start bearing, about 2 teaspoonfuls of ammonium sulphate, or its equivalent in some other nitrogen fertilizer, should be mixed into the soil between 4 inches and 12 inches around each plant to maintain good yields.

Flowering shrubs demanding a slightly acid to neutral soil may be handled in much the same way, except that only about a tablespoonful or 2 of the mixed fertilizer is used around small ones and ordinarily no supplemental nitrogen. For large shrubs, the rate should be calculated according to the approximate area it would shade with the sun directly above it. When the shrubs are established—set out—the soil should be well fertilized with the minerals, especially phosphorus and potash. The different sorts vary widely in depth of planting.

To go back to the kitchen garden: Sweet corn, lettuce, chard, and the other salad crops may be given a little extra nitrogen in mid-season, placed in the soil about 2 inches to the side of the plants, say about ¾ cupful of ammonium sulphate per 100 feet of row or its equivalent in some other nitrogen fertilizer with rows 2 feet apart. More is used with wider rows and less with narrower ones. If a mulch of good compost is added after the plants are well established, these amounts of nitrogen fertilizer may be reduced by about one half.

For lawns, the basic treatment may be supplemented with annual applications of about 10 pounds per 1000 square feet of a 10-10-10 or its equivalent. Many use more nitrogen than this. In fact, nearly all recommend heavier nitrogen applications than the author in early spring, and they may be correct. A lot depends upon the hazards of disease and weeds, especially crabgrass. If other hazards are minor, fertilizer can be applied each spring and a supplemental application or two of nitrogen in midseason, each about 5 to 10 pounds per 1000 square feet of ammonium sulphate or its equivalent.

In the Middle Atlantic States and specifically in Maryland, the author has had better success by avoiding spring applications of nitrogen, and by keeping the soil well supplied with phosphorus, potassium, and magnesium, and with lime to about pH 6.5. White clover is used in the lawn mixture and furnishes some nitrogen. If nitrogen is used in the spring, an excellent response in growth of luscious grass is had. But with the warm, humid days of late spring and early summer, such fungus diseases as *damping off* and *brown patch* become very bad. With the permanent grasses weakened, the nitrogen stimulates crabgrass and other weeds.

If nitrogen is withheld in the spring so that the grass is dependent upon the clover and its own root reserves, diseases are less serious. Then in early midsummer an application of nitrogen is given to the grass under the trees, and perhaps another in late summer. In early autumn, after the danger of disease is essentially past, the whole lawn is given a fairly heavy application of a mixed fertilizer containing nitrogen, usually a 5-10-10 or 5-10-5, so that the grass goes into the winter strong and with good root reserves.

For an established tree or shrub, a few holes may be made between the trunk and the drip line with a rod or soil auger some 2 to 4 feet deep and these filled with superphosphate or with that and a potassium fertilizer as needed.

For acid-loving plants soil structure is highly important. Assuming that the structure is made proper with acid organic matter or by supplying acid sandy materials, fertilizer treatment should include a medium application of phosphorus, mixed with the whole soil when the plants are put out, and subsequent light spring applications of nitrogen, potassium, magnesium, and iron as needed. With abundant good compost, which has had no lime added to it, for mulching, no other fertilizer may be needed for acid-loving flowering plants if the soil is well prepared initially.

For the lawn and other nearly uniform areas small machines are available for spreading fertilizer evenly. With care, on a windless day, it can be done by hand. Small lumps must be broken. If a tiny amount, say of borax, is to be put on a considerable area it should be mixed with sand or superphosphate in order to spread it evenly. It is a good practice, when broadcasting fertilizer by hand from a pail, to split the application into two parts and go over the area in two sets of strips at right angles to one another.

In the perennial beds and among the shrubs and trees, one must broadcast fertilizer slowly (with patience) to avoid unevenness, especially as the different plants growing in the same bed may require quite different treatments.

Fertilizers should not be placed on wet grass or other wet leaves because the salts burn the leaves as they dry. If dry fertilizer is allowed to rest on the leaves, bad burning results after the dew moistens it. Frequently, one cannot avoid getting some of the fertilizer on the leaves. It should be washed off with the hose immediately, unless one is lucky enough to have done the job just before a hard rain.

HOW MUCH FERTILIZER TO USE

The most difficult question to answer, especially in a book of this sort, is how much fertilizer to use. Gardens vary greatly in soil conditions and past management. Many old garden soils are already very rich in phosphorus and other plant nutrients because of long use of manures and fertilizers. The amount to use also depends upon the plants to be grown, because they vary widely in tastes.

First of all, the gardener needs to estimate whether the plant-nutrient content of his soil is high or low. If he can obtain reliable tests, the results will help him. Besides such tests, he can study the growth-habits and appearance of the existing plants, according to the suggestions made already.

TABLE 7. Approximate fertility levels for optimum growth of several plants, as very high (1), high (2), medium (3), and low (4).[1]

Crop	Nitrogen	Phosphorus	Potassium
Vegetables			
Asparagus	1*	1	1
Beans	3	3	3
Beets, early	1*	1	1
Beets, late	2*	1	2
Broccoli	1*	2	2
Brussels sprouts	2	2	2
Cabbage, early	1*	1	1
Cabbage, late	2*	2	2
Cantaloupe	2	2	2
Carrots	2*	2	2
Cauliflower, early	1*	1	1
Cauliflower, late	2*	2	1
Celery, early	1*	1	1
Celery, late (on muck)	2*	2	1
Cucumbers	2*	2	2
Eggplant	2*	2	2
Lettuce, head	1*	1	1
Lettuce, leaf	1*	1	1
Onions	2*	2	2
Parsnips	2	2	2
Peas, early	2	2	2
Potatoes, early	1*	1	1
Potatoes, late	2	1	1
Pumpkins	3	3	3
Radishes	2	1	1
Rhubarb	2	2	2
Rutabaga	2	2	3
Soybeans	3	2	2
Spinach	1*	1	1
Squash, early	2	2	2
Squash, late	3	3	3
Sweet corn, early	2*	2	2
Sweet corn, late	3*	3	3
Sweet potatoes	3	3	2
Tomatoes, early	3*	2	2
Tomatoes, late	2*	2	2
Turnips	2	2	3
Turnip greens	1	2	3
Watermelons	3	3	3

TABLE 7. *Continued*

Crop	Nitrogen	Phosphorus	Potassium
Lawn grasses [2]	3	2	3
Fruits			
Apples	2	3	3
Blackberries	3	4	4
Blueberries	2	4	4
Grapes	3	3	3
Peaches	2	3	2
Pears	3	3	3
Raspberries	3	3	3
Strawberries	3*	3	4
Annual flowers, generally [3]	2	2	2
Perennial flowers, generally [3]	3	3	3
Bulbs, generally [3]	3	3	3
Shrubs, ornamental [3]			
Deciduous	3	3	3
Evergreen	4	4	4
Shade trees			
Deciduous	3	3	4
Evergreen	4	4	4

* With supplemental applications in midseason.
[1] Based in part on "Chemical Soil Diagnosis by the Universal Soil Testing System," by M. F. Morgan (Connecticut Agricultural Experiment Station Bulletin 450, pp. 579–626, New Haven, 1941). See also notes in Appendix II, especially for the ornamentals.
[2] See special section on lawns, page 145 *et seq.*
[3] See text and Appendix II for exceptions.

Secondly, the gardener needs to have in mind any peculiar requirements of the plants he intends to grow. Some of these are outlined generally in Table 7 and in the lists given in the Appendix. Recorded experience is available for the ordinary vegetables and common flowering plants, but not for many of the less common sorts. In the absence of specific information, one may assume that flowering plants having an optimum pH range between about pH 6.2 and pH 7.5 do best with medium to high fertility for phosphoric acid and potassium, and medium fertility for nitrogen. Those wanting an acid soil should generally have low to medium levels of fertility. Most wild plants do best with only medium or low to medium fertility, in contrast to the somewhat higher requirements of most cultivated sorts.

Table 8 has been arranged to give suggestions of the amounts of nutrients to use in an application for the season according to soil class, the general nutrient level of the soil, and the requirements of the plant, either very high, high, medium, or low. Thus for a single broadcast application when the garden is prepared for carrots on a loam soil of low fertility, the requirement would be 3 pounds of nitrogen, 4 pounds of phosphoric acid, and 3 pounds of potash per 1000 square feet. This would mean about 15 pounds of ammonium sulphate, 20 pounds of 20 per cent superphosphate, and 5 pounds of 60 per cent potassium chloride, or 33 pounds of a 9-12-9.[8] If good applications of manure or compost are used, the nitrogen and potash may be reduced 40 per cent, giving a recommendation of 20 pounds of a 9-20-9, or 40 pounds of a 5-10-5. If placed in bands, only 24 pounds of the 5-10-5 would be needed. From Table 9b, this translates into one cup for 10 feet of row, with the rows 2 feet apart.

TABLE 8. Amounts of plant nutrients suggested for different groups of soil classes according to general plant preferences in pounds per 1000 square feet [1]

AMOUNTS TO USE PER 1000 SQUARE FEET (POUNDS) [2]

General soil class	Estimated nutrient status	Nitrogen (N) [3] According to plant needs: [4]				Phosphoric acid (P_2O_5) According to plant needs:				Potash (K_2O) According to plant needs:			
		VH	H	M	L	VH	H	M	L	VH	H	M	L
Sandy [5]	Low	4	3	2	1	5	4	3	2	4	3	2	1
soils	High	2	1	½	0	3	2	1	0	3	2	1	½
Loamy [6]	Low	4	3	2	1	5	4	3	2	4	3	2	1
soils	High	2	1	½	0	3	2	1	0	2	1	½	0
Clayey [7]	Low	4	3	2	1	6	5	4	3	5	4	3	2
soils	High	2	1	½	0	3	2	0	0	3	2	1	0
Muck	Low	3	2	1	½	6	5	4	3	7	5	3	1
soils	High	2	1	½	0	4	3	2	1	3	2	1	0

[1] Applications are for one growing season, say about May to September. Late autumn crops, winter crops, and cover crops following a fully fertilized earlier crop should be given about one half the amounts listed.
[2] Reduce all applications 40 per cent if fertilizer is used in bands rather than broadcast. Reduce broadcast applications of nitrogen and potash by 40 per cent if a heavy application of manure or good compost is used.
[3] Most high nitrogen rates should be split into two applications.
[4] VH, very high; H, high; M, medium; L, low.
[5] Sands, loamy sands, and light sandy loams.
[6] Sandy loams, loams, and silt loams.
[7] Clay loams, silty clay loams, and clays.

To take another illustration, suppose that we have ordinary perennials growing on a fertile sandy soil, that manure or compost is used, and that the plants are individually fertilized. The amounts per 1000

[8] Unless the gardener mixes his own fertilizers, he will not be able to have exactly the formulae reached by his calculations. A 9-12-9 is close enough to a 10-10-10 for all practical purposes; or he could use nearly twice the amount of a 5-10-5. The extra phosphorus will do no harm.

square feet are reduced by 40 per cent twice, giving a recommendation of .09 pound of nitrogen, .36 pound of phosphoric acid, and .36 pound of potash. This would mean only .45 pound of ammonium sulphate, 1.8 pounds of 20 per cent superphosphate, and 0.6 pound of potassium chloride, or roughly 10 pounds of a 5-18-6. By consulting Table 9b, this translates into only 1½ tablespoonfuls per plant, with the plants spaced about 2¼ by 2¼ feet. In such an instance, a 5-10-5 would probably be as good. From this illustration, one can see how easy it would be to apply too much.

The author is not suggesting that the gardener calculate all fertilizer applications so closely. There are too many approximations and uncontrolled variables involved. Yet if he calculates several of them, to fit his principal situations, he can then estimate the amounts to use in terms of teaspoons, tablespoons, cups, and pints and make the important distinctions.

Nutrient tests and sampling. If the gardener undertakes to make tests for acidity or plant nutrients, he shall need to follow the routine explained for the particular kit recommended to him by a competent local soil scientist. Yet, in either case, whether he makes them himself or has them made for him in a laboratory, he shall need to take proper soil samples. A great deal of the value of the test results depends upon how well he does this.

At least one sample of the surface soil of each kind of soil in the garden should be taken. Such a sample should fairly represent the upper 8 inches of soil, or less if the surface soil is shallow over a contrasting layer. One should not mix samples from unlike areas of soil or from unlike horizons or layers at one spot. It is also well to take a representative sample of each kind of soil from beneath the surface soil, according to the natural layers, or, if these are absent or have been mixed in double spading, below 8 inches and above 18 inches.

To take samples, it is convenient to have a piece of oilcloth about 2 feet square, a spade, a strong narrow garden trowel (a fern trowel is ideal), containers, labels, and a notebook.

Small holes with one straight clean wall are made to the required depth. Then an even slice of the soil layer to be sampled is taken with the trowel and placed on the clean oilcloth. This may be mixed and about 1 cupful to 1 pint saved as the sample. In sampling an area of *one* kind of soil, within which no reason exists for expecting significant variations, several samples of the same surface layer may be placed together on the oilcloth, thoroughly mixed, and a representative cupful or pint taken as a *composite* sample. The same may be done for a lower layer. Unlike soils should never be thrown together into one composite sample.

Many flowering plants grow where the relatively uniform surface soil is only 4 or 5 inches thick. In such places, the surface sample should be taken only to that depth.

Waxed cardboard ice-cream containers are handy for soil samples. They may be taken also in heavy paper bags, like those used for nails. Special plastic sacks are also available for the purpose. The moist soil should be allowed to dry out before final sealing and shipment. If only moist, the samples will dry after a few days setting in a protected place in open containers. If wet, they may be spread out on clean newspaper. Care must be taken to avoid contamination of any sort with dust, fertilizer, or by exposure to smoke or gases, as in a kitchen.

In the notebook each sample should be given a number and a brief description, including its location. One cannot trust to memory and, of course, the results are useless unless related to the exact spot. For many purposes it is convenient to have copies of a sketch of the garden grounds, showing the location of the various beds and plots. It is helpful to locate each numbered sample as described in the notebook on such a sketch.

The individual samples need to be carefully numbered, inside and outside the container, if sent to a laboratory. Along with them should go a list giving a description of each soil—its slope, texture, color, drainage, and so on—its past treatment, characteristics of previous plant growth, and intended use, including kinds of plants to be grown. Also an exact location of the garden should be given so that it may be spotted on a soil map. All these notes help the soil scientist, agricultural chemist, or horticulturist who interprets the test results into suggestions.

Samples are best shipped in wooden boxes. They should be very tightly packed; otherwise the containers are liable to break and the samples be lost or become contaminated. Since many laboratories prefer that patrons use special containers and follow specific directions that they have found helpful, it is well to write and make arrangements in advance of sampling.

CONVERSION GUIDES FOR FERTILIZER APPLICATIONS TO SMALL AREAS [9]

Most recommendations about the use of fertilizer, lime, and manure are given in tons or pounds per acre (43,560 square feet), or in pounds per thousand square feet. Most gardeners find it difficult to convert these weights into terms of simple household measures for small plots, rows, and individual plants. Tables 9a and 9b are designed to do this.

All households have standard pints, cups, tablespoons, and teaspoons for liquid measures. One pint is equivalent to 2 cups, or 32 tablespoons, or 96 teaspoons. Level-full measures are understood except for those marked *h*, slightly heaped, and those marked *s*, a trifle less than full.

A pint of water weighs just a little over a pound, precisely 1.046 pounds. Many common materials have been grouped in Table 9a according to their weight relative to that of water. By the careful weighing of another material, the group to which it belongs can be determined.

Although near enough for the gardener, the values in the table are only approximate, since the weight and volume of a given material vary with moisture content and texture. The calculations are based on the assumption that the materials are scooped into the cup or other container without any packing, and that they are loose and not lumpy.

Now, of course, these tables tell the gardener nothing about the basic recommendation; but once he has this he can convert it into any convenient unit. This is very important, especially for the beginner, since different kinds of materials are used in greatly different amounts. On 1000 square feet of the same soil one may use 80 pounds of ground limestone, 28 pounds of superphosphate, 1 pound of ammonium nitrate, and only 6 ounces of borax. Unless care is taken, the gardener is likely to apply too little of some and far too much of others. Let us see how these translate into volume measures per 100 square feet from Table 9a. By locating each material in its proper group, it is seen that they are 6 pints, 3 pints, 4 tablespoons (tbs.), and 1 tablespoon respectively. By turning to Table 9b, and locating these rates in the left-

[9] Based upon a leaflet prepared by the author, AIS–18, issued April, 1945, by the United States Department of Agriculture.

hand column, it is seen that for individual plants spaced 2¼ by 2¼ feet, the rates become ½ *h* cup, 5 tablespoons, ½ teaspoon (tsp.), and ⅛ teaspoon respectively.

TABLE 9a. Weights of various fertilizing materials per acre, per 1000 square feet, and per 100 square feet and the approximate equivalent-volume measures for 100 square feet, grouped according to weight in comparison with that of water

WEIGHTS SPECIFIED PER—

Materials	Acre	1000 Sq. Ft.	100 Sq. Ft.	Volume Measure for 100 Sq. Ft.
	Pounds	*Pounds*	*Pounds*	*Pints*
Weight about the same as that of water .... Examples: *Cal-Nitro (or A-N-L), manure salts.*	1300	30	3	3
	870	20	2	2
	435	10	1	1
				Cups
	220	5	½	1
	110	2½	¼	½
				Pints
Weight about 1 3/10 that of water... Examples: Ground limestone, ground dolomitic limestone, granular sodium nitrate, potassium sulfate.	5660	130	13	10
	3485	80	8	6
	870	20	2	1½
			Ounces	
	565	13	21	1
				Cup
	280	6½	11	1
			Pounds	*Pints*
Weight about 9/10 that of water.... Examples: Ammonium phosphate, double superphosphate, superphosphate, mixed fertilizers (5-10-5, 4-8-4, etc.), muriate of potash.	1960	45	4½	5
	1650	38	3¾	4
	1220	28	2¾	3
	1000	23	2¼	2½
			Ounces	
	785	18	30	2
	610	14	21	1½
	390	9	15	1
				Cups
	300	7	11	1½
	200	4¾	7½	1
	100	2¼	3½	½
		Ounces		*Tbs.*
	50	18	2	4
	11	5	½	1

TABLE 9a. *Continued*

WEIGHTS SPECIFIED PER—

Materials	Acre	1000 Sq. Ft.	100 Sq. Ft.	Volume Measure for 100 Sq. Ft.
	Pounds	*Pounds*	*Pounds*	*Pints*
	1740	40	4	5
	650	15	1½	2
			Ounces	*Cups*
Weight about 8/10 that of water....	175	4	6½	1
Examples: Epsom salts, bonemeal.				*Tbs.*
	44	1	1½	4
			Pounds	*Pints*
	1740	40	4	6
	1525	35	3½	5
	650	15	1½	2
			Ounces	
	300	7	11	1
Weight about 7/10 that of water....				*Cup*
Examples: Activated sewage	150	3½	5½	1
sludge, Uramon, ammonium sul-				*Tbs.*
fate, granular ammonium nitrate,	44	1	1½	4
aluminum sulfate, granular borax.		*Ounces*		
	11	5	½	1
		Pounds	*Pounds*	*Pints*
	1300	30	3	5
	545	12½	1¼	2
Weight about 6/10 that of water....			*Ounces*	
Examples: Cottonseed meal, sul-	260	6	10	1
fur, fish scrap.				*Cup*
	130	3	5	1
			Pounds	*Pints*
	1100	25	2½	5
	435	10	1	2
Weight about 5/10 that of water....			*Ounces*	
Example: Hydrated lime.	220	5	8	1
				Cup
	110	2½	4	1
Manure (moist):	*Tons*		*Pounds*	*Bushels*
Loose	13	600	60	2
Packed	13	600	60	1
Dry straw or leaves packed tightly with hands	5	250	25	2

TABLE 9b. Approximate equivalent-volume measures of materials to use in the row and per plant at various rates per 100 square feet

Rates per 100 Square Feet	RATES PER 10 FEET, ROWS SPACED—			RATES PER PLANT SPACED—		
	3 ft.	2 ft.	1 ft.	5x5 ft.	2¼x2¼ ft.	2x1½ ft.
Pints	*Pints*	*Pints*	*Pints*	*Pints*	*Cups*	*Cups*
10	3	2	1	2½	1	½
	Cups	*Cups*	*Cups*	*Cups*		
6	3½	2½	1¼	3	(h) ½	(h) ¼
5	3	2	1	2½	½	¼
					Tbs.	*Tbs.*
4	2½	1½	¾	2	6½	(h) 3
3	1¾	1¼	(h) ½	1½	5	2½
2½	1½	1	½	1¼	4	2
			Tbs.			
2	1¼	¾	6½	1	3¼	1½
1½	(h) ¾	(h) ½	5	¾	2½	(h) 1
		Tbs.				*Tsp.*
1	½	6	3¼	½	1½	2½
Cups				*Tbs.*		
1½	½	5	2½	6•	1	1½
	Tbs.				*Tsp.*	
1	5	3¼	1½	4	2½	¾
½	2½	1½	¾	2	1¼	½
Tbs.		*Tsp.*	*Tsp.*			
4	1¼	2½	1¼	1	½	¼
Tsp.	*Tsp.*					
1	1	(h) ½	⅓	¼	⅙	1/12
Bushels	*Bushels*	*Pecks*	*Quarts*	*Bushel*	*Quarts*	*Quarts*
2	(h) ½	1½	6	½	3	1½
	Peck			*Peck*		
1	(h) 1	(s) 1	3	1	1½	¾

h=Slightly heaped. s=A trifle less than full.

A FINAL WORD

This has been a long chapter, yet no more important than the others. As pointed out at the start, one may have quite good success on many soils with a safe general recommendation, such as about 1000 pounds of manure per 1000 square feet and 25 pounds of a 10-20-10. But this does not fit all plants. There is no half way between such a general "shotgun" recommendation and the calculations for specific combinations of soils and plants.

8

MORE ABOUT LAWNS
AND GRADES

The first requirement for a good lawn is good soil, either a natural one or a man-made one. The basic principles of soil structure, drainage, watering, acidity, and plant nutrients apply, of course, to soils for lawns as well as to the rest of the garden. Even though application of these principles to lawns has already been suggested, it may be helpful to review the problem specifically, even at the risk of some repetition.[1]

In cool-temperate humid regions, such as New England and west into Minnesota, the "northern" grasses do well. In the lower southern states, the "southern" grasses do well. But between, the winters are too cold for the southern grasses and the summers too hot for easy growth of the northern ones.

The large machines for loosening compacted soil under a growing turf, sometimes called "aerification," and for spraying to control weeds and diseases, used by nurserymen and golf-green keepers, are not practical for the small gardener. Yet for large lawns it may be possible and economical to rent such equipment or to have the work done on a custom basis.

Other plants besides grass—other ground covers—can be used in

[1] For an excellent brief statement of some of the main points, especially about disease control and kinds of grasses, *see* "Pointers on Making Good Lawns," by F. V. Grau and M. H. Ferguson (United States Department of Agriculture Leaflet No. 281, 6 pp., 1950, Washington).

open areas. Heavily tramped places may be paved with flagstones, carefully set into the soil so that they are firm and are just a bit above the ground line. Grasses, ivy, dwarf shrubs, or small hardy perennials may be set between the slabs. English ivy, *Pachysandra*, *Vinca minor*, and many others may be used in shady places. Ivy and others may be used on steep banks where grass fails because of heat and drought. Especially in the areas with very hot summers, and with winters a bit too cold for the southern grasses, many gardeners find these other ground covers better than grass for the difficult spots and no more work in the long run. Still, these plants require care too. English ivy, for example, when once established, must be kept pruned and in bounds. It is a harder job to take out the autumn leaves that fall on it than it is to rake them off the lawn.

ESTABLISHING THE GRADE

Let us begin with the original grade. Ideally, a good soil for grass should be granular in structure and fertile for at least 12 inches. It needs to be well drained without low places or pockets where water stands for more than an hour or so after rains. In building a house, the good surface soil, if there is any, should be removed and piled up while excavations for buildings and roads are being made. This, or good topsoil from the outside, is put on the subgrade after it has been shaped, tamped, and fertilized. Heavy clays or very coarse materials removed for basements should be hauled away. Excavated material of medium texture may be used for any necessary deep fills about the garden; but no stones, boards, plaster, or other rubbish should be allowed in the soil for lawns or gardens. Stones above the size of a quart jar may be saved for little terraces and for the rock garden.

After the excavations are finished, the soil material that will be the final subsoil or subgrade may be graded in long even slopes. If the lawn area is steeply sloping, stone terraces may be used to break the slope into two or more easy slopes. The slopes should be away from the house to protect the foundations and basement against excess water. A combination wall and convex slope may be used. That is, runoff and erosion are greater on concave (upward curving) slopes and banks than on convex ones. If considerable soil is moved in this process, it should be packed with rollers or by tamping and allowed to settle before replacing the surface soil. Otherwise, if the lower soil settles unevenly after the lawn is established, the whole area may need to be torn up and regraded, except that very small depressions can be filled gradually by sifting fine surface soil over the grass, a little each spring and autumn.

It is especially important to have firm fills near the walls of the basement. Usually, excavations for the basement are made somewhat larger than its area, leaving roughly V-shaped trenches around the basement walls. All rubbish needs to be cleaned out of such trenches. If any danger of seepage exists, the basement walls are waterproofed and tile laid to remove any drainage water that may collect. With that done, these trenches can be filled with soil of medium texture and well packed. If cavities are left, storm water may find its way into them and unduly moisten the soil near the basement walls. Where possible, flower beds and other planting near the house should be anticipated at this time so that the soil proper for them can be placed where needed. Such planning can save a lot of digging and hauling later.

If the house is made on a strong slope, great care is needed to provide for interception of seepage water with tile drains and of storm water with terraces. If any flat or depressed areas cannot be graded conveniently into a slope that provides good drainage—under drainage as well as surface drainage—these need to be tapped with tile, as explained in the chapter on soil water.

Any good shade trees should be carefully protected in this process of grading. Established trees are likely to be killed if more than a very few inches of soil are laid over the original ground line near the trunk. They can be saved, however, by building circular walls of brick or stone around them to the height of the grade. For a mature tree, such a shallow well should be about 6 feet in diameter. If the grade is more than about 15 inches deep, a layer of coarse stone should be placed directly on the original ground, out to the tips of the branches. This is covered with fine stones, over which the surface soil is placed. The purpose of this is to insure that the old surface soil containing the tree roots has plenty of air. If the fill is to be very deep, it is best to lay a network of tile on the old ground surface, with two to five T-openings to the new ground surface to provide air.[2] Unless such

[2] For more detail, *see* "Care of Ornamental Trees and Shrubs," by F. L. Mulford (United States Department of Agriculture, Farmers' Bulletin 1826, 79 pp., illus., Washington, 1939).

care is taken, valuable shade trees are likely to die with heavy grades over them.

In preparing the subgrade, it should be remembered that a surface soil of 4 to 10 inches is to be added before seeding. All the form lines of the final grade should be made in the subgrade, only they are 4 to 10 inches lower in elevation than the final surface (except for special beds that may have 18 inches or so of surface soil added). If the subgrade soil is of medium texture and relatively porous but not coarse and sandy, 4 inches of surface soil may be enough for a good lawn. If, however, the subgrade material is a poor medium for plant roots, very clayey, limy, or coarse, the gardener should make the surface soil thicker to insure success.

Before the surface soil is put on, the subsoil should be given enough ground dolomitic limestone, if it is acid, to make it slightly acid or neutral. In the north, in areas where the soils are known to be acid, 150 pounds per 1000 square feet may be used on clayey soils or 80 pounds on sandy soils. In the south, about one half of these amounts are used. As explained in the chapter on soil acidity, tests may be used to establish more nearly precise applications. Every reasonable effort should be made to use ground dolomitic limestone. Either burned lime or hydrated lime, in proper amounts, can be used, but ground limestone is far better.

This subgrade should also be given good dressings of phosphorus and potash. One may use about 30 pounds of ordinary 20 per cent superphosphate and 10 pounds of potassium sulphate per 1000 square feet, or their equivalents as other materials. More precise applications can be worked out for high fertility from soil tests or from the suggestions and tables given in the chapter on plant nutrients.

These materials should be spread evenly and worked into the upper 3 or 4 inches of the subgrade. If the soil is clay, a good dressing of well rotted manure, compost, or peat should also be worked in with the chemicals.

Now the surface soil, saved at the start, may be replaced. If this is poor, additional good topsoil should be added to make a good, deep rooting zone of granular, fertile soil. After grading into place, it should also be given ground dolomitic limestone, fertilizer, and organic matter according to need as explained in the chapters on these subjects. If the soil is acid, between 25 and 150 pounds of ground dolomitic limestone per 1000 square feet is needed, depending upon the degree of acidity, soil texture, and location. A rough, general recommendation for fertilizer is 25 pounds per 1000 square feet of a 10-20-10, or twice as much of a 5-10-5. Much better estimates can be made by following the suggestions and tables in the chapter on plant nutrients for high fertility. If the soil is low in organic matter, well rotted manure or peat moss may be added and mixed well with it. Finally, the soil is firmed with a roller and smoothed by raking.

Once prepared, the lawn may be made by using sods, carefully cut and firmed into place. Although faster than seeding, this method is more costly. Good grass turf, free of weeds, is very expensive. It is the only good method, however, for establishing grass on strong slopes. Where sod is placed on steep slopes, numerous wooden stakes, about 7 to 10 inches long, should be driven through it into the subgrade, else the sods are likely to buckle and slide down the slope in rainy periods before the roots have grown into the subgrade. They may be driven down to the level of the turf and allowed to rot away.

Instead of full sodding, sprigs or plugs may be set out, especially of sorts for which seed is unavailable, like St. Augustinegrass, centipedegrass, Zoysia, and some strains of Bermuda, used mainly in the warm humid areas. In semiarid regions some avoid tall seedstalks in a lawn of buffalograss by transplanting into it plugs of only the female plants.

Commonly, well prepared soils for lawns are seeded either with a seeder or by hand on a windless day. The seed can be mixed with fine dry soil or sand to dilute it. The seed may be divided into two lots, as suggested for hand application of fertilizer, and broadcast in strips at right angles to each other to get more even coverage. The seed is covered by gentle raking. After the seeds are in, they may be firmed in the soil by light rolling. If the soil is rich in clay, rolling should be omitted, because crust formation is encouraged. About 100 pounds of clean straw may be spread on each 1000 square feet on sloping soils to help hold the soil against raindrop splash or wash while the seedlings are getting themselves established. On large areas this can be pressed into the soil a little way to hold it by running a disc over the surface with the blades set straight. For small lawns, or small sloping areas, special nets for the purpose may be fastened over the surface to hold the soil and seed. After the turf is established, these gradually rot.

Young grass seedlings or transplants need frequent light watering. As the grass becomes older, the applications can increase in amount and decrease in frequency. The soil should not be allowed to dry out in the surface rooting zone while the plants are small.

GRASSES TO USE

Rapid progress is being made in research with grasses. The gardener should check with grass specialists in his state agricultural experiment station or at the Plant Industry Station, Beltsville, Maryland, before laying out an extensive new lawn, to find what varieties and strains may be best for his situation. New and improved strains and combinations of strains are continually being developed. Grau and Ferguson [3] suggest:

Temperate humid regions

Kentucky bluegrass, red fescue, Alta fescue, bentgrass, redtop, ryegrass, and *Zoysia japonica*.

Warm humid regions

Bermudagrass, centipedegrass, carpetgrass, St. Augustinegrass, and species of *Zoysia*.

Semiarid regions

Without irrigation: Buffalograss and the grama grasses; and in the northern areas, also the Fairway strain of crested wheatgrass.
With irrigation: Kentucky bluegrass and bentgrass in the northern areas and Bermudagrass in the South.

Some selected features of the grasses are given in Table 10.

Commonly, lawns are seeded with combinations of grass. Small white clover is often seeded with Kentucky bluegrass. Some object to it, especially if small children play on the lawn, because of the ease of getting "grass" stains from the clover leaves. Kentucky bluegrass and white clover make a good combination for hot sunny places, too cold in winter for the southern grasses. By cutting the grass only to

[3] *Op. cit.*

TABLE 10. Requirements and adaptability of certain lawn grasses to selected conditions [1]

	Seeding rate per 1000 sq. ft. (pounds)	Mowing height (inches)	Light	Soil fertility requirement	Soil moisture requirement [3]	Soil drainage requirement [4]
Kentucky bluegrass	2	1½–2	Partial shade to full sun [2]	High	High	Good
Red fescue	2	1½–2	Shade to partial shade	Medium	Medium	Good
Alta fescue	2	1½–2	Full sun	Medium to high	Medium	Good
Bentgrass	¼	½	Partial shade to full sun	High	High	Fair
Redtop	2	1½–2	Full sun	Medium to high	Medium to high	Good
Ryegrass	2	1½–2	Full sun	Medium to high	Medium to high	Fair to good
Zoysia japonica	(plants)	½–1	Partial shade to full sun	Medium	Medium to high	Fair
Bermudagrass	¼	½–1	Partial shade to full sun	High	Medium	Good
Centipedegrass		½–1	Full sun	Medium	Medium	Good
Carpetgrass	¼	½–1	Shade	Medium	High	Fair
St. Augustinegrass	(plants)	½–1	Partial shade	Medium to low	High	Fair
Zoysia species	(plants)	½–1		Medium	Medium	Fair
Buffalograss	¾	1½–2	Full sun	Medium	Low	Good
Grama grasses	1	1½–2	Full sun	Medium	Low	Good
Crested wheatgrass (Fairway strain)	2	1½–2	Full sun	Medium	Low	Good

[1] Based largely on suggestions of Grau and Ferguson, *op. cit.*
[2] Partial shade, especially where days are hot and sunny.
[3] Those marked "medium" have some drought tolerance; those marked "low" are highly drought resistant.
[4] Those marked "fair" are most tolerant of some poor drainage.

151

1½ to 2 inches high, the clover helps shade the crowns of the blue-grass. Further, the clover furnishes the bluegrass some nitrogen. Blue-grass responds well to nitrogen added in early spring, but if hot, humid days follow, it is more subject to "brown patch." By keeping the soil well supplied with phosphorus, potassium, and other mineral nutrients, clover grows well and the bacteria on the roots fix nitrogen. As the clover roots die, some of this becomes available to the blue-grass. This release of nitrogen stimulates the bluegrass to crowd out the clover; but as the clover declines, nitrogen declines, and then the clover can crowd against the bluegrass. High applications of nitrogen tend to cause the grass to crowd out the clover. By avoiding spring applications, the disease hazard is reduced. Late summer and autumn applications can be used to strengthen the grass, but not enough to crowd out the clover. Thus, one may obtain a balance of the two.

Near the northern limit of its range, say near Philadelphia, some have had success with combinations of Zoysia and bluegrass. The Zoysia turns brown in winter, but the bluegrass remains green. Farther south, in Maryland and Virginia for example, the Zoysia usually crowds out the bluegrass in summer but turns brown during the winter. It does not die. It remains as a good turf, but a brown one. For sunny places in the Middle Atlantic States, say from Richmond to Philadelphia, where bluegrass does poorly, Zoysia is becoming popular, especially the "Zoysia 52."

In this intermediate region some use a combination of ryegrass and Bermudagrass. The ryegrass is green during the winter, but gives way in summer to the Bermuda, which, in turn, becomes brown in late autumn.

In cool regions one may sow grass seed in early spring or late sum-mer. Where very hot days are probable, it is far better to seed in late summer or very early autumn. In an old lawn bare or thin places may be seeded in late summer or in early spring. Bare places showing up in late spring may be seeded with annual lespedeza for a temporary cover during the summer. Zoysia plugs are best set in midsummer.

CARE OF THE LAWN

Clipping. The lawn should be mowed as soon as the young grass is high enough. In cool humid regions lawns on good soil can be cut as short as 1 inch. Where heat and drought are common, the mower should be set to leave the grass fairly long, about 1½ to 2 inches high. Clipping the grass very short starves the roots and underground stems and exposes the crowns to the hot sun. Clipping too short is a common cause of poor lawns. The lawn thickens and grows better if the grass is cut frequently and not allowed to get very high. If mowed frequently, the clippings fall back on the soil to help maintain organic matter and fertility. But heavy clippings of infrequent mowings leave a smothering mat, which encourages fungus diseases during hot, humid periods unless removed.

The layout of grassy paths and flower beds should be done with the use of the mower in mind, otherwise much hand clipping is required to keep the garden neat. By keeping the flower beds raised 3 or 4 inches in relation to the lawn, and well mulched, the spread of grass into them can be held to a minimum.

Fertilizing. It is explained in the chapter on plant nutrients how fertilizers keep the amounts of available mineral nutrients high in the soil. If dolomitic limestone is used on acid soils, both calcium and magnesium are supplied. If ordinary limestone is used, Epsom salts should be added to the other fertilizers at an annual rate of 1 to 2 pounds per 1000 square feet. Only needed lime should be used. Some city gardeners injure their lawns by repeated applications of burned or hydrated lime with the mistaken view that they are fertilizers. Where disease and weed hazards are not great, about 25 pounds per 1000 square feet of a 5-10-5 may be used in the spring, or whatever mixture seems best from a detailed study of the suggestions contained in the chapter on plant nutrients. In cool humid regions somewhat more nitrogen can be used. Where disease hazard is bad, however, the nitrogen increases it and furnishes nutrients for weeds in the places where the grasses are weak. Thus, in Maryland, the author finds it best to add the fertilizer under the trees in midseason and on the lawn generally in early autumn.

Watering. Except for young seedings, the lawn should be watered thoroughly at wide intervals, not lightly. Light watering encourages surface roots that do not endure and stimulates shallow-rooted weeds without helping the main grasses. If the soil is well prepared and kept properly fertilized and limed, most lawns do not need much extra water except during periods of real drought. Of course lawns in desert areas or in semiarid areas made up of species from humid regions require regular irrigation. Many of the grasses grown in the North and in semiarid regions normally go through a resting period in summer. Watering may encourage them to unseasonal growth and thus weaken them. But, of course, grasses like Kentucky bluegrass do die during prolonged drought unless well watered.

Rolling. In spring while the soil is moist, but not soggy, rolling pushes down any little mounds thrown up by frost. It does no good to roll when the soil is dry, and it compacts the soil too much to do so when it is wet. Clayey soils are badly injured by walking on them when wet.

Weeds. The best measures against weeds are combinations of practices that maintain a good thick turf. Of next importance is the general rule of keeping them out and not allowing any to go to seed.

Where weeds are bad, the broad-leaved sorts can be controlled by spraying with 2,4-D. This is sold under many different trade names and with directions for its use furnished. It injures most of the bent-grasses and especially the clovers. This material kills many kinds of shrubs and flowers. Once a sprayer has been used for 2,4-D, it is very difficult, almost impossible in the home, to clean it well enough to avoid injury to other plants sprayed with pesticides from the same sprayer. Thus, a special sprayer should be reserved for its use. Solutions of 2,4-D can be applied with a sprinkling can. The lawn should be marked into strips in some way because the operator needs to walk very rapidly to avoid excessive applications. Many other chemicals for weed control are now under test and the gardener may be able to get helpful up-to-the-minute suggestions from his state agricultural experiment station.

Once the lawn is clean, a little work from time to time keeps the weeds down relatively easily as compared to letting them go for several weeks or months. Weeds need to be removed by cutting them well below the crowns with a sharp knife, spud, or narrow trowel. If simply mowed, most come back directly.

Only seeds from reliable suppliers should be used in the lawn. Many coarse grasses and other weeds are introduced with grass seeds. "Special" lawn grass-seed mixtures are most likely to be contaminated.

Other hazards. The control of diseases and insects is beyond the scope of the author's competence. They must be looked for. Advice should be obtained from local experiment stations. Mosses are a nuisance in shady places, especially if the soil is acid. These places are better covered with plants other than grass. Mosses and algae may also grow in wet places where water stands on the lawn too long. Dogs are a nuisance and females may cause small spots of dead grass in an otherwise good turf. Masses of fallen leaves should not be left on the grass; they smother it. After the leaves have been raked in early winter, the gardener needs to search for and remove little piles that may have blown in afterward. Large masses of ice and snow, piled on the lawn in winter, hurt the grass if they remain for a long time after the air temperature has become fairly warm.

Finally, if the present lawn is poor, the gardener should examine the soil carefully to a depth of 20 to 30 inches. If the soil is compacted, very gravelly, full of trash, or otherwise in poor shape, he will do better by tearing it up and reworking the whole grade properly than by trying expensive halfway measures nearly every autumn and spring.

9

STARTING PLANTS AND MOVING THEM

Special soil and protection are helpful in starting plants. The large technical field of plant propagation in horticulture is beyond the scope of this book on garden soils. Here we shall look at some of the simple practices used in the home garden as they relate to soil management.

IN THE HOUSE

Some tender vegetables and flowering plants can be started from seed in the house and be of good size to transplant into the garden when frosts are over. Soils used in pots or boxes for this purpose should have only low to medium fertility and a high content of sand. Little seedling plants are subject to death by a fungus that causes "damping off." High moisture, poor ventilation, and an abundance of nitrogen-rich, easily decomposed organic matter (not sphagnum peat) increase the disease. Suggestions for making suitable soils are given a little later.

In most homes plants can be put on stands near the windows or on the window sills themselves. For best results humidity and temperature should not vary widely. About 65° F. is all right for most seeds, although some prefer it cooler. Tomatoes and many other seedlings can be started at 70° F., but the contrasts between day and night should not be great. Gas fumes are likely to be harmful, and plants often fail in kitchens unless they are especially well ventilated.

156

Young growing plants are sturdier if grown at lower temperatures, around 50° to 65°, than ordinary living-room temperatures; but few homes can arrange for such a special room with adequate light.

As the plants gain size, they need room and sunlight. But bright sunlight falling directly on little seedlings in a warm room is likely to kill them. The temperatures on the leaves become so high that transpiration cannot go on fast enough to keep them cool. As they become larger, they can endure more sunlight; but at first they need to be shaded. If all the light comes from one side, they should be so placed that they can be turned each day or so.

The soil is placed in flower pots or clean cans with holes in the bottom for drainage. Large holes may be covered with broken crockery and a 1-inch layer of gravel or coarse cinders, which prevent the soil from passing through. Small boxes about 2 or 3 inches deep are good. The lower ½ inch of the box may be filled with gravel or cinders.

Where convenient, it is good practice to set the cans or pots in a pan or tray, so they may be watered from the bottom by adding water to the pan. The soil is well moistened at the start, after the seeds are planted; then boxes or pots are watered from the top only after the surface becomes dry. When watered, they should be watered well, getting as little as possible on the young plants themselves. The plants cannot be forgotten. The air becomes very dry in many houses and water loss is rapid. A two-day lapse in a warm, dry room may be enough for the soil to dry out and the plants to wilt beyond recovery. (But if you forget them some day, do not give up hope at once; it is remarkable how well badly wilted plants may recover, if watered in time.)

Seeds should be covered only lightly. They may be placed gently on the prepared soil surface and then covered by sprinkling screened soil over them in a thin sheet, approximately as thick as three times the average diameter of the seed.

If the plants are to be transferred out-of-doors while fairly small, they may simply be thinned in the boxes or pots to give each one room, say to about ½ to 1 inch apart. If the plants are to be allowed to grow larger in the house or are to be transferred to a cold frame for two or three weeks, the little ones should be transplanted into individual 2- or 3-inch pots any time after they have formed their first *true* leaves. If handled carefully, so that the roots do not dry out, and if the soil is well firmed around the roots, the plants grow better and make better transplants for the garden by reason of this intermediate transplanting.

These repotted plants may be left in the house on a stand or on the window sill; or placed in a cold frame until danger of frost is past. The cold frame is better, because it gives the plants a chance to "harden off" a bit. If moved directly from a warm house to the garden, the shock of the new exposure to cool nights, warm days, and wind is greater than for those moved from the cold frame.

For starting plants that are difficult to transplant, the seed may be sown directly in small pots—"thumb" pots. Several annual flowering plants, for example, can be started in the house three to five weeks before the frost-free date and put in the garden after that date for early blooms. Some of these are difficult to transplant. They may be seeded in small pots and then transplanted directly to the garden without disturbing the roots, if the small ball of earth is carefully removed from the pot or the pot broken and removed from the soil in pieces.

Some use sphagnum moss or vermiculite instead of soil for starting seeds, in order to avoid "damping off." A good way to start seedlings is in a watertight flat or low box filled with vermiculite, as recently described by Dr. Emsweller.[1] Waterproof, fiber-resin paper can be folded at the corners to fit the flat exactly, in order to line the bottom and come up on the sides to a height of 1 inch. The lower layer of the flat is filled with gravel. A small flower pot is placed right side up in the center of the flat. Because it conserves moisture to cover the flat with a glass plate, the top of the pot should not be higher than the edges of the flat. Above the gravel, the flat is then filled about halfway with coarse vermiculite. A layer of fine vermiculite is placed above it, so that the top of the material is about ½ inch below the top of the side boards.

After firming, the seeds are sown in the surface as in soil-filled boxes or flats. Because the vermiculite, unlike soil, contains essentially no plant nutrients, these are added to water, which is supplied by subirrigation through the flower pot. The water spreads out through the gravel and moistens the vermiculite above it. At first, ordinary

[1] *See* "Growing Annual Flowering Plants," by S. L. Emsweller (United States Department of Agriculture, Farmers' Bulletin No. 1171, 26 pp., illus., Washington, 1950).

water is used to moisten the material and the seeds. Water enriched with 1 tablespoonful of a 5-10-5 fertilizer per gallon is used when the seedlings first emerge, and once a week thereafter. Ordinary water is used for any necessary additional waterings. If the plants are left in the boxes after they reach normal transplanting size, the enriched water should contain a bit more nitrogen, about 1 tablespoonful of 5-10-5 and either a teaspoonful of sodium nitrate or ½ teaspoonful of ammonium nitrate.

Subirrigation through the sunken flower pot is not absolutely necessary but is far easier than watering from the top. A very thin layer of sphagnum moss peat sprinkled over the seeded surface reduces drying around the seeds. Still better to reduce drying is a glass plate laid over the flat until the seedlings are well started.

HOTBEDS AND COLD FRAMES

Some gardeners use hotbeds for starting young plants. A simple hotbed or cold frame consists essentially of a box, partly in and partly out of the ground, with a gently sloping glass sash for a cover that may be raised or lowered. The hotbeds are artificially heated. In the old days they were heated with a 12- to 24-inch mass of fermenting horse manure placed in a pit under a 5-inch layer of bedding soil. Such manure is hard to find and most hotbeds are now heated with hot water or, more commonly for small home gardens, with electric wires.[2] The glass cover sash is commonly hinged so that it may be raised easily for ventilation on warm days. Small outfits can be purchased or custom-built with automatic controls that turn the current off and on to maintain a constant temperature in the bed.

Especially for the large garden, plants may be grown in the hotbed in heavy paper, soil-filled boxes, about 3 x 3 or 4 x 4 inches, for transplanting directly to the garden.

Cold frames are more commonly used in the home garden. They are simple frames with hinged or removable, sloping glass covers. The only heat is that received from the soil beneath and the sunshine falling through the sash cover. Young plants that are started in the house or in a hotbed may be grown in the cold frame for two to five

[2] *See* "Hotbeds and Cold Frames," by W. R. Beattie (United States Department of Agriculture, Farmers' Bulletin No. 1743, 28 pp., illus., Washington, 1941).

weeks before transplanting to the garden. Cold frames are also used for wintering tender plants that would freeze to death in the open garden, and for starting cuttings.

Recently, especially good boxes have been designed for starting seeds and cuttings. These can be placed on a bench in the basement or other service room. The seeds or cuttings are placed in waterproof trays filled with vermiculite instead of soil. The fungus causing "damping off" does not grow in this material. The box has automatic temperature controls and fluorescent lights.

The engineering details for making hotbeds, cold frames, and starting boxes may be found in several general garden books, in bulletins of the state agricultural experiment stations and of the United States Department of Agriculture, and in the catalogues of garden suppliers.

OUTDOOR SEED BEDS

Although seeds of cabbage, cucumbers, and even tomatoes for the late kitchen garden, and of annual and perennial flowering plants can be planted in their permanent locations, most do better if sown in special seed beds and transplanted later. Among the perennials especially, there are a few plants difficult to transplant. Yet ordinarily, plants that have been transplanted two or three times are stockier and have stronger and bushier root systems than those grown in place from seed. Those wanted early must be sown in pots or boxes kept in the house or in hotbeds. But many can be planted out-of-doors just as well, especially perennials and annuals for late flowering.

Special seed beds should be laid out in a partially shaded, well drained place protected from strong winds. Ideally, the bed should have moving, partial shade, especially during the middle of the day. Often, good seed beds may be made in the woods or among trees, *provided* the roots are cut off at the margins and do not rob the surface soil of moisture. Such a bed may be bordered with 6-inch boards set edgewise about 4 inches beneath the surface and 2 inches above the soil line. If a shady place is not available, a covering frame of slats or of cheesecloth may be used over the bed.

The soil should be highly granular and mellow, but firm beneath the very surface. It may be carefully worked over to a depth of 6 to 8 inches. A granular loam or sandy loam is best. Sticks, stones, and hard clods should be taken out, and well matured compost, peat moss, or well rotted manure added. If rich in clay, sand should be added. The soil should have medium fertility. Ordinarily, only a little phosphorus and potash is added, but no nitrogen beyond that in the manure or compost. If the soil is poor, it should be removed and filled with that described on page 165.

The seed beds need to be firm and moist. If air pockets exist, the soil dries out too much and tiny rootlets die from lack of water. After the bed is well worked up, it may be packed with the feet, leveled, and any low places repacked until the main body is firm except for a loose surface layer of about ½ inch.

Such beds should be moist but not soggy. In contrast to the main garden, watering should be frequent and light. A gentle spray that does not disturb the surface soil is best.

The seeds are best sown in rows about 2 to 3 inches apart that are carefully marked and labeled, because some sorts require several weeks or even months for germination. Little weeds need to be removed as they appear. By knowing exactly where the rows are, the beginner can avoid mistaking his seedlings for weeds.

Various sorts of seed require somewhat different temperatures for germination. Many of the perennials, for example, even do best if planted in the fall and allowed to go through the winter in the cold soil. Others do best if planted very early in the spring while the soil is still cool. Still others are easier to start after the soil becomes warm; if these are planted in cold soil, they rot rather than germinate. Most annual flowers and vegetables start well with a soil temperature of about 65° or 70° F. and an air temperature of around 60° F. or a bit higher. The germination of many seeds is promoted by the normal fluctuations in temperature between day and night.

A large part of the seeds sown in prepared seed beds should be sown in fairly early spring while the soil is still cool. A few do better, however, if sown in the late autumn or very early spring. For the humid, temperate, eastern part of this country, examples include seeds of azaleas, hardy chrysanthemums, wintergreen, Christmasrose, and many sorts of iris and lilies.

Several others important in this area prefer fairly warm soil in late spring or summer (but shaded from the sun). Among them are seeds of amaryllis, campanula, carnation, cockscomb, columbine, cosmos, dianthus, delphinium, digitalis, hardy helianthus, lantana, evening primrose, poppy, portulaca, salvia, and scabiosa.

Seeds planted in outdoor beds are usually covered about three to five times their average diameter. Very small seeds, such as those of digitalis, tobacco, and petunia, are just barely covered with a sprinkling of soil. After the seeds are placed, the soil is made firm by pressure with a small flat board or brick.

TRANSPLANTING

Shortly after the young seedlings have their first true leaves, they may be transplanted, either into another bed or into their permanent location. If thinned to 1 or 2 inches in the row, they may be left in the seed bed until they are of fair size. But if left too long, plants are likely to be spindly and the root systems small relative to the size of the tops. Double transplanting from the seed bed to a nursery and then into the garden is usually best. But good results can be had by taking the small, but well established, plants directly from the seed bed to the garden. The author commonly transplants from the seed bed into 2- or 3-inch pots, which are buried to their full depth in the nursery until plants are ready for transplanting into the garden.

The soil in the seed bed should be moist prior to taking out the plants with a small, sharp trowel. As much soil as possible should adhere to the roots. They are moved into holes somewhat larger than the block of removed soil with the plant in it. This soil should also have been watered to the ideal moisture content. As explained in the chapter on plant nutrients, fertilizers, especially phosphorus, may be sprinkled in the bottom and on the edges of the hole just in advance of putting in the plant. This fertilizer should not touch the young roots, but should be placed so they will soon grow into it.

Firming the soil around the roots is especially important. No air pockets should be left. As soon as the plants are in, they should be watered.

Generally, the soil needs to be leveled (to take out knee prints and the like), but with very slight depressions some 6 inches in diameter and about ½ inch deep around the plant. On slopes, terraces or stone guards are placed on the down-slope side, as already explained. Some plants, tomatoes for example, should be set considerably deeper than they were rooted in the nursery or pots. Many may be set just a little deeper, but most should be set at the same level as they had in the nursery or seed bed. Strawberries, for example, should be set at exactly the same level. They and several other sorts are injured if their crowns are either covered with soil or exposed to drying winds.

If the soil is to be mulched—and in most instances this is best—the mulch of compost, sawdust, or leaf mold should be put on just before watering.

Nearly all young transplants should be shaded for the first few days unless the sky is cloudy and the air cool. The easiest way to do this is with ordinary wooden shingles. The sharp ends of two or three of these may be thrust into the soil about 4 to 5 inches from the plant at angles to protect it from the bright sun between two hours before noon and five hours after. They should be firm enough not to blow away or fall on the plants. Glassine and other preformed paper covers are available too. For small plants in a straight row, 12-inch boards may be laid against slanting stakes for shade. A lattice or frame of cloth can be fastened over a small planting on stakes about 12 inches high.

Often transplants are taken from old beds, nurseries, or even from the woods. Such plants should have their roots pruned, prior to removal, from time to time, by cutting around them with a sharp spade. This gives a high proportion of roots that can be taken up with a ball of earth. Suppose, for example, that the gardener wants a young oak tree for the garden. If a nice one can be located in a woods and its roots pruned with the spade a year or two in advance, it will have an increased chance of survival when moved. By adding a little fertilizer in the cracks made by the spade, new roots are further stimulated.

Many plants can be moved after they have gained a large size, or in off seasons if a large ball of soil is taken with the roots. With trees and shrubs, a circular trench is dug around the soil to be left to the depth of the main roots, and then by digging under the main ball of roots, a large ball of soil with the roots intact is loosened. As the work progresses, the ball is wrapped tightly with burlap to keep it firm. When set in the new spot, the burlap can be removed or left in place, provided the soil is firmly packed without air pockets. The burlap soon rots in the moist garden soil.

Smaller plants without big tops can be moved conveniently by aid of metal cylinders made simply by cutting out the bottoms of tin cans of large size. This method is especially useful with hard-to-transplant large perennials and small shrubs in loose sandy or crumbly soils. The cylinder is slipped over the plant and worked down into the soil by pressure, and by cutting a narrow trench for it with a trowel. The soil inside the cylinder should remain firm and intact and tight against the wall of the cylinder. With the cylinder firmly in place, plant and soil may be loosened from the subsoil with a heavy trowel or spade. When set in the new location, the soil is firmed all around the cylinder except for one place. Usually the cylinder can be worked up with the hands and a trowel and out over the plant. If this cannot be done without loosening the soil around the plant, the cylinder may be cut with tin snips, which reduces the tension, and then slipped out.

Most shrubs and trees need pruning after transplanting to reduce water loss.

The gardener must be careful not to get his plants too close together. Digitalis plants 12 inches apart seem widely spaced while they are little, but are very badly crowded during flowering time. They should be 24 inches from one another at least.

Definite rules for spacing cannot be laid down because plants vary so much in size. Then too, in the flower beds the gardener normally has several kinds growing together. Results are best if the gardener makes a drawing of his beds to scale and sets little stakes in the ground where the various plants are to go. In this way he can allow enough room for each plant so one won't interfere with the other.

The problem of spacing is most difficult with slow-growing sorts, especially trees and shrubs. Most people space them too close together, and especially too near the house or fence. A shrub that will reach a diameter of 6 feet should be set at least 3½ feet from the house; otherwise it will lean away from the house and be ill-shaped at best. The appearance of thousands of houses is spoiled by the large, ill-shaped evergreens that were set only 2 or 3 feet from them while the shrubs were little.

By making a plan to scale the holes for trees, shrubs, and large perennials can be planned in relation to the ultimate size of the plant. Temporarily, the intervening space may be used for bulbs, annuals, or other plants to be removed later.

All the annual plants, of course, and many of the perennials are transplanted in spring or early summer. Some prefer to transplant evergreens in spring. Generally, however, the author prefers autumn for transplanting most woody plants except in areas of very cold winters. Roses and many other non-evergreens should be transplanted in early winter after they are essentially dormant. With late autumn planting, after hot days are over, the soil and roots have all winter to settle and become firmly pressed together. Then when spring comes, there is less danger of the roots being unable to supply water. But plants moved into place in autumn need to be well watered and protected from heavy winds. Some need protection from the winter sun. The trunks of deciduous trees should be loosely wrapped with burlap or canvas that will stay on until a year from the following spring. In areas with very cold winters, if heavy freezing soon follows autumn transplanting, plant roots may dry out more than with spring transplanting. In such areas, most gardeners prefer spring transplanting, especially of evergreens.

It is usually better to transplant roses in early winter than in spring. Azaleas, rhododendrons, blueberries, cotoneaster, and many, many others can be moved either in autumn or early spring. In fact, if one wants to take care, most plants can be moved in summer; but few gardeners will take enough care for success.

Then there are some plants, oriental poppies and iris for example, that are best moved during a semidormant period in late summer.

SOIL FOR STARTING PLANTS

For the pots and flats used for starting plants in the house, a fairly good soil can be made by mixing equal parts of good surface soil from the garden, clean sand, and sphagnum moss peat. Such soil is also satisfactory for the cold frame. If the garden soil is already sandy, no more sand need be added.

A good soil base for hotbeds, cold frames, and nurseries may be made by composting turf cut from a good grass sod. Small slabs about 8 by 12 inches and 4 to 5 inches thick may be piled with the grass side down, and allowed to rot. After the roots are well rotted, the soil is partially dried and sifted. Ideally, the grass should be growing in a fertile soil of intermediate texture, a loam.

A good soil for seeds or cuttings can then be made by mixing 2 or 3 parts of this "basic loam" with 1 part of clean sand and 1 of dried peat, especially sphagnum moss peat. To each bushel of the mixture one may add 3 level tablespoonfuls of superphosphate and, except for acid-loving plants, 2 of ground limestone.

For tuberous-rooted begonias and similar plants that are to grow to maturity in the pots, one may use somewhat more organic matter, say 2 parts of the "basic loam," 2 of the sphagnum moss peat, 1 of clean sand, and 1 of dried sheep or cow manure. To this may be added the superphosphate.

Potting soil for ordinary young plants already started but destined for the garden should contain a somewhat higher proportion of soil and should be a bit more fertile. Two parts of the "basic loam," or of good garden soil if loam is not available, and 1 part of finely pulverized compost or peat will do. If the garden soil contains more clay than in a loam, some sand should be added to the mixture. To each bushel of this mixture add 2 level tablespoonfuls of ground limestone (except for acid-loving plants) and about 3 of a 10-20-10 or 6 of a 5-10-5.

The recently announced synthetic organic conditioners, used as directed, are also very helpful in developing granular potting soil. (See page 55.)

If the gardener can do so (unfortunately not many can), the "basic loam" and sand used for seeds may be partially sterilized with steam for about an hour and until the soil temperature has reached 180° F.

10

PLANNING THE GARDEN

Nature has produced any number of kinds of both soils and plants. Through natural selection and adaptation combinations of plants cover the soil pattern. Natural soils have limitations for use, some within much narrower ranges than others. Plants that would die if set or sown in a wild place do well with care and protection. Through science and art the gardener can greatly extend and improve the natural combinations and patterns.

In practicing his art the gardener does not work against nature, not "against the grain"; he conducts the producing forces toward his own ends. The contrast between wild land and a garden is the result of thought and care. One is not "natural" and the other "unnatural," as some emotional conservationists imply; rather, one is natural only, while the other is cultural but still no less natural for being cultural.

Yet this does not mean, of course, that we can grow any plant anywhere. Perhaps we could if we were willing to go to enough expense and trouble. I have seen beautiful bananas growing in Iceland, but that is stretching things a bit far. I have seen garden plans developed for central England used successfully in New Zealand. But near by were better gardens using partly the local plants and others well adapted to a nearly frost-free site. When the gardener moves from one soil area to another, he should not expect to take his detailed garden plan with him. Although principles are applicable generally, details and methods for the best garden vary widely from place to place.

Each home gardener might state his problem this way: What are the best combinations of plants for the soil (or soils) I have that will most nearly satisfy the comfort of my family with the time and expense we can devote to it? At one extreme, the plants easiest to grow in the soil as it is may be selected; at the other extreme, the soil can be substantially reworked, even remade, to produce plants not naturally adapted. Most seek some compromise between, to save labor and expense on the one hand, and to grow plants that give particular satisfactions on the other.

Many failures, perhaps most of them, result from careless selection of plants not naturally adapted without making the soil changes and carrying on the management practices necessary for success. This can happen easily because an easy-to-grow plant on one soil is often a hard-to-grow one on another. Perhaps even more important is a kind of "spring-fever" garden disease that attacks many people. The symptoms of this disease are a big spring planting with lots of bustle, a messy summer garden with crowded, dying plants overrun with weeds and by the strong growers, and an unsightly autumn tangle needing a fire to clean it or a snowfall to cover it.

The plan for an individual garden depends largely on what gives satisfaction. Food lovers may stress the fresh green things from the kitchen garden. Others want mostly an outdoor living room. Some want both, and are willing to do the work. What one gardener regards as a relatively simple procedure—simple in relation to the satisfaction *he* gets from the probable result—seems downright arduous to another. No garden practice can be called generally practicable or impracticable for all gardeners. Thus the family garden should be planned according to the "work" budget. If it becomes hard work in the sense of an unpleasant responsibility, its purpose as an outdoor living room for relaxation is defeated. The gardener should honestly appraise his probable sustained interest and not plan beyond a fair work budget.

The work budget is generally far more important to the home garden than the financial budget. Certain tools, materials, seeds, and plants are necessary. A large sum, of course, can be used this way; but it is not necessary to spend a great deal of money to have a satisfactory home garden; nor do large expenditures insure success, if, indeed, they even contribute to it. Many kinds of beautiful flowering plants can be raised from seed. Shrubs and trees can be bought as small plants, and some may be grown from seed or cuttings. Even collected wild plants have a place in the garden, although most of these are inferior to the cultivated sorts. A proper compost pile can substitute for expensive manures and organic soil conditioners. Standard fertilizers can be used just as well as the costly packaged "plant foods."

FORM OF THE PLAN

The garden should be planned, consciously, with a balance among all the factors and with an eye to the future. A little time spent in soil examination and in study of the form, hardiness, and soil requirements of plants can make the difference between success and failure.

An easy way to get a plan is to call in an experienced nurseryman or landscape gardener, just as one may have the rooms in the house decorated, furnished, and arranged by an expert. Although such expert advice can be very useful, if relied on exclusively, either outside or inside living rooms are more his than yours. A large part of the fun of gardening, like any other living, is the planning of unique combinations and designs to fit one's own tastes and circumstances. Others can advise, so that the gardener knows the whole range of possibilities from which to make his plan, but no one else can do it quite so satisfactorily. After all, the home garden is a living room, not a public park.

Among the ornamentals, size, color, shape, and flowering time need to be considered for pleasing combinations. Many garden books and bulletins give lists of plants according to these characteristics, and catalogs of garden seeds and plants from reliable firms suggest these characteristics in their descriptions. Most lists are weak on soil requirements or play safe by specifying for most plants "a rich loam soil," which the gardener may not have. The lists given in this book are only suggestive for a first start. A complete list would be unwieldy beyond words because of the many kinds of plants and the variations within these according to variety and strain.

The gardener should not give too much weight to form and color alone in his selection, especially as shown in colored illustrations. Many plants that are beautiful under ideal conditions lack the hardiness and disease resistance necessary in his garden. Some are more susceptible than others to special local hazards, such as Japanese beetles. Considerable research has been done to develop improved varieties of vegetables resistant to diseases, heat, and other hazards. Some research has also been done with ornamentals. But considerable breeding work with flowers has concentrated so much on form and color that the plants themselves are very tender and require almost continuous care. This is true of many of the "choice" tea roses. Unless the gardener is prepared to give such plants the great care they demand, he is far better off with something less dramatic but hardy under the conditions he has and with the care he will actually give the plants.

For permanent plantings the garden plan should be made with an eye to the mature plants, perhaps ten years in the future. Then annuals and others easy to move can be worked between the long-lived ones. A good job requires a scaled diagram that allows space for the future growth of the permanent and semi-permanent plants.

A good basic diagram for the plan may be made to scale by measuring the distances along the boundaries and between fixed features and by plotting the corners, the house and other buildings, walks and roadways, large trees and shrubs, and similar permanent features to scale on a large sheet of paper. If distances are far, a few permanent markers can be made at specific points by driving stakes into the ground deeply enough not to interfere with lawn mowing or other operations.

Paper ruled into small squares is easiest for plotting. A convenient scale is about 1 inch on the diagram for 2 feet on the ground for a very small home garden or for a complicated part of a larger garden, and up to 1 inch for 4 or 5 feet for a large garden. If several copies of such a diagram of the permanent features are made, long-time plans can be laid out on one copy and plans for successive years on others.

Little pasteboard discs may be cut to the proper scale to represent the various spaces required for large perennials, shrubs, and trees and moved about on the diagram in trial positions. When a decision is reached, the location can be outlined in pencil. Pieces of other shapes can be used for small beds and borders. After the plan is worked out, the new distances must be transferred to the garden and little stakes set where the plants are to go.

The annual diagram serves as the guide for planting and seeding for the season. The names of the plants and dates of seeding or transplanting can be written directly on the diagram or on a supplementary sheet attached to it, with symbols for the plants to correspond to symbols on the diagram. Flowering dates, harvest dates, notes on the condition of the plants, fertilizer applications, and the like can be kept on another sheet keyed to the diagram. In this relatively simple way the gardener can keep track of all his plants—their names, locations, and growth habits—and have a useful record of how things worked out. Such records of experience are invaluable for planning the next year's garden.

On a copy of this same diagram the gardener can spot the exact location of soil samples taken for analysis and record the results. Otherwise, notes and correspondence about results are likely to be lost or forgotten.

POINTS TO REMEMBER

It may be helpful to review briefly the main points to check about each kind of plant as it is fitted into the garden plan.

Form and color. One needs to develop a sense for visualizing combinations of colors of leaves and flowers. Reds and purples may be all right side by side if the blooms come at different times, but may clash badly if in flower together. Usually one wants the tall dark evergreens as background for lower, daintier things. Tallish, dense plants can conceal sharp corners and cut off unsightly places. Low plants can be used on the ground in openings to distant views through the tall ones.

Some like formal gardens with regular geometric patterns. To be good at all, these must be very good indeed. This author favors curved lines, especially for the intimate home garden. Except for rows in the kitchen garden I avoid straight lines in favor of uneven plantings with irregularly but smoothly curved borders.

By careful planning one may have some green leaves and some color throughout the garden during the season, with a good "show" or two in different places as the season advances. The gardener should avoid concentrating all the bloom in spring or early summer with no bright spots for late summer and autumn too.

This is enough. In a book on garden soils we can do no more than recognize this large area of horticulture and landscape artistry, about which there is no dearth of excellent books.

Give them room. The gardener's plan should be based on the size of mature plants. Crowding is a common cause of poor gardens. Evergreens, for example, are often so crowded together or against a building that the lower branches die and the plants become leggy and unsightly. Once the lower branches die, new ones do not grow and the plant is ruined as an ornamental for the intimate garden. Heavy plantings on a naturalized hillside to be viewed at a distance are a different matter.

Especially on hot, moist days plants need fresh air and ventilation. Crowding promotes diseased and spindly plants that fall over easily in the wind.

Sun and shade. Plants vary widely in their requirements for light. Some are more shade-tolerant when young than when older. No matter how pretty, a sun-loving perennial cannot be used under a shrub or tree. Nor can a shade-loving one be grown in an exposed rock garden. The gardener, planning in spring before the leaves are out, may overlook the dense summer shade of deciduous trees and shrubs.

The sun requirements of many plants are often somewhat overstated, especially as applied to areas having a good many bright, sunny days. Often it is root competition rather than shade that does the damage. Many shade-loving plants can be grown in the sun if kept well mulched so that roots are cool.

The lists in the Appendix give some notes on sun and shade requirements for a start. More complete lists are available in general garden books dealing with ornamentals.[1]

Remember the roots. The roots need room and the proper soil environment. Some do best in clayey soils, others in sandy soils. Some prefer acid soil; most thrive best in slightly acid to neutral soil; and a few want alkaline soil. Some are best in a dry site; some grow in wet places; while most prefer a moist, well drained soil. Some have the best form if grown in soils of low fertility; some need high fertility; and so on.

In selecting groups of plants for combination plantings the gardener should check the soil requirements of the separate plants as well as their height, form, color, hardiness, and light requirements.

[1] An excellent book for helping plan the shade garden is "Gardening in the Shade," by H. K. Morse (205 pp., illus., Scribners', New York, 1939).

Perhaps we should say requirements and tolerances of soil and light. Some plants that do well in sun may also do nearly as well in shade. Some plants that do best on one kind of soil also do nearly as well on others. Many are quite specific. Then too, some plants "like" one another better than others. With similar shade and other growing conditions the roots of some trees and shrubs compete with low plants more than do those of others. Elms and maples are worse than oaks, for example, and forsythias worse than cotoneasters or azaleas. In fact, strong-growing iris and other herbaceous plants can choke azaleas badly. Bittersweet is another robber.

It takes a lot of cutting-and-trying to develop combination plantings that fit together on a given kind of soil—fun for the long winter evenings with plant descriptions and the garden diagram.

Strong and weak. Some plants in a particular garden are naturally very strong growers. Many spread vigorously, by runners or rhizomes, and engulf the others. These strong growers need to be cut back and kept within bounds or they are likely to ruin the appearance of the planting as a whole. English ivy, for example, makes a good ground cover, but should not be allowed to encroach into the lawn, over the flower beds, or into the shrubs. If permitted to root in the soil directly under many fine plants, such ground covers may weaken them seriously. Morningglory, kudzu, and other vines useful in big places with lots of room may become a great nuisance in the intimate garden.

The gardener should try to go over his plantings frequently with pruning shears and trowel to check the strong growers as well as the weeds. Some ardent weed pullers have an unconscious reluctance to cut back the strong growers. They think of them as "plants" not "weeds."

Protection and staking. Some plants need protection while they are little and should not be planted where they cannot be given it. Many shrubs may be grown in protected places and transplanted later as medium-sized plants to windy spots that they would not endure as young plants. Some flowering shrubs, azaleas for example, have very brittle stems and small plants cannot endure where people are likely to walk on them. In such exposed places thorny shrubs of fair size are better. Children soon learn to keep away.

The gardener needs plenty of stakes. Of course the sturdier his plants, the fewer he needs. But many annuals and perennials need a little support from slender cane or bamboo stakes to keep them from blowing over in strong wind when flowers and leaves are heavy with moisture. Plants should be staked before they fall over or lean badly, because once over, they begin to grow abnormally. Rather than a few heavy stakes with unsightly strings around the whole plant, the gardener may use small, slender canes, stained green, for the principal stems. These can be fastened to the slender stake with green string or paper-covered wires, which need only a twist to hold them. Such inconspicuous stakes protect the plants without marring their appearance.

Change the annuals. In the kitchen garden and flower beds the same kind of plant should not be grown in a particular row or group of rows year after year ordinarily. It can be done if the soil requirements are carefully met and if no serious soil-borne disease develops. But it is safer to shift the vegetables about within the garden from year to year. In a large kitchen garden a different one quarter or one third of it may be planted to a green-manuring crop each year. Such a practice improves the soil in most gardens and reduces the disease hazard.

The same principle applies to annual flowers and even to some perennials. Many perennials need to be replaced after a few years anyway. It is best to replace one kind with some other kind, to shift the beds around.

Any diseased plant should be uprooted and destroyed at once and be replaced with a different kind.

Plan to try them first. Each gardener is bound to have his own successes and failures. If the reader has experiences like those of the author, sometimes he can account for them and often he cannot. Before spending money on some particular kind of plant it is safer to make a few trials to see how it does in the local soil with the care that it will actually receive. Some plants do well if sprayed every week without fail; but if the gardener cannot plan on doing this, he had better look for something nearly as good but more disease-resistant.

Such trials are especially advised for new kinds of plants. As his experience grows, the gardener gradually accumulates a list of plants that he knows do well in his own garden. Of those he tries for the first or second time, many will doubtless do poorly or die; but gradually he adds to his list of good ones.

Vegetables for the family. A kitchen garden can be planned to serve the family throughout the growing season. Heavy plantings of early radishes and lettuce, for example, are wasteful. For the small garden in the temperate region, more can likely be had from well-cared-for tomatoes than from any other crop in the kitchen garden. Kinds of salad crops can be planned for the whole season and, in the South, for the winter too. (See Appendix III.)

As the size of the kitchen garden increases, crops for canning may be added to those for direct use during summer and autumn. In fact, a well managed kitchen garden can be planned to supply nearly all the family needs for vegetables. Plantings for small fruits and even for tree fruits may be added also. This takes a lot of work. Ordinarily it is not practical to add tree fruits to the home garden unless one has enough to justify high-pressure spray equipment. It is difficult to control pests with hand or wheelbarrow equipment. Suggested plans for such gardens of various sizes may be had from some of the bulletins listed near the end of the Appendix, in those to be had for the asking from the local state agricultural experiment station, or through the use of the principles already discussed and the lists in the Appendix.

It is possible for a family to raise nearly all of its food on a very few acres. But few people already employed at something else are willing to make the sacrifice of nearly all of their spare time for the necessary work. The problem of the small subsistence farm is another subject. Too many have been led into the large subsistence garden or small farm by the glamorous accounts of success without looking carefully into the skills required and especially into the sacrifices of time demanded for success. Beyond regular employment at a job life holds other values and offers other interesting things to do besides gardening.

APPENDICES

I

SOIL MAPS

Soil maps have been published by the United States Department of Agriculture for about one half the counties of the country. These have grown out of cooperative soil research of the United States Department of Agriculture and the state agricultural experiment stations since 1899. Soil surveys are made primarily for use by farmers and by scientists and advisors working with farmers. Few are made at large enough scale and in sufficient detail to locate a small home garden on them accurately, especially the older ones made before the use of aerial photographs became general in the middle 1930's. Yet they can be very useful to the gardener. By using the map, he can locate his garden fairly well and can read from the map legend the names of the soils in the immediate vicinity. Then by looking at the soil (or soils) in his own garden and comparing his observations with the descriptions of the soils in the text report accompanying the map, he can learn their proper names, such as Miami silt loam, Clarksville cherty loam, and Plainfield loamy sand.

By knowing the name of his soil the gardener is in very much better position to receive specific advice and suggestions from scientists in both the state and federal experiment stations. Each proper name, like Miami, for example, is associated with a whole set of soil characteristics, including the thickness, texture, structure, color, and chemical composition of the various layers in the soil profile, the slope of the soil, the parent rock material, and soil drainage.

Published soil maps may be consulted in most public libraries and in the offices of county agricultural agents. State agricultural colleges and experiment stations have them. Old ones are out of print, but recent ones may be purchased from the Superintendent of Documents, Washington, D.C. Copies of new manuscript maps, yet unpublished, may be consulted in the offices of many county agents.

II

SOME SOIL PREFERENCES
OF SELECTED PLANTS

The following lists indicate some of the *local* soil preferences of plants commonly grown in the home garden—vegetables and fruits and some flowers, shrubs, and other ornamentals. General notes on hardiness and exposure to sun are given. No attempt has been made to sort the plants according to quality, color, and other important botanical characteristics. Such lists are already available in general garden books. Besides, the catalogs of reliable seed and nursery firms give plant descriptions.

Most plants grow over a fairly wide range of soil conditions, although some are more specific in their requirements than others. That is, two kinds of plants may both grow better in a loam soil than in a clay loam, but one may also do nearly as well in the clay loam and the other only very poorly. Then too, the plant itself may grow well over a wide range of conditions, but a disease hazard may be worse in one part of the range than in another. The optimum soil for any kind of plant has a combination of many characteristics, and often good results may be had even if some one characteristic is far from the ideal, provided the others are all favorable.

For pH ranges—acidity and alkalinity—great dependence has been placed on the excellent compilation of Professor Spurway.[1] But even these figures given in the tables are not always exact. Many acid-loving plants, for example, can be grown reasonably well in nearly neutral soil *if* the gardener is careful to supply available iron, to avoid alkaline fertilizers and

[1] "Soil Reaction (pH) Preferences of Plants," by C. H. Spurway (Michigan State Agricultural Experiment Station, Special Bulletin 300, 36 pp., 1941).

lime, and to maintain a deep mulch of acid-forming organic matter, such as leaf mold from oaks, sawdust, or pine needles. Some plants preferring a neutral soil can be grown fairly well in a strongly acid one, provided good supplies of plant nutrients, especially calcium, potassium, magnesium, and phosphorus are made available. Although many plants do very well in soils *naturally* neutral or slightly alkaline, the same plants may do more poorly in acid soils changed by liming to pH 7.0 or 7.5 than in those given lime only to pH 6.5. Rarely is it wise for the gardener to raise the pH of strongly acid soils higher than to about 6.5 or 6.6.

In the lists that follow the relationships between pH values and descriptive words are:

pH		*pH*	
Below 4.5	Extremely acid	6.6–7.3	Neutral
4.5–5.0	Very strongly acid	7.4–7.8	Mildly alkaline
5.1–5.5	Strongly acid	7.9–8.4	Moderately alkaline
5.6–6.0	Medium acid	8.5–9.0	Strongly alkaline
6.1–6.5	Slightly acid	9.1 and higher	Very strongly alkaline

The approximate definitions of general soil textural terms used in the notes are:

Sand	Sands and light loamy sands
Light sandy soils	Loamy sands, and light sandy loams
Sandy soils	Light sandy loams and sandy loams
Soils of medium texture	Heavy sandy loams, loams, and light silt loams
Clayey (or heavy) soils	Heavy silt loams and light clay loams
Clay (or very heavy) soils	Heavy clay loams, silty clays, and clays

These lists are not precise. The records of most observations about soils are very "sketchy." This compiler has not had experience in his own garden with all of the plants listed. Efforts have been made to check the statements, but for many the evidence is conflicting or vague because of inadequate soil descriptions. Possibly a few are still in error, and many are not so detailed as could be wished.

As supplements to the detailed explanations of soil management practices in the text, these notes may give the gardener a start—a beginning point for further reading about particular plants or for testing in his own soil.

1. *Vegetables*

Vegetables, like herbs, small fruits, and fruit trees, do best in sun. All require good drainage unless otherwise specified. Soil pH preferences are given in parentheses after the name of the plant. For a few plants supplemental lower and higher pH limits are given within which plants do fairly well if other growth factors are favorable.

Planting rates, depths, distances, and dates are set out in Appendix III. For varieties see references in Appendix IV, *For Further Reading.* "Growing Vegetables in Town and City," by Victor H. Boswell and Robert E. Webster (United States Department of Agriculture Miscellaneous Publication No. 538, 40 pp. illus., 1950), is an excellent brief guide to the kitchen garden.

Artichoke, globe (6.5–7.5). Requires fertile soil of medium texture. Tender. Mulch in winter with cool ashes; remove in spring.

Artichoke, Jerusalem (6.5–7.5; as low as 5.5). Requires soil of medium texture and good fertility. Long growing season, but not heat tolerant.

Asparagus (6.0–8.0; as low as 5.5). Requires deep, highly fertile soil of good structure. Avoid light sandy soils. Abundant organic matter, good compost, or well rotted manure and phosphate should be added in upper 24 to 30 inches when soil is prepared. After planting, and each year, a good application of nitrogen and potash fertilizer may be needed.

Beans, lima (6.0–7.0). Wide range of soil, including light sandy loams and clay soils if well fertilized. Must avoid surface crust as seedlings emerge. Sensitive to overliming.

Beans, snap (6.0–7–5). Wide range of soil, including light sandy loams and clay soils if well fertilized. Must avoid surface crust as seedlings emerge. Sensitive to overliming.

Beets (6.0–7.5; as low as 5.5). Do best on fertile sandy soils or soils of medium texture, but grow better on clay soils than most root crops. Lime often needed. Sensitive to boron deficiency.

Broccoli (6.0–7.0). Prefers fertile soils of medium texture but does well on sandy soils and clayey soils, even clay soils. Quite hardy. Lime often needed. Must have plenty of moisture. Can be grown on muck soils too. Often benefits from supplemental nitrogen fertilizer (in midseason). More cold-hardy and less heat-tolerant than cabbage.

Brussels sprouts (6.0–7.5). Prefer fertile soils of medium texture but do well on sandy soils and clayey soils, even clay soils. Quite hardy. Lime often needed. Must have plenty of moisture. Can be grown on muck soils too. Often benefit from supplemental nitrogen fertilizer (in midseason). More cold-hardy and less heat-tolerant than cabbage.

Cabbage (6.0–7.5). Cool season crop, with soil requirements like broccoli, but tolerates some heat.

Cabbage, Chinese (6.0–7.5). Like cabbage, but even more "cool season."

Cantaloupe (6.0–7.5; as low as 5.5). Prefers fertile sandy soils, especially in humid regions, but can be made to do fairly well on clayey soils where carefully prepared to allow good root growth. Needs warm season.

Carrots (5.5–7.0; as low as 5.0). Prefer a fertile, granular soil, especially sandy loam soils, but grow fairly well on clayey soils of good structure. In soil of poor structure, roots are stubby, pronged, and crooked. Do well on muck soils.

Cauliflower (5.5–7.5). Prefers fertile soils of medium texture but does well on sandy soils and clayey soils, even clay soils. Must have plenty of moisture. Cool season needed but not so tolerant of severe cold and heat as cabbage.

Celery (5.8–7.0). Requires very fertile deep granular soils, especially sandy loams, loams, or good muck soils. Needs cool season and a good moisture supply in the soil *all* the time. In warm regions grown only in cool season.

Collards (6.0–7.5). Prefer fertile soils of medium texture but do well on sandy soils and clayey soils, even clay soils. Need good moisture supply. Tolerant of cold and more tolerant of heat than cabbage.

Corn, pop (6.0–7.5). Does best on fertile soils of medium texture or clayey soils, but fairly well on sandy soils and clay soils. Does poorly on light sandy soils unless irrigated as well as fertilized. Needs warm growing season. Benefited by supplemental nitrogen fertilizer in midseason.

Corn, sweet (5.5–7.5; as low as 5.0). Does best on fertile soils of medium texture or clayey soils, but fairly well on sandy soils and clay soils. Does poorly on light sandy soils unless irrigated as well as fertilized. Needs warm growing season. Benefited by supplemental nitrogen fertilizer in midseason. Can be grown on muck soils where there is no frost hazard.

Cress, water (6.0–8.0). Needs wet fertile soil, ideally in pools of clean fresh water fed by a spring or stream from limestone rocks. After plants are established, water should be about 1 foot deep over soil. Hardy.

Cucumbers (5.5–7.0). Prefer a fertile soil of medium texture or a sandy one, but grow on granular clayey soils or even especially well prepared clay soils. Very responsive to well composted manure. Need a warm season.

Eggplant (5.5–6.0).[2] Similar to tomatoes but requires a longer and warmer season and is even more sensitive to low nutrient supply.

Endive (5.8–7.0). Requires a fertile soil of medium texture or granular clayey soil. Does best in cool seasons. Hardy. Must be shaded in warm seasons. Better than lettuce for autumn.

Garlic (5.5–8.0). Similar to onion. Prefers sandy or medium-textured soils; avoid clay soils.

Horseradish (6.0–7.0). Prefers deep fertile soil of medium texture but grows on any soil in which roots can go deeply. Can become a weed.

Kale (6.0–7.5). Similar to cabbage and broccoli. Hardy in late autumn and early spring.

Kohlrabi (6.0–7.5). Similar to cabbage and broccoli. A cool season crop but stands some heat.

Leeks (6.0–8.0). Similar to onions.

Lettuce (6.0–7.0; as low as 5.5 and as high as 8.0). A cool season crop for mild winters in warm regions and for summers in cool regions. Few varieties are heat resistant. It does best on very fertile soils of medium texture but can be grown on well fertilized, well irrigated sands and on very well prepared clay soils during cool periods. Can be grown on muck. Needs supplemental nitrogen fertilization where left in garden for second crop of leaves. In warm seasons partial shade is essential for good plants.

Mustard greens (6.0–7.5). A cool season crop for the winter in warm regions and autumn and spring in temperate regions. Does well on fertile soils, well supplied with water, over a wide range of texture.

Okra (6.0–7.5). Similar to tomato.

Onion (5.8–7.0; as low as 5.0 and as high as 7.5). Requires a fertile soil. Sandy loams or loams are best, although they can be grown on muck and *well* granulated clayey soils. Onions from seeds often do poorly in clay or clayey soils, especially with high heat, while a crop may be had from sets. They may be grown widely if extremes of both heat and cold are avoided. In temperate regions seeds should be in the soil very early.

2 Keep below pH 6.1 as a precaution against disease.

Parsley (5.0–7.0). Grows on a wide range of fertile soils. Hardy but needs good moisture conditions.

Parsnip (5.5–7.0). Requires relatively long, medium to cool season on deep, fertile, well granulated soils. Sandy loams and loams are best. Will grow on muck. Cannot endure drought. Unless clayey soils are unusually well prepared, roots are stubby, pronged, or crooked. The same bad effects are caused by pebbles, stones, or coarse, unrotted organic matter in the soil. Where allowed to grow too long they become tough. The flavor is better if harvested after heavy frost.

Peas (6.0–7.5; as low as 5.5). A cool season crop, more hardy than beans, unable to withstand heat or drought, for moderately fertile soils of medium texture. Can be grown on well granulated clayey soils and well irrigated light sandy soils.

Peppers (5.5–7.0). A warm-season crop similar in requirements to tomatoes but even less cold-resistant.

Potatoes (Irish) (4.8–5.6).[3] Can be grown widely but do best in cool moist areas on sandy loams, loams, and heavier soils of very good structure. Do well on fertile muck soils. Will do well on light sandy soils with fertilization and irrigation. Cannot endure poor drainage or drought. Do *very* poorly on clay soils of poor structure. The scab organism often attacks susceptible varieties severely on soils with pH values above 5.6, especially where lime is used on acid soil. Thus, most varieties cannot be grown in garden soil that has been limed to the optimum for most other vegetables.

Pumpkins (5.5–7.5). This tender long-season crop can be grown on a wide variety of deep fertile soils where there is plenty of room. Although sandy loams and loams are best, they grow nicely on well prepared clayey and clay soils.

Radishes (6.0–7.0; as low as 5.0). These do best on the sandy soils of moderate to high fertility, but can be grown on clayey soils if well prepared, especially the early crop. They may be sown in small, sand-filled trenches in clay soil. They do poorly in heat or drought.

Rhubarb (5.5–7.0; as low as 5.0). Does best in cool, moist regions with rather cold winters. It does well in many well drained, highly fertile soils, but not the light sandy ones. When set out, the soil should be spaded deeply and abundant compost, or well rotted manure, and phosphate incorporated in the upper 15 to 25 inches.

Rutabaga (5.5–7.0; as low as 5.0 and as high as 7.5). This cool-weather crop is similar in requirements to turnips, except that it is even less heat-resistant.

Salsify (6.0–7.5). Similar to parsnips.

Shallot (5.5–7.0). Similar to onion.

Soybeans (6.0–7.0; as low as 5.5). Widely adapted to fertile, well drained soils of good structure. Endure drought fairly well. Do poorly on clay soil of poor structure. Where grown for the first time seed or soil should be inoculated with legume organism.

Spinach (6.0–7.5; as low as 5.5 or as high as 8.5). Generally, a hardy cool-weather crop grown during spring and autumn in temperate regions, summer in cool regions, and winter in warm regions. Does best on fertile soils high in organic matter and well drained. It can be grown on clay soils if these are well prepared. Does poorly on light sandy soils unless irrigated as needed. After plants are well started, supplemental nitrogen fertilization should be given.

Squash, crookneck (6.0–7.5). Requirements similar to those of pumpkin.

[3] Plants grow well up to pH 6.5 and even higher, but disease control is difficult over pH 5.6.

Squash, Hubbard (5.5–7.0). Requirements similar to those of pumpkin.

Sweetpotatoes (5.2–6.0; as high as 7.5). Require a long, warm growing season. Best results are had on moderately fertile sandy loams. Can be grown on rather poor light sandy soils. The clay soils should be avoided. Often they are planted in ridges, some 4 or 8 inches high, in soil previously mixed with about 10 pounds of a mixed fertilizer per 100 feet of row. About a month after the plants are up, an equal amount of fertilizer may be applied as a side dress. Excess nitrogen should be avoided. Many yields are low because of too little fertilizer and late planting.

Swiss chard (6.0–7.5). Requirements similar to those of spinach. Somewhat more heat-resistant than spinach and lettuce. With care, can be grown on clay soils.

Tomato (5.5–7.5; as low as 4.5). A warm-season crop that grows well on a wide variety of soils. They can be grown on light sandy soils if watered as needed, and on clay soils if the soil is very carefully prepared in advance by the incorporation of organic matter to prevent packing. Fertilizer rich in phosphate and with fair supplies of nitrogen and potassium should be mixed into the soil around and beneath the roots when the plants are set out. Then nitrogen should be added again after the fruits are well set. They cannot endure drought. After plants are established, it is well to mulch the soil. Care must be taken to be sure of little ridges near the plants placed so water will enter the soil around the roots and not run off. In places with hot summer seasons light partial shade is an advantage, although much shade reduces the content of vitamin C.

Turnip (5.5–6.8). A cool-weather crop adapted to the sandy loams, loams, and silt loams, but not to the clay soils unless they have unusually good structure. It cannot endure much heat. Special fertilizers are not necessary if the soil is moderately fertile.

Watermelon (5.5–6.5; as low as 5.0). A long-season crop needing warm weather, a fertile, well drained but moist, sandy loam or loam soil. By digging fairly large holes some 18 to 20 inches deep, and replacing poor clayey soil with a mixture of well rotted manure or good compost and well fertilized soil, fairly good success may be had. It requires much space.

2. Herbs

Except as noted, most herbs have the best quality if grown on relatively dry soils of only moderate fertility. Optimum soil pH values are suggested in parentheses after the name. Some are uncertain.

Anise (5.5–7.0?). Well drained sandy soil of moderate to good fertility. Needs full sun.

Balm, lemon (6.0–8.0). Wide soil tolerance. Prefers clayey, fertile moist soil. Partial shade or full sun. Spreads very easily.

Basil, sweet (6.0–7.0?). Well drained moderately fertile soil. Full sun.

Caraway (5.5–7.0?). Well drained moderately fertile soil. Full sun.

Catnip (5.5–7.0?). Wide range of soil. Prefers fertile soil of medium texture in sun.

Chives (6.0–7.0). Moderately to highly fertile soil in full sun.

Coriander (5.5–7.0?) Moderately fertile soil of medium texture in full sun.

Dill (6.0–7.0?). Moderately to highly fertile soil of medium or clayey texture in full sun.

Fennel, common (5.0–6.0). Moderately fertile soil in full sun.
Geranium, sweet-leaved (6.0–8.0). Tender. Moderately fertile, relatively dry soil of medium texture. Full sun.
Horehound (6.0–7.0?). Sandy soil in full sun.
Lavender (6.5–7.5). Relatively dry sandy soil in full sun.
Marjoram, sweet (6.0–7.0?). Tender. Moderately fertile, very well drained soil in full sun.
Mint (6.0–7.5?). Moderately fertile, moist soil of medium to clayey texture. Nearly full sun to shade.
Rosemary (6.0–7.0?). Very well drained sandy soil in full sun.
Sage, garden (6.0–7.5?). Moderately fertile, very well drained sandy soil in full sun.
Savory, summer (6.0–7.0?). Moderately fertile soil of medium texture in full sun.
Savory, winter (6.0–7.0?). Well drained sandy soil in full sun.
Sorrel (4.0–7.0). Wide range of well drained, moderately fertile soil in full sun.
Tarragon (6.0–7.5?). Well drained sandy soil in sun or partial shade.
Thyme (5.5–7.0?). Very well drained soil of sandy or medium texture in full sun.

3. Small fruits

This list is arranged like the one for vegetables. Optimum soil pH values are given in parentheses after the plant name.

Blackberries (5.0–6.0; as low as 4.5). Do best on fertile soils of good water-holding capacity in which roots may penetrate deeply. Cannot endure poor drainage. Ordinarily do better on sandy loams and loams than on clayey soils. On droughty soils or those with shallow rooting zones they can be grown with low terraces to save water and especially heavy use of good compost or well rotted manure in the surface soil and heavy mulches on the surface. A very little lime is often necessary on the most acid soils.
Blueberries (4.0–5.0; as low as 3.5 and as high as 6.5). Do best on imperfectly drained, acid sandy soils or shallow peat over sand, provided the surface soil is not swampy or ponded, even for a week or so. If well drained sandy soils are used, irrigation is necessary in dry periods. Although acid soils are needed, some imperfectly drained sandy soils are even too acid and a very little lime is needed. The plants should have a deep mulch of sawdust, pine needles, or other acid-forming organic matter. Blueberries can be grown on clayey soils by mixing sand and organic matter in the upper 24 inches and using heavy mulch. Sulphur may be used, in advance of planting, to increase the acidity of slightly acid or neutral soils. A little phosphate and potash should be mixed with the soil at planting time. They need some fertilization with acid-forming nitrogen fertilizers.
Cranberries (4.2–5.0; as high as 6.0). Grown in cool regions on acid peat bogs with a controlled water table so they may be flooded and the water table lowered but not beyond the reach of the roots. Ideally, the acid peat (or muck) overlies sand at about 12 to 15 inches with a hardpan underneath the sand. Rarely practicable for the home garden except where such a soil occurs naturally.
Currants, black (6.0–7.5). Similar to raspberries.
Currants, red (5.5–7.0). Similar to raspberries.
Dewberries (4.5–6.0; as low as 4.0). Similar to blackberries but not so hardy.
Gooseberries (5.0–6.5). These grow on a wide variety of soils. Most varieties prefer

sandy soils; others, such as Poorman, clayey soils. They need a good mulch, especially where the season is warm.

Grapes (5.5–7.0). Some varieties of grapes can be grown almost anywhere. They prefer a moderately fertile, well drained soil of medium texture and with some gravel or rock fragments in it. When established, ample phosphates should be mixed into the soil. With good general soil preparation to encourage deep rooting, free drainage, good water-holding capacity, and a balanced supply of nutrients, and with watering in dry periods, they may be grown on a wide range of soils.

Raspberries, black (5.0–6.5; as low as 4.5). See red raspberries.

Raspberries, red (5.5–7.0; as low as 5.0). Generally, these do best in cool and temperate regions. Some varieties may be grown near Washington and a little farther south if kept heavily mulched. They do best on a deep, well drained soil of moderate to high fertility and sandy or medium texture. Sandy soil with a clay layer or hardpan at 30 inches is excellent *provided* that there are no "pockets" or spots of poor drainage, even for a few weeks, in the soil above the hardpan. But by careful preparation of the soil to encourage deep rooting, they may be grown fairly well on clayey soils. Phosphate should be worked into the soil at planting time and some potash and nitrogen used also. A little lime is sometimes needed. The plants should be kept mulched and may need watering since they cannot endure much heat or drought. Poor plants are often the result of unsuspected poor drainage in the soil beneath the surface.

Strawberries (5.0–6.5; as low as 4.5 and as high as 7.0). Strawberries can be grown in nearly all parts of the world where gardens are found if the locally adapted varieties are used. Although they prefer the sandy loams and loams, with good soil preparation they may be grown on sand soils and clay ones. They require moderate fertility, *good drainage*, and a dependable supply of moisture. They will not endure drought, especially heat and drought together, so supplemental irrigation is often necessary. In doing this while berries are ripening one should avoid wetting the plants. Very strongly acid soils should have a light application of ground limestone. Phosphates and potash should be worked into the soil before planting and fair applications of nitrogen given during the season. Good mulches of sawdust, pine needles, or chopped straw are helpful.

4. *Some fruit trees*

All the fruit trees listed require sun. Optimum soil pH-values are given in parentheses after the plant name.

Apples (5.0–6.5). Varieties vary widely in hardiness, but generally they are not adapted to severe cold or high heat, although they will endure more cold than peaches. They need well drained soils of moderate texture but do well in clayey soils, *provided* no hard layer or poor drainage prevents good root growth. Phosphate should be worked into the soil at planting time for these and other fruit trees, and supplemental nitrogen fertilizers used, especially where grass grows under the trees. Extremely fertile soils are not the best for apples, since fruiting is poor and winter injury more likely. They require watering in periods of severe drought.

Apricots (6.0–7.0). Similar to peaches.

Cherries (6.0–7.0). Similar to apples except they may be grown in sandy soils, even in light sandy soils if well irrigated in dry periods.

Citrus, including grapefruit, lemon, and orange (6.0–7.5; as high as 8.3). These fruits for warm, nearly frost-free regions require a fertile soil of sandy or medium texture that is well drained, but moist. They are quite sensitive to deficiencies of the minor nutrients, such as zinc, manganese, and iron, and of excesses of boron. They may be grown in clayey soils if drainage is good so that roots grow well and salts do not accumulate. At least some irrigation is needed in most places.

Peaches (6.0–7.5). These prefer sandy soils in regions where the winter temperature does not fall much below 0° and late spring frosts are uncommon. They overlap the soils suitable for apples, but extend into warmer areas and are not so hardy. If the garden soil is well prepared for deep rooting they may be grown on clayey soils.

Pears (6.0–7.5). Although somewhat similar to apples, pears prefer a moderately fertile soil of medium to clayey texture that is well drained and permits good root growth. Heavy nitrogen fertilization or very highly fertile soil must be avoided since the trees will be more subject to disease and the twigs to dieback.

Plums (6.0–7.5). Similar to pears, except that they favor a more fertile soil.

Quince (6.0–7.5). Similar to plums.

5. A *few herbaceous perennials*

This list includes only a few species of some of the main sorts of perennials, with a few that are commonly regarded as biennials.

Where only one species is listed, the soil pH range is given in parentheses immediately after the name; otherwise, it is given after the species name at the end of the paragraph.

Exposure to sun is suggested by the first letter in parentheses after the soil notes or the species name according to the following symbols: FS, full sun; S, sun or very light shade; PS, partial shade or only 3 to 8 hours of sun; and Sh, shade or little or no direct sunshine.

Hardiness for the area from about Baltimore to Boston is suggested by the second letter in parentheses as H, hardy, and HH, half-hardy.

Thus *Lobelia cardinalis* has an optimum soil pH range of about 5.0 to 6.0, likes partial shade, and is hardy.

Acanthus mollis (Bears-breech) (6.0–7.5). Deep soil with excellent drainage. (S; HH)

Achillea (Yarrow). Moderately fertile soil; grows fairly well in poor soil. Good for dry slopes. (S; H). A. *ptarmica* (Sneezewort y.) (6.0–7.5); A. *rosea* (5.0–7.5).

Aconitum (Monkshood). Fertile soil. Subject to injury with extreme heat and drought. Should be left long in one place. (S to PS; H). A. *autumnale* (6.0–8.0); A. *bakeri* (5.0–6.5); A. *fischeri* (5.0–6.0).

Aethionema cordifolium (Lebanon stonecress) (5.5–7.0). Well drained, sandy or gravelly soils. Can endure drought, but not wet. Good for rockery or hillside gardens. (FS; H)

Althea rosea (Hollyhock) (6.0–8.0). Highly fertile, well drained soil of medium texture or well prepared clayey soil. Needs good moisture supply. (FS; H)

Alyssum saxatile (Goldentuft) (5.5–6.5). Well drained soil. Useful in rock garden. (FS; H)

Anchusa myosotidiflora (6.0–7.5). Deep, well drained soil of medium texture. Avoid clay soils unless carefully prepared. Irrigation necessary during dry periods. (FS; H)

Anemone (Windflower). Fertile soil, especially well drained in winter. Needs good watering in dry periods. Some mulch covering for cold winters. (S to PS; HH). *A. japonica* (6.0–8.0); *A. canadensis* (5.0–7.5); many other sorts.

Anthemis tinctoria (Camomile) (6.0–8.0). Wide tolerance of soil including clay soils. Can become pest. Useful in rockery or hill gardens. Fair drought resistance. (S or PS; H)

Aquilegia (Columbine). Prefers sandy soils rich in organic matter, but will grow in clayey soils well prepared with compost. Avoid clays for large hybrid sorts. (PS; H). *A. canadensis* (5.5–7.0); *A. caerulea* (6.0–7.5); *A. chrysantha* (6.0–7.0); *A. flabellata* (5.5–6.5).

Asclepias. Prefers well drained sandy loams or loams, but grows in well prepared clay soil, although more likely to freeze in winter. Often crowds other plants. Good for dry slopes. (S; H). *A. tuberosa* (Butterflyweed) (5.0–6.5); *A. curassavica* (Milkweed) (6.0–7.5).

Aster (Hardy aster). Hardy asters grow on a wide range of moderately fertile soils. Not tolerant of drought. Prefer sun but do fairly well in partial shade. Spring transplanting better than fall in clay soil. (S or PS; H). *A. alpinus* (5.5–7.0); *A. novae-angliae* (6.0–8.0); *A. novi-belgi* (5.0–7.5).

Astilbe arendsi. Does best in moderately fertile, moist, well drained soil. Grows well in rockery if mulched. (S to PS; H)

Aubrieta deltoidea (Purple-rockcress) (6.0–7.5). Well drained soils of sandy or medium texture. On moist clay soils likely to die in winter. Good in rock garden. (FS; H)

Baptisia (Wildindigo). Prefers deep fertile soil with ample space but grows on light sandy soils. Fair drought resistance. (FS; H). *B. australis* (5.0–6.5); *B. tinctoria* (5.0–6.0).

Bocconia (or *Macleaya*) *cordata* (Plumepoppy) (6.0–7.5). Prefers a relatively dry fertile soil. Can become a weed. (FS; H)

Boltonia (False-starwort). Soil of medium fertility. (S; H). *B. asteroides* (5.0–6.0); *B. latisquama* (5.0–6.0?) is useful for moist places.

Callirhoë involucrata (Poppymallow) (5.5–6.5). Does well in very well drained sandy soil. Can be used on dry slopes. (FS; H)

Campanula (Bellflower). Prefers fertile soil of sandy or medium texture. Needs mulch, especially in winter. (FS to PS; H to HH). *C. excisa* (5.0–6.0); *C. pusilla* (6.0–7.5); *C. waldsteiniana* (5.0–6.5); many others.

Cassia marilandica (Wild Senna) (6.0–8.0). Relatively moist soil of moderate fertility. (S; H)

Centaurea cyanus (Cornflower) (6.0–6.5). Wide range of moderately fertile well drained soils. (FS; H). Several other species (5.0–7.0).

Cerastium arvense (Snow-in-summer) (6.0–7.0). Wide range of soils, including dry banks. (FS; H). Many other species.

Ceratostigma plumbaginoides (Chinese leadwort or Plumbago) (6.0–7.0). Moderately fertile well drained sandy loam or loam. Can be used in rock garden. (S to PS; H to HH)

Chrysanthemum. Requires moderately fertile soil of medium texture, but can be grown in well prepared clay soils. Needs abundant phosphate and potash and moderate nitrogen. Needs plenty of room. Responds to good mulch. (S; H). *C. alpinum* (4.5–7.0); *C. arcticum* (Arctic daisy) (6.0–7.5); *C. coccineum* (5.5–6.5); *C. morifolium* (Pompons) (6.0–7.5, as low as 5.0 and as high as 8.0); *C. maximum* (Shasta daisy) (6.0–8.0); many others.

Cimicifuga americana (Bugbane) (5.0–6.0). Moist soils with plenty of organic matter. (S to Sh; H). Many other species; *C. racemosa* is good for wet places.

Convallaria majalis (Lily-of-the-valley) (4.5–6.0). Prefers somewhat moist fertile soil with plenty of organic matter. (PS or Sh; H)

Coreopsis (Tickseed). Does well in somewhat moist fertile soil. May need some winter mulch. (S; HH to H). *C. grandiflora* (6.0–7.5) is good for wet places; *C. lanceolata* (5.5–7.0).

Delphinium (Larkspur). Prefers fertile soils of medium texture. Likely to die in wet soil during winter. Very good in North where days are long. Not good in hot humid areas. (FS; H). *D. belladonna* (6.0–7.0?); *D. grandiflorum* (6.0–7.5).

Dianthus. Needs well drained soil of moderate fertility. Plants easily crowd one another. Several sorts good in rockery and hill garden. *D. barbatus* (Sweet William) (6.0–7.5); *D. caesius* (Cheddar Pink) (6.5–7.5); *D. deltoides* (Maiden Pink) (6.5–7.5); *D. glacialis* (Ice Pink) (5.0–6.5).

Dicentra (Bleedingheart). Prefers fertile soil of sandy or medium texture with high content of organic matter. (PS to Sh; H). *D. spectabilis* (6.0–7.5); *D. eximia* (5.0–6.0).

Dictamnus albus (Gasplant) (6.0–7.0?). Needs well drained soil of medium texture. Difficult to move. (S to PS; H)

Digitalis purpurea (Foxglove) (6.0–7.5). Does best in fertile soil rich in organic matter and phosphate. Grows fine in well prepared, well drained clayey soils. After ground freezes a light mulch of pine needles is good. Crowns and lower leaves should not be wet. There are many other good sorts. Most are treated as biennials. (FS to PS; H)

Doronicum plantagineum (Leopardsbane) (6.0–7.0). Can grow in wide range of fertile soils, including clayey soils. Cannot endure much drought. (S to PS; H)

Echinacea purpurea (Purple Coneflower) (5.0–7.5). Does well on wide range of soils. Will grow in dry poor soil. (S; H)

Epimedium musschianum (Barrenwort) (6.0–7.5). Prefers moist peaty sandy loam or loam; but will do well in rockery. Needs a little winter protection. Avoid cultivation or moving plants. (PS; H)

Erodium, sp. (Heronsbill) (about 6.0–7.0?). Well drained sandy or gravelly soil. Useful in exposed dry places. (S; H)

Eryngium amethystinum (Seaholly) (about 6.5–7.5?). Prefers sandy soils. Hard to move. Fairly drought resistant. (FS; H)

Eupatorium coelestinum (Hemp Agrimony; Mistflower) (5.0–7.5). Does well in wide range of soils but best in well drained sandy loams of moderate fertility. (PS to S; H)

Euphorbia corollata (Flowering spurge) (5.0–6.0). Can be grown in dry places, hill gardens, and rock gardens. (S; H)

Gaillardia aristata (Blanketflower) (6.0–7.5; as low as 5.5). Prefers fertile sandy soils but can be grown on clay soils well prepared with sand and leaf mold or compost. Fair drought resistance. (FS; H)

Gentiana. A little difficult. Does best in fertile soil rich in organic matter. Needs watering in dry periods. Disturb plants as little as possible. (PS; H). G. *crinita* (Fringed Gentian) (6.0–8.0) treated as biennial; G. *andrewsii* (Closed Gentian) (5.0–6.0).

Geranium pusillum (Cranesbill) (6.0–7.5). Does best on moderately fertile soils of medium texture. Many other sorts; some not drought resistant. (PS; H)

Gerberia jamesonii (Transvaal Daisy) (6.5–7.5). Grows in relatively moist soil of medium texture rich in organic matter. Needs light winter protection in temperate regions. (FS; HH)

Geum chiloense (Avens) (6.0–7.5). Can be grown on well drained soil that is not wet in winter. Needs watering in dry periods, and light winter mulch where cold. (S to PS; HH to H)

Gypsophila paniculata (Babysbreath) (6.0–7.5). Needs well drained moderately fertile sandy loam or loam. Not good in clay soils. Can be grown in dry places; on soils of low fertility with good rooting zone. (FS to S; H)

Helenium autumnale (Sneezeweed) (5.0–7.5). Grows in wide variety of well drained fertile soils. (S; H)

Helianthemum chamaecistus (Sunrose) (6.0–7.5). Prefers very well drained places, like rock and hill gardens. Can endure drought, but needs some winter protection in temperate regions. Hard to transplant. (FS; HH to H)

Helianthus (Sunflower). Does well on a wide range of moderately to highly fertile well drained soils. Needs frequent transplanting. Some sorts good in dry places but most like moisture. (FS to S; H). H. *angustifolius* (Swamp Sunflower) (6.0–7.5); H. *decapetalus* (var.) *multiflorus* (Golden Sunflower) (6.0–7.5); H. *giganteus* (Giant Sunflower) (6.0–8.0).

Helleborus niger (Christmasrose) (6.0–8.0). Grows in wide range of fertile soils. Prefers sun in winter and shade in summer. Needs some winter protection in temperate regions. Difficult to transplant. (PS; HH to H)

Hemerocallis (Daylily). Can be grown on wide range of soils, including dry banks and moist places. Needs frequent transplanting. Can be naturalized in bad places. (If grown in shade or partial shade, the plants lean very badly toward the sun.) (FS to PS; H). H. *fulva* (Tawny Daylily) (6.0–8.0); there are many kinds.

Heuchera (Alumroot). Prefers moist fertile loam soil; not good in clay. Used in rock gardens. (S. to PS; H). H. *sanguinea* (Coralbells) (6.0–7.0).

Hibiscus (Rosemallow). Prefers a moist site but will grow in fairly dry or wet soil. Needs mulch. (S to PS; H). H. *moscheutos* (6.0–8.0).

Hosta (Plantainlily). Moderately to highly fertile moist soil. Useful in wet or moist shady places. (PS to Sh; H). H. *plantaginea* (6.0–7.5).

Hypericum (St. Johnswort). Well drained sandy soil. Useful in rock garden. (PS; H). H. *perforatum* (6.0–8.0).

Iberis (Candytuft). Well drained, moderately fertile moist soil. (S; H). I. *sempervirens* (5.5–7.0).

Iris cristata (5.5–7.0; as low as 4.5). Likes partial shade and fairly moist soil. (S to PS; H)

Iris germanica (6.5–7.5). Needs well drained soil of medium or clayey texture. Can be used in relatively dry rock gardens. (S; H)

Iris kaempferi (5.5–6.5). Needs well drained surface soil, but will endure wet soil beneath. Medium to clayey texture. (S; H)

Iris prismatica (4.5–6.0). (S to PS; H)

Iris sibirica (5.5–6.5?). Same as *I. kaempferi*. Inclined to be a bad robber in mixtures. Also will do quite well in dry places. (S; H)

Iris verna (4.0–5.0). (S to PS; H)

Iris versicolor (5.0–7.5). Likes wet feet. (S to PS; H)

Kniphofia uvaria (Torchlily) (6.0–7.5). Moderately fertile moist sandy loam or loam. (S; HH)

Limonium (Sea-lavender). Moderately fertile sandy soils; not good in clay soils. (S; H). *L. tataricum* (6.0–7.5).

Liatris (Gayfeather). Grows in wide range of soils; prefers moist moderately fertile soil not too rich in clay. (PS to Sh; H). *L. graminifolia* (4.5–5.0); *L. scariosa* (5.0–6.0).

Lobelia cardinalis (Cardinalflower) (5.0–6.0). Prefers moist soil of moderate fertility. Not good in dry places. (PS; H)

Lupinus polyphyllus (Washington Lupine) (6.5–7.5). Moist soil of moderate to high fertility. Little drought or heat tolerance. Hard to transplant. Other species are more acid tolerant. (S to PS; H)

Lysimachia punctata (Spotted Loosestrife) (5.0–7.5?). Grows on almost any kind of soil. Very strong grower and a nuisance on fertile soils. (FS to PS; H)

Mertensia virginica (Virginia Bluebells) (5.5–7.0). Well drained moist fertile soil of medium texture and deep rooting zone. (Sh; H)

Myosotis scorpioides (Forget-me-not) (6.0–8.0). Grows under a wide range of soils. Prefers moist soil of moderate fertility. (S to PS; H)

Oenothera (Evening Primrose). Grows on wide range of moderately fertile, well drained soil. Fair drought tolerance. Good in the rock garden, but a strong grower, and can be a weed. (S; H). *O. fruticosa* (5.0–6.0).

Paeonia albiflora (Chinese Peony) (6.0–7.5). Does best in highly fertile, well drained moist soils of medium texture in full sun. Intolerant of shallow soil or wet subsoil. Needs plenty of room. (FS to PS; H)

Papaver (Poppy). Does well on wide range of moderately fertile soil. Does better on clayey soils than on very sandy ones. Likes moist soil except in semi-dormant midseason, but *P. orientale* does fairly well in dry places. Transplant in August. (FS; H). *P. nudicaule* and *P. orientale* (6.0–7.5).

Penstemon (Beardtongue). Does best in fertile, mellow, well drained moist sandy loam. Intolerant of wet or shallow soil. (S to PS; H to HH). *P. hirsutus* (5.0–7.0); many sorts.

Phlox paniculata (and others) (6.0–8.0). Well drained moderately fertile soil of intermediate texture. Neither very sandy nor very clayey soils are good. Needs moisture but not wet surface soil or subsoil. Especially sensitive to magnesium deficiency. (FS to PS; H)

Phlox subulata (Creeping Phlox or Mosspink) (6.0–8.0). Well drained soil of medium to clayey texture and moderate to high fertility. Good for rock garden without extremes of wet and dry. (FS; H)

Physostegia virginiana (False-dragonhead) (5.0–7.5). Grows on wide range of soils, but prefers moist, well drained loams of moderate fertility. Better on clayey soils than on very sandy ones. Strong grower and can be a nuisance in small gardens. (FS; H)

Platycodon (Balloonflower). Does best on well drained soils of medium texture —sandy loams and loams. Needs winter mulch. (PS; H). *P. grandiflorum* (5.0–6.0).

Primula polyantha (Primrose) (5.5–7.0). Well drained moist soil of high fertility.

Intolerant of drought. Needs some winter mulch. (PS; H). *P. vulgaris* (English Primrose) (5.5–6.5; can go as high as 7.5).

Rudbeckia (Cornflower). Grows well on wide range of moderately fertile lands. (FS and S; H). There are many sorts including biennials. *R. hirta* (Black-eyedsusan) (5.5–7.0).

Salvia farinacea (6.0–7.5). Used on wide range of moderately fertile well drained soils. (S; HH)

Saxifraga virginiensis (6.0–8.0). Mostly for well drained stony hill gardens or rock gardens. Many other sorts. (PS; H)

Scabiosa caucasica, etc. (5.0–7.5?). Well drained soils of moderate to high fertility. Only fairly tolerant of drought. (FS to S; H)

Sedum. Mostly used in rockeries and rocky hill gardens of moderate fertility. Needs good drainage, especially in winter. Good drought resistance. Grows well on very sandy soils but also on clayey ones. (FS to S; H). (*S. sarmentosum* and *S. spurium* grow also in partial shade.) *S. spectabile* (5.5–7.0). Many sorts.

Sempervivum tectorum (Hen-and-chickens) (6.0–8.0). Ideal for rocky hill gardens. Does best with moderate to high fertility and good drainage. Not tolerant of high acidity. Good drought resistance. (FS or S; H). Many other sorts.

Statice pseudoarmeria (6.0–7.5). Grows best in well drained sandy loams of moderate to high fertility. Not good in very clayey or wet soils. (S; HH). Many other sorts.

Stokesia cyanea (Stokes-aster) (6.0–7.5). Well drained, moderately fertile soil of medium texture. Fair drought resistance. Not good for very clayey or wet soils. (FS; H)

Thalictrum (Meadowrue) *T. dipterocarpum* (5.5–7.5). Does best in sun while others grow also in partial shade. Prefers organic-rich, well drained soil with deep rooting zone and moderate fertility. (S to PS; H to HH)

Trollius (Globeflower). Grows in imperfectly drained or swampy to well drained moist soil of moderate to high fertility. Not drought tolerant. Very good for low places. (S to PS; H). *T. europaeus* (5.5–7.0); *T. ledebouri* (5.0–6.0).

Veronica. Needs moist but well drained soil of low to moderate fertility. Low sorts good for rockery. (S; H). *V. spicata* (5.0–6.0); *V. subsessilis* (5.5–7.5).

Viola (Violet). *V. cornuta* does best in highly fertile soil while most other sorts do well in partial shade and only moderately fertile soil. *V. blanda* (6.0–8.0) (PS; H); *V. canadensis* (6.0–8.0) (PS; H); *V. cornuta* (5.5–7.5) (S; H); *V. odorata* (6.0–7.5) (PS; HH); *V. pedata* (5.0–6.0) (PS; H).

Yucca filamentosa (5.5–7.0). Grows well in dry soil of low fertility. Prefers sandy soil but will grow in well drained clayey soil. Excellent drought resistance. Not good for intimate garden. (FS to S; H)

6. *Selected annual flowers*

The probable range in soil pH preferred is given in parentheses after the name. At the end of the paragraph the exposure to sun is suggested by S for full or nearly full sun and PS for partial shade. The numbers following S or PS in parentheses refer to times for planting seed according to the following key: (1) Inside for early plants; (2) outdoors in early spring, about 3 to 5 weeks before frost-free date; (3) outdoors after frost-free date; (4) late summer or early autumn; and (5) late autumn.

Abronia (Sand Verbena) (about 6.0?). Sandy soils. (S; 3, 4)

Ageratum (6.0–7.5). Wide range of moderately fertile well drained soils. (S; 1, 3)

Alyssum (Sweet) (6.0–7.5). Wide range of moderately fertile well drained soils. Useful in the rock garden. (S; 2, 5)

Antirrhinum (Snapdragon) (6.0–7.5). Prefers moderately fertile well drained soil of medium texture. (Where winters are mild, some sorts grow as perennials.) (S; 1, 2, 3, 5)

Calendula (Pot-marigold) (5.5–7.0). Does best in moist, moderately fertile well drained soils, but can grow in rather poor soil. Suffers from strong heat. Tolerates some shade. (S; 1, 2, 3, 5)

Callistephus (China Aster) (6.5–7.0). Does best in well drained sandy loams of moderate fertility, but can be grown in well prepared clayey soils. Not drought tolerant. (S to PS; 1, 3)

Celosia (Cockscomb) (6.0–7.5). Prefers a moderately fertile well drained sandy soil, but can be grown in clayey soils of good structure. (S; 1, 3)

Centaurea (Cornflower) (6.0–6.5). Wide range of well drained soils. Prefers moderate fertility, but can grow on poor garden soil. (PS; 2, 3, 5)

Clarkia (6.0–6.5). Best in well drained, moderately fertile sandy soil. Not tolerant of high heat. (PS or S; 1, 2, 4, 5)

Cleome (Spider Plant) (6.0–6.5?). Moderately fertile sandy soil best. (S to PS; 1, 2, 3, 5)

Convolvulus (Dwarf Morningglory) (6.0–7.0?). Grows well on a wide range of well drained soils. Hard to transplant. (S; 1, 3)

Coreopsis (Calliopsis) (5.0–6.0). Wide range of moderately fertile well drained soils. (S to PS; 1, 2, 3, 5)

Cosmos (5.0–8.0). Wide range of moderately fertile well drained soils. Can become weed. (S to PS; 1, 2–3, 5)

Dahlia (6.0–7.5). Wide range of moderately fertile well drained soils. Can be grown on well prepared clay soil. Phosphorus and potassium should be relatively higher than nitrogen. (Roots can be stored for next season.) (S; 1, 2–3)

Delphinium (Larkspur) (5.5–7.5). Needs moderately to highly fertile, moist soil of medium texture. Not good in high heat. A bit hard to transplant. (S; 1, 2, 5)

Dianthus (China Pink) (6.0–7.5). Wide range of moderately fertile well drained soils. (Many bloom second year if protected in winter.) (S; 1, 2, 3, 5)

Gaillardia (Blanketflower) (6.0–7.5). Wide range of moderately fertile well drained soils of sandy to medium texture. Can be grown on very well prepared granular clay soils. (S; 1, 2, 5)

Gypsophila (Babysbreath) (6.0–7.5). Wide range of moderately fertile well drained soils. Not good on clay soil unless very well prepared. (S; 1, 2, 3)

Helianthus (Sunflower). Wide range of moderately fertile well drained soils. (S; 1, 3)

Iberis (Candytuft) (6.0–7.5). Wide range of moderately fertile well drained soils. Needs some shade in hot regions. (S; 1, 2, 3, 4)

Impatiens (Balsam) (6.0–7.5). Prefers well drained, moist soil of medium texture and high fertility. (S to PS; 1, 3)

Ipomoea (Morningglory) (climber) (6.0–7.5). Grows on wide variety of soils. Can become a nuisance in the intimate garden. (S; 1, 2)

Kochia (Summer-cypress) (5.5–7.5). Wide range of moderately fertile well drained soils. (S; 1, 2, 3)

Lathyrus (Sweet Pea) (6.0–7.5). Cool, moist soil of high fertility and good structure. Not tolerant of drought or heat. Some plant seed in well prepared trenches that are gradually filled as plants grow. Mulches reduce surface soil temperature. (S; 1, 2, 5)

Lupinus (Lupine). Requires somewhat more acid soil than most annual flowers. Does best in cool, moist soil of moderate fertility and medium texture with plenty of organic matter. Not tolerant of high heat. (S to PS; 1, 3). *L. hirsutus* (5.0–6.0); *L. luteus* (5.0–6.0); and *L. hartwegi* (6.0–7.0).

Mathiola (Stock) (6.0–7.5). Does well only in cool moist climates. Prefers soils of medium texture with moderate to high fertility. (S; 1, 3)

Mirabilis (Four-o'clock) (6.0–7.5). Grows on wide range of moderately fertile well drained soils. The roots may be stored over winter. The plant grows as a perennial in tropical regions. (S; 1, 2, 3, 5)

Nicotiana (Flowering tobacco) (5.5–6.5?). Grows on wide range of moderately fertile, slightly to medium acid, well drained soils. (S to PS; 1, 3)

Papaver (Poppy) (6.0–7.5). Grows on wide range of moderately fertile, well drained soils, but does best on sandy loams and loams. Hard to transplant. (S; 1, 2, 3, 5)

Petunia (6.0–7.5). Grows on a wide range of well drained soils but prefers medium textures and moderate to high fertility. (S to PS; 1, 3)

Phlox (Drummond Phlox) (5.5–7.0). Prefers well drained, moderately fertile soils of sandy to medium texture kept well supplied with moisture. (S; 1, 3)

Portulaca (5.5–7.5). Grows on a wide range of soils, including dry sandy soils. Good to fill in bad places in a hill or rock garden. (S; 1, 2, 3, 5)

Ricinus (Castor-bean) (6.0–7.5). Grows on a wide range of well drained soils but prefers moderate to high fertility. Some drought resistance. Excellent for bad places but too big for the intimate garden. (S; 1, 3)

Salpiglossis (6.0–7.5). A bit hard. Does best in sandy loams of moderate fertility. (S to PS; 1, 3)

Salvia (Scarlet sage) (6.0–7.5). Grows on a variety of well prepared soils but prefers sandy loams of moderate fertility. (S; 1, 3)

Scabiosa (4.8–7.5). Grows on a wide range of well drained soils of moderate fertility. (S; 1, 3)

Tagetes (Marigold) (African: 5.5–7.5; French: 5.0–7.5). Although it can be grown on a wide variety of well prepared, well drained soils, it prefers moderately to highly fertile sandy loams and loams. (S; 1, 2, 3)

Tropaeolum (Nasturtium) (Climber) (5.5–7.5). Grows on a wide range of well drained soils of low to moderate fertility. High fertility reduces flowering. (S; 1, 3)

Verbena (6.0–8.0). Seems to do best on moderately to highly fertile well drained soils of medium or clayey texture. (S; 1, 3)

Viola (Pansy) (5.5–6.5). Grows on a wide range of moderately fertile soils. Can be planted in late summer and carried over with winter mulch or in cold frames. Not tolerant of high heat. (S to PS; 1, 4)

Zinnia (5.5–7.5). Grows on a wide range of well drained, moderately to highly fertile soils. Tolerant of heat. Some drought resistance. (S; 1, 2, 3)

7. A *few shrubs*

This list includes only a few.[1] The optimum range in soil pH is given after the name in parentheses at the beginning of the paragraph or after individual species near the end of it. Optimum exposure to sunlight is suggested by the first symbol in parentheses near the end of the paragraph as FS, full sun; S, sun or light shade; PS, partial shade; and Sh, shade. Hardiness is suggested approximately by the second symbol in the parentheses as H, hardy (about Ohio); HH, half hardy (hardy in Washington); and T, tender.

Many groups of shrubs, such as viburnums and cotoneasters, have many species and varieties that vary from one another in soil requirements and in form and color. With some groups the author is uncertain of the best soil pH and can give figures for only a few.

Abelia grandiflora (6.0–8.0). Prefers sandy loams but grows on wide variety of soils including reasonably well prepared clays. Heat tolerant. In Washington and North, tips die back in winter and must be pruned. (FS to PS; H)

Andromeda. Does best in organic-rich soils similar to those for evergreen azaleas. (Sh; H). *A. glaucophylla* (3.0–5.0); *A. polifolia* (Bog-rosemary) (4.5–6.0).

Azalea [2] (4.5–5.0 for most, but for *Mollis* and *Ghents* a bit higher). Most azaleas prefer a well drained, acid, organic-rich sandy loam with good mulch. They have low drought resistance and the evergreen sorts need moisture in winter as well as summer. The *Mollis* grow well in sun. A few deciduous sorts are hardy in the North (*A. viscosa* and *A. schlippenbachi*); and some endure wet feet (*A. austrina* (tender) and *A. viscosa*.) By careful preparation of the soil to produce an acid, organic-rich sandy loam or loam, azaleas may be grown on almost any well drained non-limy soil, where hardy, if kept well mulched with acidic materials. If the natural soil is clay loam or clay, it must be removed and replaced with sandier soil. Azaleas are very sensitive to iron deficiency, showing as chlorosis of growing points and young leaves. Iron deficiency is worsened by lime or anything that increases the soil pH. Excessive applications of phosphorus, and especially of phosphorus and nitrogen together, worsen it. When set out, the soil should be lime-free and acid, and moderately well supplied with phosphorus and other mineral nutrients. Nitrogen may be added in the spring as an organic, such as cottonseed meal, or in spring and early summer in small quantities as ammonium nitrate or sulphate of ammonia. Nitrogen should be low in late summer and autumn to avoid green succulent stems that winter may kill. With good compost added in spring, no other fertilizer is required after planting. The deciduous sorts are, generally, more tolerant of sun than the evergreens. In sun the evergreens

---

[1] For an excellent list see "The Book of Shrubs," by Alfred C. Hottes (428 pp., illus., De La Mare, New York, 1942). The author gives soil notes on many of the plants listed.

[2] These are now commonly included in the genus *Rhododendron*. There are a great many kinds, both evergreen and deciduous. See "Rhododendrons and Azaleas" by C. G. Bowers (549 pp., illus., Macmillan, New York, 1936). Some additional kinds have been developed since this book was published.

are stockier and have smaller flowers; in dense shade the flowers are large but few. Most can be grown in sun or even full sun, but flowers wilt soon and if they also get reflected light from a wall the plants may die. They are more subject to winter injury in sun. Partial, moving shade is best. They can be naturalized well with oaks. Young plants are considerably less cold-hardy than mature ones. (S to Sh; H and HH)

Berberis (Barberry). These grow on a wide variety of well drained soils. The soil should be nearly neutral and well supplied with mineral nutrients. Once established, they are fairly drought resistant. Can be used on strong slopes. (FS to PS; H and HH). *B. thunbergi* (6.0–7.5). The many sorts vary in hardiness. Some fairly hardy, nice ones are evergreen (*B. sargentiana* and *B. julianae*).

Buxus (Box). Require well drained, moderately to highly fertile soil of medium to clayey texture. Near the Philadelphia area and north they are subject to winter injury especially in sun. They are badly burned by winter or summer sun, with poor roots or drought. When moved, they should have the same relative position to the sun, if possible. (S to PS; HH). There are many sorts. *B. sempervirens* (6.0–7.5).

Calluna (Heather) (4.5–6.0). If given good acid mulch, heather can be grown on a wide range of acid soils but prefers peaty or organic-rich soils of medium texture. Likes moisture, but once established is fairly drought resistant if kept mulched.

Calycanthus (Sweetshrub) (6.0–7.0). Does best in moderately to highly fertile, well drained soil of medium to heavy texture. Will endure some poor drainage. Strong grower and a bit too coarse for the small garden. (S to PS; H)

Camellia. These plants are grown in the South, a few as far north as Washington, on well drained, moist, acid, organic-rich sandy loams and loams. The soil requirements are similar to those of azaleas. (PS; T to HH). *C. japonica* (4.5–5.5).

Chaenomeles (Flowering Quince) (6.0–7.0). Grows on a wide variety of well drained soils of moderate fertility. (S to PS; H)

Chionanthus (Fringetree) (5.0–6.0). Does best on well drained but moist, moderately fertile soils of medium texture. (S; H)

Clethra (Sweet Pepperbush) (4.5–5.0). Moist, acid, organic-rich soils are best but will grow on well drained soils of medium texture if not dry. (PS to Sh; H)

Comptonia (Sweetfern) (5.0–6.0). Does best in well drained, organic-rich, light sandy soil of low fertility. Can be used on banks and other dry places if not clayey or limy. (FS to PS; H)

Cornus (Dogwood). Most sorts do best on a slightly acid to neutral soil of good drainage and moderate fertility (except for *C. canadensis*), and will grow in sun or partial shade. Most grow well in strongly acid soil, along with azaleas, rhododendrons, and mountain laurel, with which they may be naturalized. Hottes gives lists for moist places, including *C. stolonifera*, and others for dry places, including *C. baileyi*. (S to Sh; H). *C. canadensis* (4.5–5.5); *C. florida* (5.0–7.0); *C. mas* (6.0–8.0); *C. stolonifera* (6.0–7.0).

Cotoneaster. These grow on a wide variety of moderately fertile, well drained soils. Once established they have fair drought resistance. The dwarf sorts do well in rockeries and hill gardens. There are a great many sorts, some evergreen and some deciduous. (FS, S; H to HH). *C. horizontalis* (6.0–7.0); *C. tomentosa* (6.0–8.0).

Daphne. A bit difficult. Most do best in well drained organic-rich sandy loam. Not good in clay. They can be used in *well* prepared soil in rockery but have little drought resistance. When set out, they need protection from sun. (S; H). *D. cneorum* (6.5–7.5); *D. mezereum* (6.0–7.0).

Deutzia (6.0–8.0 for several varieties). Grow on well drained soils of moderate fertility and prefer those of medium or sandy texture. (S, PS; H)

Elaeagnus. Grow well on a wide range of soils. Especially adapted to dry regions and situations because of their great drought resistance. (FS; H). The many kinds include *E. angustifolia* (Russian-olive) and *E. argentea* (Silverberry) (6.0–7.0).

Erica (Heath). Similar to *Calluna*. (S; H). *E. carnea* (4.5–6.0).

Euonymus. These plants grow well on a wide variety of well drained, moderately fertile soils. More subject to attacks of scale in shade than in partial shade or sun. High nitrogen and moisture in autumn increase winter killing. (S to PS for most; H to HH). *E. radicans,* var. *regata* (Winter creeper) (6.0–7.0).

Forsythia. No shrub grows on a wider range of soils. The soil should be fairly well drained at least, but may be sand or clay. Can be used in bad places including droughty spots. Best results are had with moderate fertility. It has a high drought resistance and is a bad robber of other nearby weaker growers. Must have plenty of room and occasional root pruning in mixed plantings. There are many sorts. (FS to PS; H). *F. intermedia* (6.0–7.5); *F. suspensa* (5.0–6.5).

Fuchsia. Prefers moderately to highly fertile soil of medium texture. Plants are injured by heat or drought and do best where both soil and air are humid. (S to PS; HH). *F. hybrida* (5.5–6.5).

Gardenia (Capejasmine). Grows well on acid, organic-rich sandy loams and loams in the warm southeastern part of the United States. The soil requirements are similar to those of azaleas. (PS; T to HH). *G. veitchi* (5.0–6.0).

Hamamelis (Witchhazel). These grow on a wide range of well to fairly well drained soils of moderate fertility. Fair drought resistance. (PS to S; H). *H. virginiana* (6.0–7.0).

Hibiscus rosa-sinensis (Chinese Hibiscus) (6.0–8.0). Grows best on well drained, moderately to highly fertile soils of medium to clayey texture. Needs good moisture supply. (S, PS; T to HH)

Hibiscus syriacus (Shrubalthea or Rose-of-Sharon) (6.0–7.5). Grows on wide range of moderately fertile soil, including clay soils, but does not do well on light sandy soils. (S, PS; H to HH)

Holodiscus (Rockspirea) (5.5–6.5). Wide range of moderately fertile soils of medium textures. (S; HH)

Hydrangea. Grows on a wide variety of fairly well to well drained soils. Needs moisture. With high fertility plants require much pruning. The several sorts vary somewhat in hardiness and soil requirements. (S to Sh; H to HH). *H. arborescens* (6.0–8.0); *H. grandiflora* (6.0–7.0); *H. macrophylla* (blue) (4.0–5.0); *H. macrophylla* (pink) (6.0–7.0); *H. paniculata* (6.0–7.0).

Hypericum (St. Johnswort). Grows on wide range of soils, but prefers the sandy sorts. Not good on clay. Most kinds want fairly good to good drainage, but *H. densiflorum* can grow with wet feet. (PS; H to HH). *H. patulum* (5.5–7.0).

Ilex (Holly). The hollies grow on a wide range of moderately fertile soils. They prefer sandy loams and loams but can be grown on clayey soils too. *I. crenata* is very good for the intimate garden because it is hardier than box. Once well established, it has fair drought resistance. *I. glabra* and *I. verticillata* also grow in somewhat poorly drained or wet soils. Lime-containing materials need to be avoided. The soil and management requirements approach those of azaleas but these are easier. *I. cassine* (5.0–6.0) (S. Sh; T to HH). *I. crenata* (Japanese Holly) (5.0–6.0) (PS; HH to H). *I. glabra* (Inkberry) (4.5–5.0) (PS; HH). *I. verticillata* (Winterberry) (PS; HH to H).

Kalmia. These plants have soil requirements similar to those of azaleas. *K. angustifolia* will endure wet soil. Kalmias are not tolerant of a high pH and must have relatively sandy soil for good growth. The soil is prepared as for azaleas. They are also subject to chlorosis from iron deficiency, perhaps even more so than azaleas. A deep mulch of acid-organic material is very helpful. Unless well cared for and used with azaleas or other acid-lovers immediately in front of them, they become too coarse and leggy for the small intimate garden. *K. angustifolia* (Sheep-laurel) (4.5–5.0) (S, Sh; HH to H). *K. latifolia* (Mountain-laurel) (4.5–6.0) (PS, Sh; HH to H)

Kolkwitzia (Beautybush) (6.0–7.5). Does best in moderately fertile soil of excellent drainage. (S; H)

Laburnum (Goldenchain tree) (6.0–8.0). Needs a well drained soil of moderate to high fertility and good water-holding capacity. Best in mild northern areas; not good in high heat. (S; H)

Lagerstroemia (Crapemyrtle) (5.0–6.0). Grows on wide range of well drained, non-limy, moderately fertile soils. (S; HH)

Ledum (Labradortea) (3.0–5.0). Prefers cool, moist, very acid peaty and sandy soils in cool regions. Can be used in shady, cool, northern rockeries with well prepared acid sandy soil mixed with peat. Also grows in wet acid peaty soils. (S, PS; H)

Leucothoe (5.0–6.0). This splendid evergreen has about the same cultural requirements as described for azaleas. Useful in moist sandy and peaty soils but can be grown nicely in clayey soils that have been *well* prepared with sand and acid-organic matter. Needs continuous acid mulch. Can be grown on gentle slopes with stones set to hold water so the soil does not dry out. Prefers partial shade but grows in light sun or heavy shade. Dense ground covers should not be permitted to root close to the plants. (S, Sh; HH to H)

Ligustrum (Privet). These shrubs grow on such a wide range of well drained soils that they are popular for city planting in bad situations. Most kinds are quite hardy. (S, PS; H or HH). *L. ovalifolium* (6.0–7.0).

Lonicera (Bush Honeysuckle) (*L. tatarica* and many others) (about 6.5–8.0). These hardy plants grow on a wide range of well drained or fairly well drained soils. For success with the rarer and daintier sorts the soil should be well fertilized with minerals and the plants kept moist and mulched until established. Useful in rock and hill gardens. Best in sun or light shade. They do poorly in heavy shade. (S, PS; H)

Magnolia. Magnolias do best in well drained soils of medium texture and moderate fertility except for *M. glauca*, which prefers wettish soil. Magnolias suffer from drought and should have plenty of moisture. Any lime-containing materials need to be avoided and the plants should have an acid mulch. (S; HH). M. *soulangeana* (Saucer Magnolia) (5.0–6.0); M. *stellata* (Star Magnolia) (5.0–6.0); M. *virginiana* (Sweetbay) (4.0–5.0).

Mahonia aquifolium (Oregongrape) (6.0–8.0). The Oregon hollygrape is, perhaps, the hardiest of the broad-leafed evergreens. It does best on sandy soils, even fairly well on dry sandy soils, but can be grown on well prepared clayey soils. If fertilized with minerals and given a good mulch the plants are nicer. (S, PS; H)

Malus (Flowering crabapple) (6.0–7.5). The many kinds of crabapples grow on a wide range of moderately fertile well drained soils. High fertility should be avoided, otherwise plants are likely to be too big and rangy. They can be used on poor stony areas if carefully established. Adequate phosphorus, potassium, and magnesium should be added and the soil properly limed (if required) at the start. One needs to be sure of magnesium on acid soils. (FS, S; H)

Myrica (Bayberry). Naturally found in acid sandy or peaty and sandy soils. After they are established, they grow on quite dry sandy soils. Said to endure sea spray. Soil requirements are generally similar to those of azaleas. In the South M. *cerifera* is used on wet sandy soils too. M. *cerifera* (Southern Waxmyrtle (4.0–6.0) (S, PS; HH); M. *pensylvanica* (Northern Bayberry) (5.0–6.0) (S, PS; H).

Myrtus (True Myrtle) (6.0–8.0). Does well on wide range of well drained soils but not tolerant of drought. (S; HH)

Nerium (Oleander) (6.0–7.5). Naturally grows in moist places but is used on wide variety of moderately to highly fertile soils of medium to clayey texture that are kept moist. (S; T)

Philadelphus (Mockorange). Does well in wide range of moderately fertile well drained soils. Needs room. (S; H). There are many sorts. P. *coronarius* (6.0–8.0).

Pieris japonica (Lily-of-the-valley-shrub) (4.0–6.0). This excellent broad-leafed evergreen has roughly the same soil requirements as azaleas. It prefers acid, well drained, sandy loams or loams with a heavy mulch of acid-organic material, but properly prepared soil can be made from clayey soils. The roots should not be allowed to become dry. (PS; HH to H)

Prunus. These shrubs grow on a wide range of well drained soils of moderate fertility and sandy to medium texture. Generally not good on clay soils unless quite well prepared. Prepare soils as for *Malus*. (S; H). Flowering almonds (6.0–7.0); Flowering peaches (6.0–7.5); Flowering plums (6.0–7.5).

Pyracantha (Firethorn) (6.0–8.0). Grows in wide range of well drained, moderately fertile soils. Once established, endures some drought. With care can be used in hill gardens. Adequate mineral nutrients are added at the start. (S to PS; HH to H)

Rhamnus (Buckthorn). Grows in wide range of well drained, moderately fertile soil. A bit hard to move. (S, PS; H). R. *cathartica* (6.0–8.0).

Rhododendron (about 4.5–6.0). Rhododendrons have essentially the same soil requirements as those described for azaleas, which see. They prefer well drained but moist acid sandy soil with deep acid-organic mulch. Especially good to naturalize with oaks and dogwoods on acid sloping soils along with low azaleas and acid-loving ground covers. Unless the soil is very well prepared and managed, the plants become too coarse and leggy for the intimate garden. But they can be kept very attractive. They have little drought resistance. (PS; H to HH). *R. maximum* (Rosebay) (4.5–6.0); *R. carolinianum* (4.5–6.0); *R. catawbiense* (5.0–6.0).

Rhus (Sumac). The sumacs are ideal for hillsides of poor soil and other half-wild dry places. Once established they have great drought resistance. Some sucker so freely that they are hard to keep in bounds, especially in fertile soil. *R. copallina* (Flameleaf Sumac) (5.5–7.0) (S; H); *R. glabra* (Smooth Sumac) (5.0–6.0) (S, PS; H); *R. typhina* (Staghorn Sumac) (5.0–6.0) (S; H).

Ribes (Currant). Most sorts grow on a very wide range of moderately fertile well drained soils. They can often be used in steep places under partial shade where few others grow well. (PS; H). *R. sanguineum* (6.0–8.0) (PS; HH).

Rosa (Rose) (about 5.5–7.0 for most). Roses need well drained, fairly loose soils of medium to clayey texture and moderate to high fertility. They do not do well in light sandy soils unless kept well watered. Since it is commonly said that roses like lime and clay, many overdo both. Clay soils are satisfactory if they have good structure and are well drained. They may be improved for roses by digging out the heavy clay to about 30 inches. A 6-inch layer of gravel or coarse cinders may be put down and the soil replaced after mixing with the proper amount of ground dolomitic limestone to reach about pH 6.5, some superphosphate, potash, and organic matter, and enough sand to reduce the texture to at least a clay loam. Water needs to drain freely from the underlying soil. Roses are best transplanted in early winter because of the importance of *firm* contacts of the roots with the soil before any hot days come. Manure, especially fresh cow manure, appears to be the best nitrogen fertilizer, but good compost and a little nitrogen salt can be used. On acid soils where summer days are hot, roses are a bit difficult, especially where the air is humid too. In bright, sunny areas they do as well or better in partial shade as in sun, especially moving shade. Some use too much lime. Roses do well in naturally neutral or mildly alkaline soils. But if the pH of naturally acid soils is raised to pH 7.5 or higher, the balance among nutrients is likely to be upset. (See chapter on *Soil acidity and how to change it.*) If dolomitic limestone is not available, ordinary liming materials need magnesium sulphate added. (S; H to HH)

Rubus (Flowering Raspberry) (5.0–6.0). Prefers moist, highly fertile soil, either well drained or poorly drained. Good for naturalizing in a big garden but too coarse and suckers too much for the intimate garden. (S, PS; H)

Shepherdia (Buffaloberry) (6.0–8.0). A very hardy shrub for northern areas. It grows on a wide range of soils of medium texture. Once established, it has good drought resistance. (FS to PS; H)

Spiraea (about 6.0–7.0). Most of the spiraeas do well on a wide range of well drained soils of low to moderate fertility. Some sorts, such as *S. tomentosa* (Hardhack), also grow in wet places. This same one can also be used on steep banks. Once established, most sorts endure ordinary drought without watering. Although good for naturalizing and for the large garden, most are a bit large and coarse for the intimate garden. But they are easy to grow. (S, PS; H)

Symphoricarpos (Snowberry). Can be grown on steep banks, but does better in moderately fertile, well drained soil. One of the few shrubs for winter color (berries) on rather poor soil in the shade. (S, PS; H). *S. microphyllus* (Pink S.) (6.0–7.0); *S. orbiculatus* (Coralberry) (5.5–7.5).

Syringa (Lilac) (6.0–7.5), for most. Lilacs grow well on a wide variety of well drained moderately to highly fertile soils. They do very poorly in acid sandy soils of low fertility. (S; H)

Taxus (Yew). *T. canadensis*, or ground hemlock (5.0–6.0), grows on a wide variety of acid soils. It is good for rock and hill gardens. (S to Sh; H). *T. cuspidata* (6.0–7.0) has many forms including shrubs, trees, and slow-growing trees that may be held as shrubs by pruning. They require a moderately fertile soil of good drainage, but one able to keep the plants well supplied with moisture.

Tsuga (Hemlock) (5.0–6.0). These plants are, of course, trees that reach a great size. But by pruning they may be kept small and compact, and are useful as tall shrubs. Except for *Taxus*, hemlock is the only evergreen tree that the ordinary gardener can keep to size with pruning. It is not too particular in its soil requirements. The soil should be acid and moderately moist. Great variations in subsoil moisture from wet to dry are bad for hemlock. (S, PS; H)

Viburnum. There are a great many sorts of viburnum. Most of the unlisted sorts probably grow best in soils of about pH 6.5, except V. *nudum*, which needs more acid soil. Both V. *dentatum* and V. *lentago* can be used in wet places under light sun to partial shade.

Viburnum acerifolium (Mapleleaf V.) (4.0–5.0). Does well on moderately fertile, acid, light sandy soils or those of medium texture. Has fair drought resistance and does well under trees. (PS, Sh; H)

Viburnum alnifolium (Hobblebush) (5.0–6.0). For moderately fertile acid soils of medium texture and good drainage. (S, PS; H)

Virburnum lantana (Wayfaringtree) (5.0–7.0). Grows on a wide variety of moderately fertile, well drained soils, including dry soils. (S; H)

Virburnum opulus (Cranberrybush) (6.5–7.5). Grows on wide variety of moderately fertile, well drained soils. Less acid tolerant than most. Not good for the small garden. (PS; H)

Virburnum tomentosum (Japanese Snowball) (6.5–7.5). Grows on wide variety of moderately fertile, well drained soils. (S; H to HH)

Weigela (6.0–7.0 for W. *florida*). Does best in moderately to highly fertile, well drained soil from sandy loam to clay loam. A bit too big and coarse for the small garden. (S; H)

Zanthorhiza (Yellowroot) (5.0–6.0). Does best on moist acid soil of moderate to high fertility as along streams (PS, Sh; H)

Zenobia (5.0–6.0 for Z. *pulverulenta*). Prefers moist, but well drained, acid, organic-rich sandy loam or loam like that best for azaleas and rhododendrons. (PS, Sh; H)

8. *Vines*

This small selection does not include the host of vines suitable for tropical and subtropical regions or for the glasshouse.

The small letter following the name indicates type: *w*, woody; *p*, perennial; and *a*, annual. The figures in parentheses that follow indicate optimum range in soil pH. The first letter in parentheses at the end of the paragraph suggests exposure: FS, full sun; S, sun and light shade; PS, partial shade; and Sh, shade. The second letter suggests hardiness of perennial sorts: H, hardy (about Boston); HH, half hardy (hardy for Washington, D.C., and south); and T, tender.

Actinidia arguta (Tara Vine) *w* (6.0–7.0?). Well drained, moderately to highly fertile soil. Not good in high heat. (S, PS; HH to H)

Akebia quinata (Fiveleaf Akebia) *w* (6.0–7.0?). Does well on wide range of moderately fertile, well drained soils, including well prepared clays. (FS to PS; H)

Ampelopsis brevipedunculata (Porcelain A.) *w* (6.0–7.0?). Well drained soil of medium texture and well prepared clayey soils. (S; H)

Aristolochia durior (Dutchmanspipe) *w* (6.5–8.0?). Moderately to highly fertile soil of medium texture to clay. (PS; H). Other tender and half-hardy sorts.

Bougainvillea (Bougainvillea vine) *w* (*B. spectabilis*) (5.5–7.5). Grows on wide range of well drained soils in tropical and subtropical regions. When established, can endure water and drought. More beautiful with high fertility; more hardy with low fertility. (FS, S; T, and such a pity!)

Calonyction aculeatum (Moonflower) *a* (6.0–7.5?). Well drained moderately to highly fertile soils. Needs good supply of water. (S)

Campsis chinensis (Chinese Trumpetcreeper) *w* (6.0–7.0). Highly fertile soil, well drained and rich in organic matter, is best. (S; H)

Celastrus scandens (American Bittersweet) *w* (4.5–6.0). Grows on a wide variety of well drained soils of low to high fertility. Responds well to moderate fertilization, but lime should be avoided. A *serious* robber of other plants. It is a bit too coarse and needs too much room for the small garden. If used near fine shrubs, the roots must be pruned frequently. (FS, S; H)

Clematis w (many sorts). Prefer moderately to highly fertile well drained sandy loams or loams but can be grown on well prepared clayey soils. They need a large rooting space, both laterally and in depth. The plants have little drought resistance. Many sorts prefer shade on the lower part of the plant. Should be well mulched to keep roots cool. (FS, S; H). *C. crispa* (5.5–6.5); *C. jackmani* (5.5–7.0); *C. paniculata* (6.0–7.0).

Dolichos lablab (Hyacinthbean) *a* (6.0–7.5). Seeds may be sown on frost-free date in well drained soil of moderate fertility. Plants very hard to transplant. (FS, S)

Euonymus (Wintercreeper) *w*. See list of shrubs.

Gourds, ornamental *a* (most about 6.0–7.0). Seeds may be sown on frost-free date in well drained soil of moderate to high fertility. They need much room and are too coarse for the intimate garden. (FS, S)

Hedera helix (English ivy) (many varieties) *w* (6.0–8.0). Prefers moderately to highly fertile, well drained soil of medium to heavy texture. If carefully established, English ivy does well under adverse conditions. Young plants should be set in soil properly limed and well fertilized with phosphorus. In sunny places they should be artificially shaded the first year. On banks the stems should be tipped in to get a mass of roots to hold water and prevent soil erosion under the stems. Once well established, they have good resistance to drought. When used in mixtures, both roots and stems must be kept pruned or the ivy will choke other fine shrubs and perennials.

It is easy to get new plants by tipping in stems. For well rooted plants to put in steep banks, it is best to root them within sunken flowerpots. The gardener must remember that young plants will not endure drought or bright sun. (FS to Sh; HH to H)

Humulus japonicus (Japanese Hop) *a* (6.0–7.5). Seed may be sown in late autumn or early spring in a wide variety of well drained soils. Although tolerant of low soil fertility, heat, and drought, the plants respond to moderate fertilization and watering. Supports must be elastic; otherwise the plants "pull themselves out by the roots." (FS, S)

Hydrangea petiolaris (Climbing Hydrangea) *w* (6.0–7.0?). Need deep, fertile, organic-rich soil of medium texture or well prepared clayey soil. Young plants need winter protection. (S, PS; HH to H)

Ipomoea (Morningglory). See list of annuals.

Lathyrus latifolius (Perennial Pea) *p* (5.0–6.5). Grows well in moderately fertile, well drained soil. Can be used on banks, over old stumps and logs, and on low fences. (FS, S; H). (For *L. odoratus*, Sweet Pea, see list of annuals.)

Lonicera (Honeysuckle) *w* (most about 6.0–7.5). These grow on a very wide variety of well to fairly well drained soils. They are excellent for steep banks and semiwild hills. If used in the small garden or in combination with other plants, both roots and stems *must* be kept pruned or other fine plants will be overrun. To prevent erosion on banks, stems must be tipped in to get thick root mat. Two examples include: *L. japonica* (Japanese H.) (S, PS; H); *L. sempervirens* (Trumpet H.) (PS; H).

Lycium halimifolium (Matrimonyvine) *w* (6.0–8.0). Same as for *Lonicera*, except not tolerant of wet places. (S; H)

Lygodium palmatum (Climbing Fern) *p* (4.0–5.0). Requires an acid, organic-rich, sandy moist soil. Prefers high temperatures and humidity. (PS, Sh; H)

Menispermum canadense (Common Moonseed) *p* to *w* (5.0–7.5). Grows on wide range of moderately fertile, well to fairly well drained soils. Used in semiwild places. (S, PS; H)

Parthenocissus w. These grow on a wide range of well drained soils, but do best on well fertilized ones. *P. quinquefolia* (Virginia creeper) (5.0–7.5) (S, PS; H); *P. tricuspidata* (Boston Ivy) (6.0–8.0) (FS to Sh; H).

Phaseolus multiflorus (Scarlet Runner Bean) *a* (6.0–7.5). Grows on a wide range of well drained soils but responds well to fertilization. Needs moist soil because it lacks drought resistance. (FS, S)

Polygonum auberti (China Fleecevine) *w* (6.0–7.5). Grows on a very wide variety of well drained soils and under adverse conditions. (FS to PS; H)

Pueraria thunbergiana (Kudzuvine) *p* (about 5.5–7.0). Although kudzuvine prefers clayey soils, it can grow in most any well drained soil if the roots are set deeply in soil fertilized with minerals. Once established, the plants have fair to good drought resistance. They are rapid growers and need careful training and pruning if used in the small garden or they overrun other plants, even large shrubs and small trees. With care in setting the crowns, fertilization, and early watering, kudzuvine is excellent for dry clay banks. Not good for the intimate garden except as trained on porch or definite trellis. As with other vines, ends must be tipped in repeatedly if they are to control soil erosion on steep banks. (FS, S; HH to H)

Tropaeolum (Nasturtium). See list of annuals.

Vitis labrusca (Fox grapes) *w* (5.5–7.0). Grow on moderately fertile, well drained soils. Useful in semiwild garden or under adverse conditions. (S to Sh; H)

Wistaria floribunda (Japanese Wistaria) *w* (6.0–8.0). Requires well drained, moderately fertile soil of medium texture with plenty of room for the roots, both laterally and in depth. They require moisture, especially for flowering. (FS, S; H)

9. Ground covers

The small selection that follows is confined mostly to hardy sorts. The small letter immediately after the name indicates the type: *p*, herbaceous perennial or creeper; *s*, low shrub; and *v*, woody creeper. Figures for the probable optimum soil pH are given in parentheses.

The first letter in parentheses at the end of each paragraph indicates optimum exposure: FS, full sun; S, sun or light shade; PS, partial shade; and Sh, shade. The second letter suggests hardiness: H, hardy (about Boston to Columbus, Ohio); HH, only hardy for about Washington, D.C., and south; and T, tender.

Aegopodium podagraria (Goutweed) *p* (about 6.0–7.0). Grows on a wide range of soils, including dry sunny or shady spots. Responds to good fertility. Useful in places where grass will not grow. (S, PS; H)

Ajuga reptans (Carpet Bugle) *p* (6.0–7.5). Grows on a wide variety of soils including places too shady for grass. May become a weed in the rockery. (S, PS; H)

Akebia quinata (Fiveleaf Akebia) *v*. See list of vines.

Arctostaphylos uva-ursi (Bearberry) *v* (4.5–6.0). Prefers well drained sandy soil. Grows well in cold northern areas. Good for sandy or rocky slopes. (S, PS; H)

Arenaria verna caespitosa (Moss Sandwort) *p* (about 6.5–7.5). Prefers moderately fertile, well drained soils of medium texture. Good between stepping stones but can become a weed in the rockery. (S, PS; H)

Asarum canadense (Canada Wild Ginger) *p*. (6.0–8.0). Moderately to highly fertile, moist soils. (S, PS; H)

Calluna. See list of shrubs.

Convallaria (Lily-of-the-valley). See list of perennials.

Cornus canadensis (Bunchberry) *p* (4.5–5.5). Needs cool, moist soil of low to moderate fertility. Cannot endure heat, so used only in northern regions and in the mountains. (PS, Sh; H)

Coronilla varia (Crownvetch) *p* (about 6.0–7.5?). Grows on wide variety of well drained, non-acid soils, including steep banks. Too near a weed for the small garden, perennial beds, or rockery. (S, PS; H)

Dennstaedtia punctilobula (Hayscented Fern). See list of ferns.

Epigaea repens (Trailing-arbutus) *v* (4.5–6.0). Must have organic-rich, acid, sandy soil of only moderate fertility. It cannot be transplanted from the wild, but plants can be had from seeds planted in pots. (S, PS; H)

Euonymus fortunei (Wintercreeper). See list of shrubs.

Euphorbia cyparissias (Cypress-spurge) *p* (about 6.0–7.5?). Grows on a wide variety of soils. Not recommended for the garden since it becomes a *very* serious weed in moderately fertile soil. Should be kept out of the rockery and mixed plantings. (S; H)

Galax aphylla p (4.5–6.0). Prefers moderately fertile, moist, acid soil like that required for rhododendrons and azaleas. A little difficult. (S to Sh; H)

Gaultheria procumbens (Wintergreen) *s* (4.5–6.0). Prefers moderately fertile, moist, acid soil like that required for rhododendrons and azaleas. (S to Sh; H)

Gazania longiscapa p (5.5–7.0). Good for dry sunny places on well drained soils of moderate fertility. In the North can be used as an annual. (FS, S; T to HH)

Hedera helix (English ivy). See list of vines. One of the best for sun or shade if kept pruned.

Helianthemum (Sunrose). See list of shrubs.

Juniperus (Juniper: low spreading sorts such as *J. horizontalis* and *J. cummunis depressa*) *s* (5.0–6.0). Grow on wide range of soils. Not good for the small garden. (S, PS; HH to H)

Leiophyllum buxifolium (Box Sandmyrtle) *s* (4.0–6.0). Prefers sandy organic-rich, moist soil like that for azaleas. A bit difficult to grow. (S, PS; H to HH)

Linnaea borealis (Northern Twinflower) *p* (4.0–5.0). Very difficult. Requires cool, acid, moist, organic-rich soil. Can be grown in remains of old logs and stumps. (PS, Sh; H)

Lonicera japonica. See list of vines.

Lycopodium (Clubmoss) *L. complanatum* or Groundcedar (4.0–6.0) and *L. obscurum* or Groundpine (4.5–6.5). Needs moderately fertile, moist, acid, organic-rich soil. (PS, Sh; H)

Lysimachia nummularia p (about 5.5–7.0?). Grows on a very wide variety of soils from very sandy to clay and from wet to dry. Does best in moist, highly fertile soil. It should be used only in wet places, in very shady spots, or on steep banks, as it becomes a *serious* pest in mixed plantings on fertile soil and in thin lawns. But for bad places it is splendid, especially if fertilized a little, partly because it grows so fast. Best not to use it in a good, fertile rockery, but all right for semiwild gardens and in wet places. (FS to Sh; H)

Nepeta glecoma h. (Groundivy) *p.* (about 5.5–7.0?). Grows on a wide range of soils but prefers moderately fertile, moist places. Becomes a serious weed in the small garden. Should be used only in semiwild hill gardens and in shady places. (S to Sh; H)

Pachysandra terminalis (Japanese-spurge) *s* (4.5–5.5, but will do quite well up to 6.5). One of the very best. Can be used with the acid-tolerant shrubs. It does best on moderate to highly fertile, moist soils of medium texture but will make good growth on well prepared clay loams. It can grow in full sun, but is much nicer in partial shade. Can do well in only slightly acid soils but should not have lime. It will endure wet and some drought, although it does poorly with both sun and drought. It needs to be kept pruned away from the weak growers, including young azaleas. This is better than English ivy in mixed plantings because it does not grow up into the shrubs and requires less cutting back. It is easily transplanted. (S to Sh; HH to H)

Phlox subulata. See list of perennials.

Rubus hispidus (Swamp Dewberry) *s* (5.0–6.0). Grows in poorly drained acid soils. (S, PS; H)

Taxus canadensis. See list of shrubs.

Thymus serpyllum (Mother-of-thyme) s, p (5.5–7.0). Grows on moderately fertile, well drained soil. (S; H)

Veronica rupestris (Speedwell) p (5.5–7.5). Does well in moderately fertile, well drained soil. (S; H)

Vinca minor (Periwinkle or Myrtle) v, p (6.0–7.5). An excellent ground cover that grows under a wide range of conditions. It prefers a moderately to highly fertile soil. In mixed plantings it *must* be kept away from the weak growers. Very useful in heavy shade and in semirough hill gardens. Nice in the rockery if kept in check. A bit of a nuisance in mixed plantings. (S to Sh; H)

Xanthorhiza (Yellow root). See list of shrubs.

10. Bulbs

Some tubers and roots are included here and some in the perennial list. The optimum soil pH is given in parentheses after the plant name. Some are uncertain. After each description a key is given to: (1) season of bloom, (2) hardiness, (3) exposure, and (4) planting depth, in that order and according to the following notations:

(1) Season: SP, spring flowering; SU, summer flowering.

(2) Hardiness: For region about like Boston to Washington, D.C. —H, hardy; HH, half hardy and need winter protection; T, tender and should be lifted and stored.

(3) Exposure: FS, full sun; S, sun or very light shade; PS, partial shade; Sh, shade.

(4) Planting depth: approximate depth in inches to the *top* of the bulb or root in soil of medium texture. Planting depths should be somewhat deeper in sands and somewhat shallower in clayey or clay soils. In most clayey soils holes should be made and refilled with a sandy, organic-rich, well prepared soil so that bulbs have beneath them this soil of medium to high fertility in mineral plant nutrients and the correct soil pH.

Thus the key in parentheses after the notes on dahlia, "(SU; T; FS, S; 5)," means "summer flowering; tender; full sun or very light shade; and planting depth of 5 inches."

Amaryllis (Belladonna Lily) (5.5–6.5). Prefers deep sandy loam, say along a south-facing wall. Tender in northern areas. Moved after flowering. (SU; H to T; FS, S; 7)

Anemone. Hardy south of Washington and planted in fall; tender in North and planted in spring. Well drained, organic-rich, sandy soil. A. *coronaria* (about 6.5?) (SP; HH to T; PS; 3½); A. *nemorosa* (4.0–6.5) (SP; H; PS; 3).

Begonia (tuberous) (5.5–6.5?). Usually started inside in a mixture of good garden soil, sphagnum peat, and sand with some manure and superphosphate. (See discussion of potting soil.) Moved to well prepared, sandy, organic-rich soil in partial shade after frost-free date. Must be moist and protected from wind. In late summer, allowed to dry and roots are lifted and stored in sand in cool room above freezing. (SU; T; PS; 2)

Caladium (Elephant's Ear) (6.0–7.5). Planted 2 or 3 weeks after frost-free date in well prepared granular soil of high fertility. Needs lots of water. Too big and coarse for the intimate garden. (SU; T; FS, S; 2)

Calla (6.0–7.0). Dormant bulbs are planted inside in 6-inch pots just below surface of fertile soil and planted outside after frost-free date. After growth is well started much water is needed. (SP; T; S; 1)

Camassia (Camass) (6.0–8.0). Grows in moderately fertile soil of medium texture. Can stand nearly full shade under deciduous trees. (SP; H; S, PS; 3)

Canna (6.0–8.0). Planted out after frost-free date. Grows on wide range of well drained moderately to highly fertile soil. Will do well in clay soil with abundant organic matter and high fertility. Nitrogen should never be relatively higher than mineral nutrients. For maximum growth *canna* needs plenty of water but resists drought fairly well on well prepared soil. (SU; T; S; 2)

Chionodoxa (Glory-of-the-snow) (about 6.5?). Moderately fertile well drained but moist soil. Stands nearly full deciduous shade. Planted in autumn. (SP; H; S, PS; 3)

Colchicum (Autumn-crocus) (About 6.5?). Planted in early autumn or late summer on moderately fertile, well drained soil. Not valuable in the small garden. (SU; H; S, PS; 3)

Crocus (6.0–8.0). Planted in early autumn in well drained, moderately fertile soil. Prefers sandy soil but does well on clayey soils carefully prepared with sand and compost. A bit of phosphatic fertilizer may be put under the bulb for the roots to grow into. Does not endure poor drainage. Can grow with deciduous trees and shrubs if it gets spring sun. (SP; H; S; 2)

Daffodil. See *Narcissus.*

Dahlia (6.0–7.5). Tubers are planted about 2 weeks after the frost-free date in well drained soil of high fertility in phosphorus and potassium, and medium fertility in nitrogen. Prefer sandy loams and loams but can be grown in more clayey soil by thorough spading to 12 to 18 inches and mixing in sand, compost, mineral fertilizer, and ground limestone (if required). The plants require stakes and these should be put in solidly before or during planting. The top of the tuber should be roughly 4 to 6 inches below the surface in a well prepared hole and covered only 2 inches. After growth starts, the hole is gradually filled. Dahlias need plenty of moisture but good drainage. After the plants are started, the soil should be well mulched to reduce temperature and hold moisture. Even in sandy soils the soil needs to be spaded and properly fertilized to 15 inches. Although the plants require moderate to high fertility, excess nitrogen in relation to the mineral plant nutrients must be avoided. The ordinary sorts need much room. The dwarfs are better for the small garden. (SU; T; FS, S; 5)

Eranthis (Winter Aconite) (about 7.0?). Planted in early autumn on moderately to highly fertile, well drained soil. Grows under deciduous shade in rockery or with shrubs. (SP; H; S, PS; 2½)

Eremurus (Desert Candle) (about 6.0–6.5?). Planted in autumn in well drained soil of medium fertility and texture and given winter protection. Hard to move. (SU; HH; PS, S; 5)

Erythronium (Dogtooth Violet) (5.0–6.0). Well drained but moist soils of moderate fertility and light sandy loam to loam texture. Use acid-forming mulch. (SP; HH; PS; 4)

Fritillaria (6.0–7.5). Well drained deep soil of moderate to high fertility. (SP; H; PS; 3)

Galanthus (Snowdrop) (6.0–8.0). Well drained, moderately fertile, moist soil. Likes deciduous but not evergreen shade. (SP; H; PS; 3)

Galtonia (Summer Hyacinth) (6.5–7.5). Planted in spring, in North, in moderately to highly fertile, well drained soils of light sandy loam to loam texture. Hardy in New York with heavy mulch. (SU; HH; PS; 6)

Gladiolus (6.0–7.0). Planted out about 2 or 3 weeks before frost-free date in well drained, moderately fertile soil. Sandy soils are best, but gladiolus can be grown in well prepared clay soils of good drainage in which manure, peat, or compost has been deeply spaded. Excess nitrogen in relation to mineral nutrients must be avoided. The plants do not like high heat. Mulches help. In sandy soils, the bulbs may be set deeply—to 6 or 7 inches. This reduces temperature of the roots and gives sturdier plants. These are better in cool or temperate areas than in warm-temperature ones. (SU; T to HH; FS, S; 4)

Hemerocallis. See perennial list.

Hyacinth (Common) (about 6.5–7.0?). Planted in early autumn in moderately fertile, well drained sandy soil or clayey soils well prepared to 20 inches with sand pockets under the bulbs. Best results are had by lifting them after the foliage is dead, storing in a cool dry place and then resetting. Most gardeners may do best with new bulbs each year. (SP; H; FS, S; 4)

Iris (bulb) (about 6.0?). Grows in a wide range of moderately fertile, well drained soils with good mulch. Good in rockeries. The Dutch and Spanish sorts are planted late in autumn and the English varieties early. (SP; H; PS; 4)

Iris (rhizomes). See perennial list.

Jonquil. See *Narcissus.*

Lilium. Lilies are planted in autumn as soon as the bulbs are mature or as can be obtained. Most prefer well drained loam or silt loam soils but can be grown in well prepared clayey soils of good structure. Few are good in sands or very light sandy loams. Mineral nutrients should be plentiful in relation to nitrogen. Manure needs to be used sparingly because of the danger of excess nitrogen. Plants may be supplied phosphorus and potash beneath the bulbs when set out. Lilies have little drought resistance. Good mulch holds moisture and reduces temperature.

L. *auratum* (Goldband Lily) (5.0–6.0). Requires well drained, organic-rich soil. (SU; H; S, SP; 4)

L. *canadense* (Canada Lily) (6.0–7.0). Wide variety of moist, well drained soils. (SU; H; S, PS; 4)

L. *candidum* (Madonna Lily) (6.5–7.5). Well drained, moderately fertile sandy loam best. Likes winter mulch. A bit uncertain. (SU; HH; S; 3)

L. *carolinianum* (Carolina Lily) (5.0–6.0). Well drained sandy soil. Can endure dry soil. (SU; H; S to PS; 4)

L. *grayi* (Grays L.) (5.0–6.0). Wide variety of well drained moderately fertile soil. (SU; H; S, PS; 5)

L. *hansoni* (Hanson Lily) (5.0–6.0). Wide variety of well drained, moderately fertile soil. (SU; H; S, PS; 5)

L. *henryi* (Henry or Yellow Show Lily) (about 6.5?). Moderately to highly fertile, well drained soil. (SU; H; PS; 9)

L. *philadelphicum* (Wood L.) (5.0–6.0). Moderately to highly fertile, well drained soil. (SU; H; S to PS; 5)

L. regale (Regal L.) (6.0–7.0). Moderately fertile soil of good structure. Suffers from drought. (SU; H; S; 9)

L. speciosum (6.0–7.0). Moderately fertile soil of good structure. Suffers from drought. (SU; H; S; 9)

L. superbum (Turkscap Lily) (5.0–6.0). Moderately fertile, moist soil of good structure. (SU; H; S to PS; 6)

L. tigrinum (Tiger Lily) (6.0–7.0). Wide variety of moderately fertile, well drained soils. (SU; H; S; 9)

Muscari (Grapehyacinth) (6.0–7.5). Moderately fertile, well drained sandy loam or well prepared clay loam. Endures deciduous shade but not evergreen. Naturalizes well in rockery. (SP; H; S; 2)

Narcissus (about 6.5?). Narcissi do well on a wide range of moderately fertile, well drained soils. They like moisture but will do well on slopes and in the rockery. The soil should be highly fertile in phosphorus and potash and moderately so in nitrogen. They can be naturalized with acid-lovers, like rhododendrons, below their optimum soil pH, by placing a tablespoon of superphosphate an inch below the bulb. Large masses of bulbs need to be dug and reset. They are planted in early autumn. They are best in semi-permanent plantings along with mulched shrubs and perennials or natural-ized in the partly open woods. (SP; H; S, PS; 4). *N. pseudon-narcissus* (5.5–6.5); *N. tazetta* (6.0–7.5) is only half hardy.

Polianthes (Tuberose) (6.0–7.0). Put out about frost-free date in well drained granular soil of moderate to high fertility, lift in the autumn, and store in sand. Avoid high nitrogen in soil relative to mineral nutrients. They can be grown in clayey soils but are late. (SU; T; FS, S; 1)

Scilla (Squill) (6.0–8.0). Grows on wide range of well drained, moderately fertile soil. Naturalizes well, even with evergreens if shade is not too dense. (SP; H; S, PS; 6 for *S. campanulata* and 4 for *S. sibirica.*)

Tritonia (Montbretia) (about 6.5?). Grows in deep, moderately fertile soil as for gladiolus. Does not endure cold or heat. In mild climates with cool summers, it may be best to lift, store, and plant after frost-free date in spring. (SU; HH; S; 3)

Trillium. Several *Trillium* species are often included in the wild flower garden, but they are excellent under shrubs in mixtures. They naturalize very well in moist, moderately to highly fertile soil with mulch, as in the woods. The flowers should not be picked. Both *T. grandiflorum* and *T. undulatum* can be used with the acid-loving shrubs. (SP; H; PS, Sh; 2 to 3). *T. erectum* (Wakerobin T.) (7.0–7.5); *T. grandiflorum* (Large-flowering T.) (5.0–6.5); *T. undulatum* (Painted T.) 4.5–6.0).

Tulipa (Tulip) (about 6.0–7.0). Tulips prefer a moderately fertile, well drained soil. They should have a rich supply of mineral nutrients and moderate nitrogen. Light sandy loams to loams are best, although they may be grown in more clayey soils if well prepared and well drained. Most clay soils are too wet in the subsoil for best results and the bulbs "run out." Many lift them after the tops die down and store them in wood ashes or sand for late autumn planting. Most gardeners, and especially those with clay soils, use new bulbs each autumn. (SP; H; S; 5 to 6)

11. Ferns

The figures in parentheses immediately after the name give the pre-ferred range in soil pH. The symbols in parentheses at the end of each paragraph suggest the optimum exposure: FS, full sun; S, sun or light shade; PS, partial shade; and Sh, shade.

Most ferns, like many other perennials, should be mulched, but not directly over the crowns.

Adianthum pedatum (Maidenhair Fern) (6.0–8.0). Moderately to highly fertile soil with good mulch. Mostly in North, but native in South. (S to PS)

Asplenium septentrionale (5.0–6.0). Wide range of soils, from moist to dry after established, if mulched. (S to Sh)

Athyrium (Lady-fern). Wide range of moist soils from acid (pH 4.5) to mildly alkaline with acid mulch. (S, PS). *A. angustum* (6.0–7.0); *A. asplenioides* (5.5–7.5).

Botrychium ternatum (Grapefern) and *B. virginianum* (Rattlesnake Fern) (5.0–6.0). Moist soil with mulch. (PS)

Camptosorus rhizophyllus (Walking Fern) (6.0–8.5). Needs moist to wet soil. Can endure moderate acidity in fertile soil. (PS)

Cystopteris bulbifera (Bladder Fern) (6.5–8.0). Moist soil with mulch. (PS)

Dennstaedtia punctilobula (Hayscented Fern) (4.0–7.0). Well drained soil, acid to neutral, moist to dry. (S, PS)

Dryopteris. Besides the examples which follow there are many others. They may be listed under *Aspidium* or *Thelypteris.*

D. *filixmas* (Malefern) (6.0–8.0). Moderately to highly fertile, moist soil. (PS, Sh)

D. *hexagonoptera* (Broad Beechfern) (6.5–7.5). Well drained soils. (PS, Sh)

D. *intermedia* (Fancy Fern) (6.0–7.0). Well drained soils. (PS, Sh)

D. *noveboracensis* (New York Fern) (4.0–7.0). Moderately fertile, well drained soil, but does not stand mulch over the crowns. (S, PS)

D. *cristata* (Crested Woodfern) (5.0–7.0). Well drained soil. (S, PS)

D. *goldiana* (Giant Woodfern) (6.0–8.0). Moderately to highly fertile, moist soil. Does not like heat. (PS, Sh)

D. *marginalis* (Leather Woodfern) (6.0–7.5). Well drained, moist soil. (PS, Sh)

D. *spinulosa* (Toothed Woodfern) (4.5–6.0). Well drained, moist soil. (PS, Sh)

Onoclea sensibilis (Sensitive Fern) (5.5–7.5). Moderately fertile, moist soil. Can become a weed. (PS)

Osmunda

O. *cinnamomea* (Cinnamon Fern) (4.5–5.5). Prefers moist, acid, organic-rich sandy soil. Slow to start. (PS, Sh)

O. *claytoniana* (Interrupted Fern) (5.0–7.0). Like O. *cinnamomea,* but will grow in somewhat drier soil. (PS, Sh)

O. *regalis* (Royal Fern) (4.0–6.0). Soil requirements as for O. *cinnamomea;* can be used in swampy places. (PS)

Pellaea atropurpurea (Purple Cliffbrake) (6.0–8.0). Shallow, neutral soil. Excellent for limestone rockery. (S, PS)

Polypodium vulgare (Common Polypody) (5.5–8.0). Well drained soil, moist or dry. (S to Sh)

Polystichum acrostichoides (Christmas Fern) (6.0–7.5). Well drained, fertile soil, moist or dry. (S to Sh)

Pteridium aquilinum (Bracken) (4.5–6.0). Any well drained, acid soil. Can become a bad weed in plantings of azaleas and rhododendrons. (S to Sh)

Pteretis nodulosa (Ostrich Fern) (6.5–7.5). Fertile soil of intermediate texture, moist to nearly swampy. (PS)

Woodsia obtusa (6.5–8.0). Well drained, moderately fertile soil. (PS)

Woodwardia areolata (Chainfern) and W. *virginica* (Virginia Chainfern) (4.0–6.0). For W. *areolata*, well drained, moist, moderately fertile soil. For W. *virginica*, moderately fertile soil, normally moist soil of garden or in wet places. (PS)

III

PLANTING SUGGESTIONS AND

Vegetable	Planting season [1]	Planting distances [2] between		Depth to cover seed or roots [4]
		Rows	Plants or hills in row [3]	
		(Inches)	(Inches)	(Inches)
Asparagus	7	30	18	8
Beans, lima (bush)	4	28	4	1½
Beans, lima (pole)	4	36	24	1½
Beans, snap (bush)	3	28	3	1½
Beans, snap (pole)	3	36	24	1½
Beets	2, 6	15	3	¾
Broccoli [7]	1, 5	30	18	½
Brussels sprouts	1, 5	30	18	½
Cabbage	1, 5	30	18	—
Cabbage, Chinese	6	24	10	½
Carrots	2	15	1½	½
Cauliflower	1	30	18	—
Chard	2, 5	24	6	¾
Collards	2, 6	30	18	½
Corn, sweet	3	36	12	1½
Cucumbers	3	72	72	1
Eggplant	4	36	30	—
Endive	6	20	10	½
Kale [7]	2, 6	24	10	½
Kohlrabi	2	15	4	½
Lettuce, head	1	15	12	—
Lettuce, leaf	1	15	6	½
Muskmelon	3	60	60	1
Mustard	2, 6	15	6	½
Okra	3	36	18	1
Onions, seeded	1–2	15	3	½
Onion sets	1–2	15	3	—
Parsley	2	15	4	¼
Parsnips	2	15	3	½
Peas, dwarf	1	18	1	1½
Peas, tall	1	24	1	1½
Peas, black-eye	3	28	3	1½
Peppers	4	30	18	—
Potatoes	1–2	30	12	4
Radishes	1	12	1	½
Rhubarb	1	42	42	4
Rutabagas	2	20	4	½
Salsify	1	20	2	½
Soybeans	3, 5	24	3	1½
Spinach	1, 6	12	4	½
Squash, bush	3, 5	48	48	1
Squash, trailing	3, 5	96	48	1
Sweetpotatoes	4	36	12	—
Tomatoes, staked	3	36	24	—
Turnips	1, 6	16	3	½
Watermelon	3	96	60	1

[1] The numbers refer to planting dates approximately as follows: (1) 4 to 6 weeks before frost-free date; (2) 2 to 4 weeks before frost-free date; (3) about frost-free date; (4) 1 or 2 weeks after frost-free date; (5) summer planting; (6) late-summer or autumn planting about 6 to 8 weeks before first autumn freeze, except in northern areas; and (7) late autumn, early winter, or very early spring. For dates, consult local Weather Bureau station or estimate from sketch maps in Figures 2, 3, 4 and 5.

[2] For the small garden. In large gardens cultivated with tractors, some rows may need to be wider.

[3] Seed is sown somewhat more thickly and plants thinned to this distance when small.

[4] On light sandy soils plant seeds about 30 to 50 per cent deeper; on clays and very clayey soils about 30 to 50 per cent shallower.

[5] These are only roughly approximate since the time varies with variety, weather, length of day (latitude), and soil conditions.

[6] Such figures can be only very rough.

[7] Hills of 4 or 5 seeds are planted and then thinned to one plant.

YIELDS OF SELECTED VEGETABLES

Seeds or roots per 100 feet of row	Approximate days from planting to harvest [5]	Satisfactory yield per 100 feet of row [6]	Remarks
70 plants	2–3 (years)	50 lbs.	Not for small gardens or southern regions.
¾ lb.	70	15 qts. (shelled)	
½ lb.	85	15 qts. (shelled)	Hills of about 4 plants each.
¾ lb.	55	1½ bu.	
¼ lb.	65	2 bu.	Hills of about 4 plants each.
1 oz.	60	2 bu.	
1 packet [8]	100 [9]	75 lbs.	Earlier crops with transplants.
1 packet	95	30 qts.	Best crop with transplants. Northern areas only.
70 plants	60–120 [9]	200 lbs.	Transplants best.
1 packet	80	150 lbs.	Not tolerant of heat.
¼ oz.	70	2 bu.	Hard to start in hot weather for late crop.
70 plants	95 [9]	60 heads	Needs cool region; hard for the beginner.
1 oz.	55	75 lbs.	
1 packet	110	30 lbs.	Late autumn crop in the South.
¼ lb.	75	100 ears	
½ oz.	70	100 lbs.	Hills of 4 plants. Poor for small garden.
40 plants	80 [9]	130 fruits	Not good for the beginner.
1 packet	80	75 lbs.	Late crop in the South.
¼ oz.	60	100 lbs.	Late crop in the South.
¼ oz.	55	80 lbs.	Not tolerant of high heat.
100 plants	40 [9]	70 lbs.	Not tolerant of heat; poor for the beginner.
1 packet	40	60 lbs.	
½ oz.	90–120	48 fruits	Hills of 4 plants. Not for small garden.
1 packet	30–75	75 lbs.	Not tolerant of heat; late crop in the South.
1 oz.	55	100 lbs.	
¼ oz.	135	1½ bu.	Hard for the beginner.
1 qt. sets	40	375 green	Plants may be used instead of sets.
¼ oz.	70	25 lbs.	Only a few plants needed.
½ oz.	150	2 bu.	Not good in the South.
1 lb.	60–80	1 bu.	{ Not tolerant of heat; too low-yielding
1 lb.	60–80	1 bu.	} for the very small garden.
½ lb.	85	20 lbs.	Only for warm regions.
70 plants	85 [9]	300 fruits	
7 lbs.	75–120	2–3 bu.	
1 oz.	20–50	1000	
30 roots	2 years	300 stalks	Not tolerant of high heat.
¼ oz.	95	2 bu.	For northern areas only.
1 oz.	150	2 bu.	
¾ lb.	90–150	30 lbs.	
½ oz.	50	40 lbs.	
½ oz.	75–120	80 fruits	
½ oz.	75–120	50 fruits	Hills of 4 plants. Not for small garden.
100 plants	150 [9]	3 bu.	For warm areas. Poor for small garden.
51 plants	70 [9]	4 bu.	Best for small garden.
¼ oz.	50–100	2 bu. roots or } 60 lbs. greens	Cool season crop.
1 oz.	90–120	12 fruits	Hills of 4 plants. Not for small garden.

[8] Less than ¼ ounce.
[9] For plants to grow from seed, allow following extra days: cabbage, broccoli, and cauliflower—50; tomatoes—60; pepper and eggplant—75; sweet potatoes—40; and head lettuce—30.

Average dates of the last killing frosts in spring are shown in Figure 2 for the western part of the United States, and in Figure 3 for the eastern part. The average dates for the first killing frosts in autumn are shown in Figure 4 for the western part of the country, and in Figure 5 for the eastern part.

By locating his territory on these maps, the gardener can read from the nearest lines the approximate dates for his garden. The figures are given as month and day; thus 4-30 is April 30. These sketch maps are based on data of the United States Weather Bureau between 1899 and 1938. A local weather bureau station may be able to give a somewhat more nearly precise figure.

These dates are very useful to the gardener. Tender plants like tomatoes, for example, or unhardened azaleas or other perennials, annuals, or shrubs from the window sill or greenhouse, should not be put into the garden until two or three weeks after the spring date. If the weather forecast on that day is for cold weather, transplanting should even then be delayed until the danger of a late frost is past. Many planting suggestions are given the gardener in reference to these dates, as in the previous table. The fall dates suggest the remaining time for tender plants and partly control the date for late-sown vegetables and flowers.

Within the areas shown on the map are local variations due to differences in air drainage. Cold air slides down the slopes, leaving them more nearly frost-free than low pockets. Protection by local clouds and trees makes a difference near the critical temperature. In mountainous areas the growing season is shorter—less time between the last spring frost and the earliest autumn one—at the high elevations than at the low ones, if local air drainage and exposure are comparable.

These maps are taken from "Growing Vegetables in Town and City," by Victor R. Boswell and Robert E. Wester (United States Department of Agriculture Miscellaneous Publication No. 538, 40 pp., illus., 1950)— an excellent brief guide for the kitchen garden.

Figure 2. Average dates of the last killing spring frost in the western part of the United States.

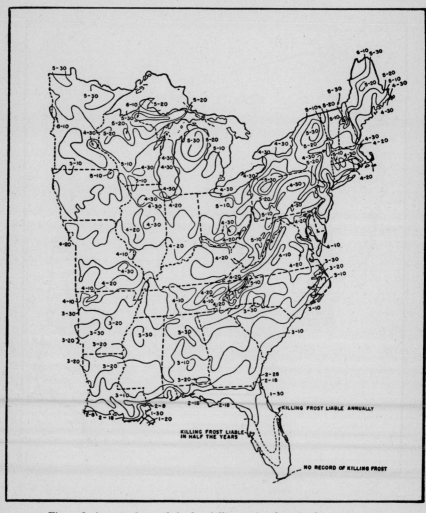

Figure 3. Average dates of the last killing spring frost in the eastern part of the United States.

Figure 4. Average dates of the first killing autumn frost in the western part of the United States.

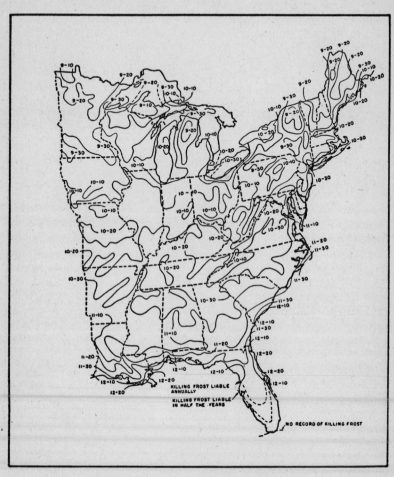

Figure 5. Average dates of the first killing autumn frost in the eastern part of the United States.

IV

FOR FURTHER READING

*

Several of the general garden books contain valuable suggestions about soils and their management. These vary widely in accuracy and specificity. Some are quite out of date on fertilizers, for example, and suggest expensive or hard-to-get materials, such as bone meal for phosphorus and cottonseed meal for nitrogen. Most general garden books assume a good garden soil to begin with, which many gardeners must first prepare from poor soil. During the last war, for example, if gardeners had not tried to use any of the kinds of soil they were warned against in books and bulletins—sloping soils, wet soils, infertile soils, soils with trash or raw clays in them, and soils partly shaded—we should have had only a small percentage of the back-yard kitchen gardens that were actually made in and around many of the big cities. Some failed, of course, but many learned how to select plants and to make over the soil for a good garden.

Since this book deals only with soil examination, improvement, and management and with the relations between plants and soils, the gardener should have also one or more horticultural books or bulletins that discuss the characteristics of plants, recommend varieties, and suggest methods of insect and disease control. Especially helpful are those books and bulletins that include lists of plants according to similar features, hardiness, and requirements of sun and water.

The United States Department of Agriculture publishes many bulletins about lawns, vegetables, flowers, and other garden plants and their adaptation and care. New ones are prepared from time to time. These may be consulted in the local library or purchased from the Superintendent of Documents (so long as they are available). Some valuable ones for the home garden are:

(1) "Growing Annual Flowering Plants," by S. L. Emsweller. Farmers' Bulletin No. 1171, 26 pp., illus., 1950.

(2) "Herbaceous Perennials," by F. L. Mulford. Farmers' Bulletin No. 1381, 84 pp., illus., 1929.

(3) "Supplemental Irrigation," by F. E. Staebner. Farmers' Bulletin No. 1846, 73 pp., illus., 1940.

(4) "Savory Herbs: Culture and Use," by M. S. Lowman and Miriam Birdseye. Farmers' Bulletin No. 1977, 33 pp., illus., 1946.

(5) "Growing Vegetables in Town and City," by V. R. Boswell and R. E. Wester. Miscellaneous Publication No. 538, 40 pp., illus., 1950.

(6) "House Plants," by F. L. Mulford. Farmers' Bulletin No. 1872, 30 pp., illus., 1941.

(7) "A Vegetable Gardener's Handbook on Insects and Diseases," by W. H. White and S. P. Doolittle. Miscellaneous Publication No. 605, 30 pp., illus., 1946.

(8) "Rockeries," by F. L. Mulford. Leaflet No. 90, 8 pp., illus., 1948.

(9) "Hotbeds and Coldframes," by W. R. Beattie. Farmers' Bulletin No. 1743, 28 pp., illus., 1941.

(10) "Care of Ornamental Trees and Shrubs," by F. L. Mulford. Farmers' Bulletin No. 1826, 79 pp., illus., 1939. Also, "Transplanting and Care of Ornamental Trees and Shrubs." Mimeograph 0–8, Bureau of Plant Industry, Soils, and Agricultural Engineering, 6 pp., 1949.

(11) "The Farm Garden," by J. H. Beattie and W. R. Beattie. Farmers' Bulletin No. 1673, 67 pp., illus., 1942.

(12) "Home Vegetable Gardening in the Central High Plains and Mountain Valleys," by M. F. Babb and James E. Kraus. Farmers' Bulletin No. 2000, 98 pp., illus., 1949.

(13) "Trees: The Yearbook of Agriculture for 1949." 944 pp., illus., Washington, 1949.

Besides these bulletins, each state agricultural experiment station (or the cooperative extension service) publishes bulletins on gardening. Most of these are concerned chiefly with vegetables. They vary widely in detail and accuracy on all phases of gardening, including soil management. There are also excellent general bulletins for the kitchen garden. And some stations have very useful bulletins on lawns, ornamentals, small fruits, and home orchards.

From the bulletins of the United States Department of Agriculture and of the state agricultural experiment stations the gardener can develop a good working library on the common plants and their management practices at low cost. As with the general garden books, however, most of the bulletins assume that the reader has already a good soil for his garden!

Since new bulletins, new methods, new materials, and new problems are continually appearing, the gardener can receive additional help through direct inquiry. In Table 11 are listed the principal state agricultural stations and a few of the substations specializing in matters of particular interest to gardeners. Besides these there are other substations. By addressing a letter to the "Director, —— State Agricultural Experiment Station," it will be forwarded to the proper specialist. For best handling, such letters should be as specific as possible. Because questions about quite different subjects—such as fertilizers and liming, soil maps, vegetables, flowers, fruits, lawns, engineering, insect control, disease hazards, and landscape design—are commonly handled by separate specialists, replies are expedited by limiting each letter to one subject.

Inquiries on specific subjects may be addressed also to the United States Department of Agriculture, Washington, D.C., or to the appropriate bureau or division. Most of the questions about soils and plants are handled by the Bureau of Plant Industry, Soils, and Agricultural Engineering, Beltsville, Maryland. Usually, however, specific questions for a particular locality can be answered more expeditiously by a specialist in the state agricultural experiment station.

TABLE 11. **Addresses of the Principal State and Territorial Agricultural Experiment Stations**

STATE OR TERRITORY	POST OFFICE
Alabama	Auburn
Alaska	College (or) Palmer
Arizona	Tucson
Arkansas	Fayetteville
California	Berkeley 4
	Davis
	Los Angeles 24
	Riverside
Colorado	Fort Collins
Connecticut	Storrs
	New Haven 4
Delaware	Newark
Florida	Gainesville
Everglades Expt. Sta.	Belle Glade
Citrus Expt. Sta.	Lake Alfred
Vegetable Crop Laboratory	Bradenton
Subtropical Expt. Sta.	Homestead
Georgia	Athens
	Experiment (Griffin)
Coastal Plain Expt. Sta.	Tifton
Hawaii	Honolulu 10
Idaho	Moscow
Illinois	Urbana
Indiana	La Fayette
Iowa	Ames
Kansas	Manhattan
Kentucky	Lexington 29
Louisiana	University Station, Baton Rouge 3
Maine	Orono
Maryland	College Park

STATE OR TERRITORY (*cont'd*)	POST OFFICE (*cont'd*)
Massachusetts	Amherst
Cranberry Station	East Wareham
Michigan	East Lansing
Minnesota	University Farm, St. Paul 1
Mississippi	State College
Missouri	Columbia
Montana	Bozeman
Nebraska	Lincoln 1
Nevada	Reno
New Hampshire	Durham
New Jersey	New Brunswick
Cranberry and Blueberry Research Lab.	Pemberton
New Mexico	State College
New York	Ithaca
	Geneva
North Carolina	Raleigh
North Dakota	Fargo
Ohio	Columbus 10
	Wooster
Oklahoma	Stillwater
Oregon	Corvallis
Pennsylvania	State College
Puerto Rico	Rio Piedras
Rhode Island	Kingston
South Carolina	Clemson
Truck Expt. Station	St. Andrews Branch, Charleston
South Dakota	Brookings
Tennessee	Knoxville 16
Texas	College Station
Utah	Logan
Vermont	Burlington
Virginia	Blacksburg
Truck Expt. Station	Norfolk 1
Washington	Pullman
Cranberry–Blueberry Expt. Sta.	Long Beach
West Virginia	Morgantown
Wisconsin	Madison 6
Wyoming	Laramie

INDEX[1]

A horizon, 10
Abelia, 195
Abronia, 193
Acanthus, 187
Achillea, 187
Acidification of soil, 104–7.
Acidity, effect on soil, 93–7
Acidity of soil, 19, 90–107 (see also pH and Soil: reaction); increase of, 104–7; tests for, 99
Acid-loving plants, 104, 121, 135
Aconitum, 187
Actinidia, 202
Adianthum, 210
Aegopodium, 204
Aerification of turf. 145
Aethionema, 187
Ageratum, 193
Air drainage, 21
Air in soil. See Soil: air
Ajuga, 204
Akebia, 202, 204
Alkali soils. See Salinity
Alkalinity of soils, 90–107. See also Soil: reaction
Althea, 188
Aluminum, 94–5
Aluminum sulphate, use of, 105
Alumroot, 190
Alyssum, 188; sweet, 193
Amaryllis, 206

Ammoniated superphosphate, 130
Ammonium nitrate, 127
Ammonium sulphate, 127
Ampelopsis, 202
Analysis of soils, 111
Anchusa, 188
Andromeda, 195
Anemone, 188, 206
Animals: in garden, 25; in soil, 41
Anise, 184
Annual flowers, 137; list of, 193–94
Anthemis, 188
Antibiotics, 41
Antirrhinum, 193
Apples, 137, 186
Apricots, 186
Aquilegia, 188
Arctic daisy, 189
Arctostaphylos, 204
Arenaria, 204
Aristolochia, 202
Artichoke, 181
Asarum, 204
Asclepias, 188
Ashes, 18, 33
Asparagus, 66, 136, 181, 212
Aspidium, 210
Asplenium, 210
Aster, hardy, 188
Astilbe, 188
Athyrium, 210

[1] When reading the soil requirements of a plant in Appendix II, be certain to scan the introduction for the specific list in which the description is given, as well as the general introduction to Appendix II for keys to symbols and terms.

223